NINE TILL THREE AND SUMMERS FREE

NINE TILL THREE AND SUMMERS FREE

LIFE AT A TEACHERS' TRAINING COLLEGE:
A MEMOIR

MIKE KENT

Matador
9 Priory Business Park,
Wistow Road, Kibworth Beauchamp,
Leicestershire. LE8 0RX
Tel: 0116 279 2299
Email: books@troubador.co.uk
Web: www.troubador.co.uk/matador
Twitter: @matadorbooks

ISBN 9781788034678

British Library Cataloguing in Publication Data.
A catalogue record for this book is available from the British Library.

Printed and bound in the UK by 4Edge Limited
Typeset in 11 pt Minion Pro by Troubador Publishing Ltd, Leicester, UK

Matador is an imprint of Troubador Publishing Ltd

This one is for Fluffle

Who, I'm certain, will be a delight to teach

PRAISE FOR MIKE KENT'S WRITING!

THE RABBIT'S LAID AN EGG, MISS!

This book will raise a smile in any reader, but it will ring several bells for anyone involved in education. Mike Kent has obviously been there and printed the T-shirt. First published in 2006, it is still valid in its hilarious depiction of the reality of running a modern school, caught between the Scylla of challenging children (and their equally challenging parents) and the Charybdis of inspectors and educational authorities, who are mostly blissfully ignorant of the sharp end!

B. Sherunkle: Former Chair of Governors

This collection of Mike Kent's popular Times Educational Supplement columns is highly addictive, giving tantalising glimpses of life as a primary school headteacher. I became totally engrossed in sharing his humour, poignancy, frustration and joys. It will revitalise test-driven, demoralised teachers and will remind parents of the sort of education they really want for their children.

Emily G: Teacher

Absolutely brilliant! Snippets of some very entertaining aspects of school life in an inner London primary school that will have the reader giggling non stop! It is a joy to read Mike Kent's books. His love of teaching and school life shines through and you certainly don't have to be a teacher to enjoy them.

Julie Jenkins: Social Worker

I loved this. I am a parent who was looking for insights into how primary schools work and how teachers think. It made me wish my children could go to his school. Quite a few laugh out loud moments. My only criticism? It was too short!

Mrs N. Stoker: Parent

TALES FROM THE HEAD'S ROOM

Humour, heroism, common sense and inspiring humanity shine through Mike Kent's writing. 'Tales From The Head's Room' demonstrates how, against all the odds, it is possible to create a centre of educational excellence, where both children and staff enjoy the learning process.

Emma Davis: Trainee Headteacher

I enjoyed reading Mike Kent's school anecdotes. Each chapter is relatively self contained and well suited for dipping into if you have a busy lifestyle. We need more school leaders like him. I hope his book inspires more potential school leaders to trust their judgement and ignore some of the loopier government initiatives!

Robert Butler: Teacher

This book is such a joy! Encouraging children to learn is what education is about and Mike doesn't let the nonsense get in his way. Heads or tails, whichever way it lands, you are going to get a highly entertaining read and have a good laugh.

K. Kool: Lecturer

I opened this book and then could not put it down! This is a must for anyone who has ever worked in a primary school or for that matter anyone with the slightest interest in education. Mike Kent's stories are hilarious but also convey the hard work, effort and dedication that teachers put into our young people to give them a great education. A great read!

Stupot: The Blue Elephant Theatre.

A LIFE AT THE CHALKFACE

An excellent read! Technology brings many changes but children remain the same. I taught Infants for thirty five years and no work could have been more satisfying. I live now with many wonderful memories and this book was a re-visit to the classroom and its unforgettable memories. Thank you!

E.R. Melville: Teacher

A brilliant book that brought back such wonderful memories of working at Mike's school. An absolutely amazing head teacher. After eighteen years I still haven't found a headteacher to match Mike Kent.

Karen Thompson: Teacher

This book is a beautifully warm, emotive and honest account of life in an inner London primary school. A wonderful insight into the varied life of a headteacher, and all the characters and situations that the author encountered in his career. Prepare to laugh and cry as this book recounts the high and low points of a career in primary education.

Rachel McMutrie: Parent

Mike Kent was obviously the kind of head teacher we would all have liked to have been. Although he does not pull any punches when he describes the trials, tribulations and stresses of headship, this book is clearly written by someone for whom headship was not just a job, but a joy and a privilege. There must be a great many people, now in their 20s, 30s and 40s, who have very fond memories of their time at his school.

Michael Evans: Headteacher

Life as a headteacher doesn't come with an unreservedly positive recommendation, but for Mike Kent it was the best job in the world. 'A Life At The Chalkface' is a love letter to thirty eventful years in a job he found endlessly challenging and fascinating. In a world of league tables and assessment spreadsheets, this book stands out as a testament to all that is best in primary education.

Lucy Edkin: Educational Columnist

Mike Kent is a rare talent. He writes beautifully and has spent most of his life in schools, first as a pupil, then as a teacher and deputy head, and finally thirty years as a headteacher in South London. So here is a rich tale, filled with meaningful insights and revealing anecdote, all set against the backdrop of school life. Read, and enjoy, his story.

Sir Tim Brighouse: Former Commissioner for London Schools

AMAZING ASSEMBLIES FOR PRIMARY SCHOOLS

This book is a must-buy for any imaginative, forward looking primary school.

John Lord: Headteacher

The activities are simple and easy to prepare and I will be using them immediately, just as long as I contact the fire brigade first!

Richard Dax: Headteacher

Mike Kent's broad experience as a headteacher and thought-provoking columnist and writer has given him the skills to produce this book, full of practical ideas to make school assemblies exciting and interesting learning experiences.

John T Morris, BA(Hons),
Med, MPhil: Director,
JTM Educational Consultants.

As a busy headteacher, this book is just what I need to capture the imaginations of children of all ages at the start of the day.

Anita Asumadu: Headteacher

Gaining inspiration for leading a school assembly can sometimes be the main obstacle, but Amazing Assemblies for Primary Schools offers an excellent collection of ideas which will inspire any teacher.

UKEdChat.com

CONTENTS

FEBRUARY

AN EXTRAORDINARY INTERVIEW

Thinking back, I was probably always destined to be a teacher.

From the time when I was old enough to reach up and chalk on the blackboard my father had made for me, I'd felt the urge to teach. Then, at the tender age of twelve, I solemnly informed my mother of my ambition to be a teacher, which pleased her enormously. She considered teaching to be one of the more respectable professions, and certainly one that would benefit from her son's abilities. Not quite in the doctor or lawyer class, of course, but respectable nevertheless. Since this was the early fifties and our lives were centered almost entirely around the street we lived on, I knew the neighbouring children well. She'd observed me spending my summer holidays playing schools in the garden, inventing and organising team games, or setting up our shed as a museum and inviting children to inspect the garden creatures I'd captured and put in labelled glass jars, and then asking them to write something about their visit afterwards.

She wasn't surprised by my decision and my father didn't really mind what career I embarked upon, providing it didn't cost him more money than necessary as funds were usually short. My father was a relaxed and quiet man, rarely ruffled, and this was probably a reflection of his upbringing in a peaceful Essex village. He'd been stationed in North Africa during the war, working as a cook... a surprising job allocation as he'd found it difficult to boil an egg prior to being summoned for service... and on returning to civvy street his artistic talents helped find him work as a draughtsman. He worked hard, eventually brought home a reasonable salary, and then left the rest of life's arrangements to his very capable wife.

I had been raised on what my mother considered to be important character-forming qualities; reading plenty of books, attending church on Sundays, not complaining about being ill, changing my underwear at least once a week (washing and drying clothes in the 1950s was a two day job), always being polite in company and not eating chips in the street. Once I'd announced my determination to train as a teacher, she looked forward to the day when her son became a respected headmaster and invited her to present bibles and dictionaries on Prize Day.

I was not by any stretch of the imagination an academic, although I'd pleased my teachers at primary school and achieved tolerable results at my rather mediocre comprehensive. The fact that my list of paper qualifications was a trifle lean didn't concern me at all. Good teachers were in short supply and I was convinced that winning a place at a teacher training college wouldn't pose the slightest problem.

In my final sixth form year, I sent an application to a college near the seaside, attracted by the possibility of writing essays on the beach and getting a suntan at the same time. The college, perhaps suspicious of my motives, turned me down without an interview. Shortly afterwards, a second interview invitation arrived, for a place at a training college in the heart of Buckinghamshire, but the Principal's aggressive grilling reminded me of the ticking off I'd received from my headmaster when I'd short-circuited the most expensive lathe in the metalwork shop, and the interview never really left the ground. The third application was for a college in Westminster, and within easy travelling distance from home. From my experience of the previous interviews, I'd thought carefully about the questions I might be asked and I looked forward to this one with a little more confidence.

I arrived much too early for the interview, having made allowances for the heavy snow which seemed to have fallen endlessly for weeks, but within minutes of my arrival the Principal had ushered me into his tiny book-lined office, gripping my hand warmly and offering me a steaming mug of hot chocolate. He commented so enthusiastically on my determination to plough through the snow that I felt like Scott of the Antarctic.

Dr Bradley was the archetypal college principal. Well-proportioned, gowned and slightly stooped, as if cramped by the lack of room in his study and the weight of his learning, his thick black spectacles and intelligent eyes gave him a fearsome appearance, but his handshake was warm and encouraging as his hand guided me to a small chair on the other side of his desk. He moved his tea tray to one side, positioned the lamp to give a little more light and then moved my written application in front of him to refresh his memory.

'So, let's get down to business, Mr Kent. I only have a short time at my disposal, and you're rather lucky to be interviewed by me. My time being so limited, I don't conduct many interviews, you see. But it's important that I do one or two, just to make sure we don't let in any old riff raff, eh?'

I gave a watery smile and shuffled uncomfortably in my seat. The Principal clasped his hands together on the desk and leaned forward.

'Humour, Mr Kent, humour. A very important quality in a teacher. Now, there are several points I need to clarify from your application. And of course, I'd like to hear your own views about primary education. You want to be a teacher. This college can train you to be one, but I'd like you to give me a few good reasons why it should.'

I'd been asked this question at the previous two interviews, and decided that sincerity might be the best way forward at this stage.

'I have only one reason,' I replied. 'I've never really wanted to do anything else.'

'I see. Well, that's admirable, of course, but it doesn't mean to say you'd be any good at it.'

Dr Bradley raised his eyebrows questioningly at the inference in his remark. Then he pushed his spectacles into a more comfortable position on his nose and leaned back in his chair.

'These days, teaching is not a soft option, Mr Kent. Many young teachers start out with admirable dedication and then discover their pupils do not share the same enthusiasm. They locked a colleague of mine in his classroom cupboard a short while ago. How do you feel about that?'

'Very sympathetic. But I don't imagine it's typical of all teenagers.'

'You're right. Most of them are worse. These were eleven year olds, Mr Kent.'

'Then I've learned something already,' I said brightly. 'I'll make sure I always carry my classroom keys with me. Or keep a spade in the cupboard so that I can tunnel out.'

Dr Bradley smiled cautiously. 'Well done! A sense of humour and a sense of vocation. Two absolute essentials in my view. You probably won't get locked in a cupboard. Your pupils may well be content with sawing the legs off your chair.'

There was a pause as he turned the page on my application paper and glanced through it. My eyes wandered round the book-lined walls of the study and the further stacks on the carpet and I wondered how many of them he had read.

'You're still in the sixth form, Mr Kent, so obviously you haven't had any teaching experience. Do you think it's a good idea to go straight into college from school? Perhaps you should gain a little experience of life in the big wide world first?'

'Possibly, but I really want to teach, so any delay seems to me a waste of time. I've already worked with the cubs and the Scout movement and helped out with groups like the Woodcraft Folk. In fact, just a short while ago I helped organise a new youth club at home, and I...'

'Woodcraft Folk, eh? And who would they be? A coven of elderly ladies who leap about stark naked in the woods at midnight, perhaps?'

My mouth dropped open. For a moment I lost my composure and giggled nervously.

'Well, no, I...'

'Don't worry, Mr. Kent. Take no notice of me. I just caught you off guard. In the classroom, children are constantly trying to catch teachers off their guard. Now, what were we talking about?'

'I was telling you about my work with the Scouts and youth clubs.'

'Ah, yes. That must have been interesting. I was a Boy Scout too, many years ago. They haven't changed much, have they?'

I hesitated, unsure how to interpret the question. Dr Bradley's piercing eyes looked at me carefully and he raised his eyebrows for an answer.

'Well… they don't stand on hilltops and signal to each other with semaphore flags any more,' I replied cautiously. 'And being involved with the Scouts has given me a lot of pleasure. I've had quite a few enjoyable camping holidays in this country. And in places like France and the Channel Islands. I was a patrol leader for some time, and that was a great teaching experience.'

The Doctor waved a mildly reproving finger in the air.

'All very admirable, but you were working with enthusiastic youngsters, who were keen to learn from you. Trying to inspire children in a classroom day after day is rather different from showing a tenderfoot how to tie a reef knot. Wouldn't you agree?'

'Maybe. But I think motivation is the important thing. Showing cubs how to tie a knot or light a camp fire is still a practical teaching experience. If I can do it well for a small group, I'm sure I could be just as successful with a large class.'

'That sounds a little conceited to me, Mr. Kent. Do you consider yourself to be conceited?'

'Yes… no… er… I simply meant…

Dr Bradley leaned back in his chair, took a packet of Capstan full strength cigarettes from the pocket of his gown and smiled reassuringly.

'Don't worry, 1 know what you meant, Mr. Kent,' he said. 'I am merely testing your patience. Children do it all the time. Now, you were talking about your practical experience, so please don't let me put you off. Tell me more.'

His cigarette lit, I talked through a haze of tobacco smoke, which he tried unsuccessfully to wave away. Still smarting a little, I described how, as a sixth former, I had been given plenty of opportunity to work with junior classes. I had found the experience enjoyable, further convincing me that teaching might offer me an interesting, varied career.

'Worthy sentiments, indeed,' Dr Bradley commented. 'But are you absolutely certain that you want to come straight into college? You've been studying for seven years, and many students find it beneficial to have a break between school and higher education. You could take a year off and try… I don't know… bricklaying or something.'

'Bricks don't have minds. And I don't think I'd be able to build them in straight lines.'

'Bricks don't answer you back, either, and that is a distinct advantage. They are also somewhat easier to put in straight lines than a bunch of ten year olds. You have cement, for a start.'

The Doctor smiled to himself and turned the page on my application form.

'You have very neat handwriting, Mr. Kent. That's supposed to denote a methodical mind. About a third of the applications we receive are unreadable, the spelling chronic and the grammar virtually non-existent. Why do you think that is?'

'Rotten teaching?'

'Possibly. Or poor teacher training, perhaps. Employers tell me that school leavers can't read, write or add up. These days the secondary school blames the junior school and the junior school blames the infant school. People of my age were taught properly, Mr. Kent. It was different in those days, eh?'

I knew I was being baited, but I refused to be drawn.

'Not necessarily. Some teachers will always be competent and others ineffectual. It's the teaching techniques that have changed.'

'Indeed. And the children have suffered. They're not taught to read any more. Nowadays, children are treated as delicate individuals who shouldn't participate in competitive sport in case they break each other's legs. Doesn't current primary school policy state that children should become… what's the phrase… agents in their own learning? In other words, please themselves?'

Dr Bradley puffed hard on his cigarette and blew a cloud of smoke across the desk. I coughed and felt vaguely nauseous.

'No, I don't think so. In the best primary classrooms, the work is suited to the individual child and structured with great care. But it's still essential for children to be taught to read.'

'Really? We're into the sixties, and these days I thought children were supposed to learn to read as they jogged along with an integrated project on head lice or something?'

'Not at all. And anyway, it depends on where you are teaching. Children from deprived inner city homes will always need a lot more skill isolation than those from the suburbs. If they can't read effectively, they won't be able to do much else.'

Dr Bradley gestured expansively: 'Thank God for that. You've put my mind at rest. I shall worry no more about the plight of primary education. We could now turn to reading methods, mathematics, calculators in the nursery class and so forth, but I shall have to be brief. Shall we look instead at your own academic achievements? You have a somewhat motley collection of GCEs. English, chemistry, economics… have you been exploring the laws of diminishing marginal utility with the aid of a test tube and a packet of litmus paper?'

'Yes, they're a bit varied,' I admitted reluctantly. 'But I'm interested in a wide range of things. And those happen to be my favourite subjects.'

'Surely it would have been more sensible to opt for subjects that complemented each other? I mean, chemistry and English? That's not a match made in heaven, is it?'

'I do have others,' I pointed out, wondering why my choice of subjects should matter so much when I wanted to teach primary children, not lecture in a university.

There was a light knock on the door. A secretary entered with a pile of letters on a small tray, murmured an apology for the interruption and withdrew cautiously. Dr Bradley glanced briefly at the envelopes and then looked up at me, changing the course of the conversation.

'Now, what about your personal qualities?' he asked. 'Have you the patience of a saint, the stamina of a horse, the staying power of a pair of braces, a delicate sense of humour like my own?'

'Yes. Fortunately I have all those qualities,' I said, throwing caution to the winds and hardly believing this interview wasn't a dream.

'Jolly good. Well, I'm convinced you could cope with a rowdy class, so let's see if we can sum up your chances. Your place here is naturally dependent on your exam results. If you do come, you'll be required to study two subject courses, as well as the primary education courses. We have a strong science department, but we also do a combined sciences course, which you may prefer. That counts for two subjects. Place all your eggs in the same test tube, as it were. I hope you pass your English, because we tend to specialise in that. What are you reading at the moment… Lawrence, Virginia Woolf, Orwell, Milton, Scouting for Boys?'

'Mickey Spillane,' I answered.

'Mmm. Are you indeed? His poetry, prose or critical essays? Oh well, don't let me catch you reading Mickey Spillane in class. Not to the under fives, anyway. Good Lord, look at the time…'

He stood up, took my arm, and ushered me to the door.

'Mr. Kent, rest assured that I shall consider your application very carefully. You seem to be able to read and write, and that counts for a lot these days. You just might have a promising career before you in the teaching profession. Your own headmaster has endorsed this view.'

'You know him?' I asked in surprise.

'Oh yes, we play golf together. A second opinion is always valuable. Can't judge the calibre of students just by reading bits of paper or talking to them, you know. They often lie through their teeth. Now, back to school and pass those exams. Economics, chemistry and English. Dear God!'

He shook my hand and strode off down the corridor. I was shaken and a little bewildered, but I had the distinct feeling that this interview just might have gone rather well…

SEPTEMBER

ARRIVAL, FIRST FRIENDSHIPS... AND MILLY

The tube train clattered to a halt and I peered through the crowd of rush hour passengers to glimpse the name of the station. Victoria. Two more stops and I would be there.

Pushing an elbow into the person crammed up against me, I forced enough room to take the letter out of my pocket for the umpteenth time. I still couldn't quite believe that I'd been accepted at St. James's. My exam results, although satisfactory, were not as good as I'd hoped. Perhaps, after all, it had been the interview and my headmaster's report that had clinched things.

For a couple of days I'd basked in the euphoria of success before my mother reminded me I'd need to buy some new clothes, the textbooks of educational theory prescribed by the college, a new suitcase and all the bits and pieces I'd need for my first year in college as a resident student. Although I was eligible for a government grant, my parents were required to contribute a sizeable amount too, but, unknown to me, my mother had been putting money aside for just such an occasion.

The doors of the train slid open and I heaved my case towards the exit escalator, battling with a cold September wind as I hurried towards the nearest taxi. The driver peered at me and chewed on the matchstick in his mouth.

'Where to, mate?'

'St. James's, please.' The driver watched, frowning, as I wrestled with the suitcase, but offering no assistance.

'St. James's what, mate? St. James's Church, St. James's Hotel, St. James's Hostel, St. James's Street, St. James' Infirmary...'

'St. James's Training College,' I interrupted. 'It's a teachers' training college in Merton Road.'

'Oh, right. New student, are you? It's not too far from here. You can walk it from the station. Don't suppose you felt like walking with that case, though.'

He turned back to the wheel, nudging the taxi into the early evening traffic. Commuters were hurrying from the station, their faces set with a grim determination to get home as quickly as possible and out of the wind, which seemed to be warning another early and very cold winter. The taxi edged across the traffic lights and turned into the main road. The driver half turned his head towards me.

'Come from London?'

'The outskirts. Ealing, actually.'

'Ealing? Queen of the suburbs they used to call it. I was born there, but it's changed a lot now. Are you going to teach, then?'

'I'm going to try.'

'Kids don't want to learn these days. I wouldn't teach them if they paid me ten times what I make as a cabby.'

Nothing like encouragement and enthusiasm for the noble teaching profession, I thought.

'Trouble is,' said the driver, gesticulating with one hand and steering with the other, 'half of 'em know what a rough time they'll have trying to find a job anyway, so they don't bother. They expect it on a plate these days. And the teachers don't have any control. I mean, what hope have you got if you can't control the kids? In the old days, they'd get a good clout round the ear. Seems crazy to me.'

I'd heard the same opinion many times, but I listened politely while the driver outlined his own methods of running the educational system, which seemed roughly on a par with the conditions existing a century ago. The taxi suddenly executed a sharp right turn and slowed down.

‘The gates are just a bit further along here. Might see you again, eh? After all, you’ll be here for a year or two.’

He made it sound like a prison sentence, I thought, as the taxi pulled neatly into the kerb outside the huge wooden gates of the college, which lay concealed behind them. On an impulse, probably motivated by the possibility of missing out on a tip, the driver lifted my case from the back seat and stood it by the gates. I paid him, added a fair tip, and then turned my collar up against the wind.

Once inside the gates I was reminded of the shock I’d had when I’d attended for interview. It was as if I’d been magically transported back several hundred years. Although the building was only a hundred years old, it had been constructed in the neo-Gothic, perpendicular style and was obviously modelled on the Oxbridge colleges, oozing a long heritage of learning and scholarship. A fortress-like gatehouse led from the main road into a front quadrangle, flanked by a chapel on the left and a large dining hall on the other. To the rear of them were the lecture rooms and theatre, practical workshops, gymnasium and the assembly hall. The cracked paving stones that made up the footpaths beneath the sprawling arches seemed to be engaged in a constant struggle with the weeds, although I noticed that since I’d last visited part of the west wall had been shorn up with immense wooden pillars, ready for yet another repair to the fabric.

In the centre of the quadrangle was an immaculately manicured lawn bordered by precisely tended flower beds that seemed distinctly out of character with the surroundings. Since the lawn provided the quickest route to the main entrance, I heaved my suitcase across it until an agonised cry brought me to a halt. A thin, suntanned man in caretaker’s overalls and a battered trilby was waving both arms and gesticulating wildly at me.

‘Off! Get off! Bloody get off!’ he shouted, his voice ricocheting around the buildings. ‘Get off! I’ve spent all day spraying and trimming, and what do you do? Bloody well walk all over it! Can’t you bloody read?’

My inclination was to leave the suitcase and run for my life, but a glance at the caretaker's face suggested that if the case so much as touched one blade of grass, all my belongings would be hurled into the nearest dustbin.

'Sorry, but I didn't see a notice...'

The caretaker waved an admonishing finger at me.

'No, I don't suppose you bloody did. I've had fifty pairs of boots buggering every blade growing on this lawn, and none of 'em saw the notice. Every year it's the same. I dunno why I bother. When I retire in two year's time you lot can grow your own bloody lawn, but while I'm still here, use the bloody pathway.'

He strode off, still muttering, and throwing caution to the winds I hurried across the rest of the lawn and climbed the steps to the main door. I was met by an older student who smiled a greeting and took the case from me.

'Welcome,' he said warmly. It was the first encouraging word I'd heard all day. 'Just put your case over here for a moment while I cross your name off the list. Now, who are you?'

'Kent. Michael. I...'

'Kent. Let's see... Ah yes, here we are. Room nineteen, top corridor. A long way to drag your case, I'm afraid. Sign this, and then I'll show you where to go. I suppose I couldn't interest you in some second hand course books? Rock bottom prices. What are you studying?'

'The sciences.'

'Oh, that's a shame,' he frowned, 'unless you fancy changing your subject to the philosophy of religion. Have you bought your books on educational theory? I can do you Dewey, Plato, Rousseau... all for the price of a pint. Well, several pints, actually.'

I explained that I'd already bought everything recommended on the college booklist, courtesy of my mother's insistence. He gave a disappointed shrug.

'The perennial problem. Freshers rushing off to buy their books before they even get here. Well, if you find anyone who wants some stuff on religious philosophers... Plato, Aquinas... or well thumbed copies of Motorcycle Monthly or Naked As Nature Intended, point them in my direction. I'll be around for a couple of days.'

He pinned the list of names back on the notice board, among details of football fixtures, societies wanting members, meetings wanting attendances and a brief note urging the bugger who'd nicked all the bathplugs from corridor five to return them immediately. The fact that the paper had turned brown suggested that the inhabitants of corridor five had gone without baths for some time.

'Okay. If you follow me, I'll take you upstairs.'

The weight of my case made this difficult, especially as he set an alarming pace. After climbing stone stairs for what seemed an eternity, we reached the third corridor. It was narrower than those below, and much darker due to the lack of windows. The air had a slightly musty smell, probably due to the deteriorating state of the roughly plastered walls. My guide came to an abrupt halt halfway along the corridor and I put my case down with great relief.

'Here we are then. This one's yours. Make yourself at home. There's a short welcome meeting for all the new students in the main hall at six-thirty. You can see the hall from your window. I'm sure you'll soon find your way around the building.'

Summoning my remaining strength, I pushed the door open and shoved the case forcibly into the room. There was a strangulated cry from behind the door and a very large lady in a dirty green overall leaned round the door. I apologised humbly.

'That's all right, cock,' she grinned, revealing teeth that might have been inherited from a pirate. 'Let yer off this time. I've finished up in 'ere anyway. New, are yer?'

'Yes. I arrived half an hour ago.'

She leaned on her broom handle and pushed strands of black hair up inside the duster tied round her head. Her tiny bright eyes were inquisitive but friendly, and the healthy pink glow of her cheeks suggested that she'd never worried about anything in her life. A podgy hand scratched around in a pocket of her overalls, and pulled out a packet of tobacco and some liquorice papers. Fashioning a skinny cigarette with the expertise of a cowboy, she looked me firmly in the eye.

'You'll like it 'ere, love. They never do a stroke of work. 'Ard enough job I 'ave just gettin' 'em out of their beds in the mornin'.' She sniffed loudly and wiped the dust from her face on part of a sheet that doubled as a handkerchief.

'Luvly view from the window. Got one of the best rooms, you 'ave, at least as far as the view is concerned. Feller killed 'imself in 'ere a couple of years ago. 'Lectrocuted 'imself. 'E was worried about 'is exams.'

'Oh dear. That's awful.'

'They all worry, sooner or later,' she went on pessimistically. 'I says to 'em, if you did a bit more work you wouldn't 'ave to worry. Don't you be one of 'em, love. 'Avin' a bit o' fun's all right, but you got to do the work as well. Stands to reason, don't it love.' She flicked her half finished cigarette into her dustpan and then picked up a duster from the bed.

'You know what?' she continued ominously. 'They say 'e still wanders about, but I wouldn't worry if I was you, love. I ain't never seen 'im yet. Mind you, I ain't bin 'ere after dark.'

'I'll let you know if I see him. Now I really should get my things unpacked.'

'Of course, love, don't let me stop yer. What's yer name, then?'

'Mike.'

'Pleased to meet you, Mike. You can call me Milly. Everybody calls me Milly. Amongst other things,' she added drily, disappearing into the next room with her clutter of brooms and buckets.

Room nineteen was small but pleasant. It contained a single bed, a slim wardrobe, a writing desk with shelving built onto it, a small set of drawers with a deep scratch across the top surface, and a full length mirror that had recently been attached to the wall. The white emulsioned walls of the room were covered with tiny, clean patches where pictures had clearly been fastened to them with sellotape by the previous occupant, but the carpet looked fairly new and made the room feel comfortable. A curved window gave an exciting view of London's skyline, with Big Ben as its centrepiece. I propped the window open to let some fresh air into the room, but a gust of cold air blew in some dust from a construction site nearby and I quickly closed it again.

I heaved my case onto the bed and started to unpack. It was the weight of the books that had made the suitcase so heavy and I gazed apprehensively at some of the titles as I stacked them on the shelf: *Psychology In Education, Modern Teaching Methodology, Philosophy In Education, Children And Their Secondary Schools*… why I needed that when I was training to teach at a primary school I'd no idea… *A Short History Of Education* which ran into seven hundred pages. I felt relieved that I hadn't been asked to buy the long version. As I finished there was a knock at the door and a beaming face topped with a shock of black hair peered round it.

'Hi there! This is one of your friendly, nosy corridor companions speaking. Mind if I come in? My name's Gerald Evans, but I hate Gerald, so make it Gerry. And I come bearing gifts: a mug of hot tea, a digestive biscuit and a carton of milk. No sugar, I'm afraid.'

I took the tea gratefully, and welcomed him into the room. He stooped slightly as he came in, his tall frame, tightly fitting suit and large hands making him seem a little awkward. Immediately, the room felt crowded and he sat down heavily on the end of the bed, which creaked alarmingly. He jumped up quickly.

'Oh God, sorry, I hope I haven't buggered your bed. Mine doesn't seem too safe either. Bit short, too. I might have to erect something or other to stop my feet hanging over the end. Anyway, I thought I'd look in as we're neighbours. I'm just across the corridor.'

His voice was soft and strong, and his questioning eyes, sturdy jaw line and natural charisma suggested he'd probably have immediate rapport with a class of children. He stretched out his long legs and thrust his hands deep into his trouser pockets.

'I only learned about my acceptance a couple of days ago,' he said. 'Odd sort of system, isn't it? I have an interview before I leave the sixth form, and then I have to wait until the day before the course starts to find out whether I'm coming here. Stunning bit of organisation, I'd say.'

'I had a bit longer than that,' I replied. 'Three weeks, to be exact.'

'Really? Perhaps they had a hard job filling up the places. After all, who except for mugs like us would want to be a teacher nowadays?' He dug into the pocket of his jacket and took out a pipe and tobacco pouch.

'I hope you don't mind me puffing,' he said guiltily. 'So many people have given up it makes you feel like a bloody social outcast. I drink occasionally, too. Pints, preferably.'

Without waiting to see whether I would agree, he put a match to the pipe and a dense cloud of acrid smoke drifted fog-like across the room. I waved frantically, trying to disperse it.

'Bugger, sorry about that,' he apologised. 'Hope nobody's got their washing out. My brother brought this muck back from abroad. I'll put it out. How long did it take you to get down here?'

'About an hour. I live in Ealing.'

'Oh, not far then. Are you planning to teach in Ealing?'

'Possibly. But I like the city. I'll probably stay in London and rent a flat. That's assuming I survive the course.'

'At least you won't have far to go if you've forgotten anything you need. You didn't bring a kettle, I suppose? There should be one in the kitchen area on each corridor, but somebody must have taken it. There's only a tiny saucepan. Do you spend a lot of time in London, living so close to it?'

'I love the theatre and cinema. I think the closer you live to London, the more you probably take it for granted. I'm a sucker for second hand book shops, though.'

'Well, I don't visit London much myself... and I'm not too far away. Slightly south of Watford. Always come down for the big movies though.'

He tapped his pipe out into the metal waste bucket and I opened the window again. The early evening air was turning much colder, but at least it cleared the smoke.

'Are you doing the primary or secondary school course?' he asked.

'Primary. I like the idea of teaching lots of different subjects. I prefer the younger ones.'

'They'd probably drive me up the wall. I'm doing the secondary course. At least they should be able to write by then. I'm doing geography as my main subject. Loved anything to do with maps at school. I quite fancied some sort of job in cartography, but the careers officer persuaded me I might have something to offer Britain's youth, so here I am.'

I looked at my watch. 'We should go soon. Only fifteen minutes to the meeting.'

Gerry stood up from the bed, dusted strands of tobacco from his jacket, thrust his pipe between his teeth and opened the door.

'Wouldn't mind a quick wash first,' he said. 'I'll just pop along to the primitive basins at the end of the corridor. Have you experienced the washroom?'

'Not yet. I haven't even finished unpacking. I'll do it while you wash.'

He strode off down the corridor and I closed the door quietly on the room that would be my home for the next three years.

(ii)

The assembly hall on the far side of the quadrangle was small but functional. Rows of chairs had been set out in front of the stage, empty except for a solitary lectern and a piece of scenery painted to look like a castle wall. The parquet floor had recently been cut back and resurfaced and there was a strong smell of polish. I sat with Gerry at the back of the hall, nearly all of the other seats being already occupied. The drone of muted conversation became louder as the hall filled, punctuated by occasional bursts of laughter.

'This is it, then,' Gerry said. 'I trust we'll be allowed weekends off, a lie-in on Wednesdays, a tray of tea brought to our bedsides on Sundays, and…'

His voice died away as Dr Bradley entered through a side door and carefully made his way to the front of the assembly. Black gown held close to him, he stepped gingerly onto the stage as if fearing the floorboards might give way. Placing a notebook on the lectern, he pushed his spectacles into a comfortable position and scanned his audience before speaking.

'Good evening, gentlemen. Firstly, I'd like to welcome you all most warmly to St. James's College. I have, of course, met some of you personally on a previous occasion and I look forward to renewing that acquaintance. The building is old, as you are doubtless aware, but like our students it also has character. And we are up to date in most other respects.' His voice, clear and fluent, reached the back of the hall without any apparent effort.

'There are several things to be mentioned before dinner, and then I'll leave you to meet each other and find your way around our labyrinth. Lectures commence on Wednesday, which will give you ample time to meet and talk with your tutors. You'll find a provisional timetable in the main corridor tomorrow. You should all be fairly knowledgeable about your individual courses from the information we posted to you. You can discuss the details with your tutors. There are certain compulsory lectures. Everyone will be required to attend physical education and of course the education lectures. You'll go out to schools on three teaching practices. The first one is short, the final one is not. The first will enable us to assess who's likely to succeed and who isn't. It'll be a bit like coming out of the trenches and going over the top; some of you will survive, others will be mown down before you've even given out the children's milk. I'm sure you will relish the challenge.'

There was a murmur of amusement as Dr Bradley paused.

'To be realistic,' he continued, 'we don't expect too much from you on your first teaching practice. Teaching in London… or come to that, in any city, is never going to be easy. I hope you will find our lecturers tolerant and supportive. It's also worth noting that a string of academic qualifications do not necessarily produce a fine teacher. There is much we can teach you about techniques, but there is no substitute for actual experience and it is therefore vital, gentlemen, that you learn from that experience.'

'I'm beginning to understand why he accepted me,' whispered a student directly behind Gerry. 'A few 'O' levels and a nice smile.'

'There will be a written examination at the end of each term. This is to ensure that you maintain a good academic standard throughout the course. You shouldn't have any difficulty keeping up with your studies if you don't waste time. You'll soon discover how easy it is to waste time at college, because unlike school, nobody will be looking over your shoulder. You will be responsible for your own learning.'

Dr Bradley stopped in mid-sentence, peered over his spectacles, and beckoned to a figure at the door. The latecomer was tall and very thin, most of his face hidden by a bushy moustache and a large black beard. A badly knitted long grey pullover hung limply over crumpled bottle-green corduroy trousers. He carried a rucksack in one hand and a banjo in the other.

'Come in and sit down,' said Dr Bradley acidly, looking at his watch. 'I'm assuming you've come to join us, or are we to be treated to a short recital on your banjo?'

A ripple of laughter ran through the assembly as the latecomer hovered at the side of the hall, looking for an empty seat. Then he leaned the banjo affectionately against the wall and sat down on a stool near the stage, apologising profusely for the disturbance. Dr

Bradley placed a hand carefully at each side of the lectern, gripped tightly and continued.

'Meals, gentlemen, are at nine, twelve and six thirty. Dress is informal for the first two, but we don't expect you to turn up for breakfast in pyjamas. We do, however, expect you to actually turn up for breakfast. It is traditional here that we wear a shirt and a tie for the evening meal. Now, clubs and societies are an important part of college life and you may join any of them. We also encourage you to start new ones.'

His speech was suddenly interrupted by the ping of a snapping string as the banjo gave up its attempt to remain upright and keeled ungracefully to the floor. The bearded owner groaned and Dr Bradley glanced sharply in his direction.

'Presumably our friend will be starting a musical appreciation group. Hopefully his strings can last out until then.' The bearded owner, embarrassed, grabbed the banjo and clamped it firmly between his knees.

'There are no lectures at weekends, but once you get involved with your studies you'll have more than enough to do. No doubt there'll be a young lady pining for you in the town where you live, so if you intend being away from college at weekends, please sign the weekend book. The Cook will need to know why you're not eating. May I also point out that this is an all male college, so don't pester the young ladies on the catering staff. We've lost several promising cooks that way.'

Gerry leaned towards me. 'At least our weekends are free,' he murmured. 'A chance for me to escape to Melanie's delights.'

'Two more points,' Dr Bradley continued, looking at his watch. 'On Friday mornings a series of guest speakers have been arranged to give lectures in this hall. Attendance is compulsory and an important part of the course. I think you'll find we've booked speakers who will challenge your views on education. And for those of you who would like it, we have an attractive chapel in the college and a short service is held there on Sunday mornings. Well, gentlemen, that's all for the present. Are there any questions?'

Several hands rose, and Dr Bradley pointed to the owner of the banjo.

'Yes, Mr… er… I'm acquainted with your instrument, but I do not recall your name?'

'Hornpipe. Dudley Hornpipe. Am I right in thinking there is some sort of clothes washing service?'

'There is a laundry service, and washing machinery of a sort in the basement, but it's even older than me and I wouldn't vouch for its reliability. Until now, I imagine your mothers have washed your clothes, but real life starts here, gentlemen, unless you intend to post your shirts home each week. There is no alternative to ironing creases from your clothes, but that is just one of life's little chores in today's world of increasing equal opportunity. However, Mrs. Marchant, our domestic bursar, will take care of your pillow cases, sheets and blankets and turn you out if you're still buried in them when she does her rounds.'

After fifteen minutes of answering similar questions on college domestic arrangements, the Doctor concluded by pointing the way to the dining room, where we were pleasantly surprised by a comprehensive buffet, attractively laid out on trestle tables around the room. It seemed that many students had already become acquainted with people on their corridors and they chatted in groups. We discovered that our corridor also housed Alex from Fintry whose Scottish dialect was so thick I couldn't understand a word he said, Ben from Eltham who seemed so nervous I wondered how he'd passed the interview and Anthony from Falmouth who seemed to have been travelling for days and was just anxious to get to bed. After several rounds of polite conversation Gerry suggested going to his room for a coffee and we were about to climb the staircase when a large metal kettle hurtled down the stairs and hit Gerry savagely in the kneecap.

'Oh shit!' cried a voice several flights up. 'Can somebody stop that kettle…'

'My leg already has,' Gerry shouted back.

'Bloody good! Wait there and I'll collect it.'

In a few moments we were joined by an exceptionally good looking, well built student, whose dark brown hair bounced on his forehead as he descended the stairs two at a time. He sighed as Gerry held up the handle.

'Look, I'm really sorry. What a day! I missed the meal because my dear old rusty Mini made an awful whistling sound on the way down and started overheating. I had to drive at five miles an hour until I got to my Auntie Jean's. She lives near here and helped me carry stuff round, but I missed the Doc's intro so I don't know what I'm supposed to be doing. I've eaten a mouldy cheese roll from a dirty little cafe round the corner and I was about to make a strong cup of tea with this kettle purloined from the bottom corridor and then the bloody handle falls off.'

'Sounds like your car's got a leaky radiator,' said Gerry. 'I can help with that. My father's a mechanic, so a few tips have rubbed off. You can get some stuff to make a temporary repair. Or it could be the head gasket. We'll find a spares shop in the morning. You'll notice that I am carrying a kettle, complete with handle. In return for fixing your motor and screwing the kettle handle on, would you like to make us a steaming cup of coffee?'

'Well… I'm not sure about that. You haven't fixed it yet. But you can have a coffee on account. What are your names?'

'Gerry. And this is Mike. You are…?'

'John. But since the age of five, I've been known as Duggan.'

'John? Duggan? Perhaps I'm being a bit thick, but I can't see the connection.'

'My dad was a keen gardener and I used to follow him round the garden with a little spade, but I was always digging up his bulbs. He'd go into the house and say to my mum 'You won't believe it, but the little bugger's just dug another one up.' Hence my name. Anyway, nice to meet you. Follow me to my palatial apartment.'

He shook hands warmly with us, and moved quickly up the stairs. He was on the same corridor as us, although his room was on a corner of the corridor and far more spacious. It contained the standard set of furniture but there was a second easy chair in the extra space. Part of the ceiling had flaked and tiny whispers of plaster had fallen onto the bed, but Duggan had obviously made a determined effort to make the room comfortable. There were small cushions on the chairs, photographs on the bookshelves and two miniature framed Monet prints on the wall. He heaved his suitcase onto the bed.

'If I carry this around much longer, I shall need a new gasket, too,' he muttered. 'Probably this is what ruptured the poor bloody Mini.' He flicked the catches open, dug one hand deep inside and pulled out a teapot.

'Is tea okay? Not sure where the coffee is. Had a spot of bother getting this. My mother wasn't keen on me borrowing the pot she brews the vicar's tea in, but I managed to convince her that my need was much greater. It brews a cup of tea with a real bite to it. Probably all the crustiness around the inside.'

I filled the kettle and went out to the kitchen area. By the time I returned, Duggan had laid out three bone china teacups, a bowl of sugar lumps, a tiny carton of long life milk and a packet of fairy cakes.

'I'm starving,' he said, peeling the wrapper off a cake. 'I suggest we drink this tea and then go in search of a decent chippy.' He poured the tea and passed the cups to us.

'There's one at the corner,' said Gerry. 'I had a quick wander round earlier this afternoon. There are pubs, second-hand bookshops, a record store, three cinemas, a couple of cheap eateries and of course the beauty of St James's Park for strolling around when Melanie visits. Pretty much everything to keep me happy.'

'Have you blokes bought your books yet?' Duggan asked. 'I was told not to buy any because the leavers always flog theirs off to the freshers at bargain prices.'

'I've spent a fortune,' I admitted.

'I've bought most of my geography set, too,' said Gerry. 'Didn't fancy rushing around half the term trying to find them.'

'Well lads, it looks like I'm down to borrowing your books for the time being. All I have is a paperback of 'Shane' and an Agatha Christie. I'm doing the combined science course. The 'A' level science papers must have got me in here. For some inexplicable reason I got quite good marks. I made a point of telling the Doc that I'd been in the Scouts for a long time and camped all over Europe. He seemed impressed and said it must have greatly broadened my experience of life.'

Gerry stood up and crossed to the window, gazing out at the night sky and stroking his long chin.

'I joined the Scouts for a while,' he said. 'The assistant Scoutmaster kept trying to put his hand up my trousers. Not only mine, either. I think he tried to put his hand up the trousers of the entire troop. It was certainly a quick way to earn a lot of badges.' He placed his bone china cup carefully back on the tray. 'Anyway, how did you two come to choose this college?'

'I didn't,' said Duggan. 'I chose the first three mixed colleges on the clearing house list. Just like every other bloke, I imagine, but all the places had gone. Then I just worked my way through the list until someone accepted me. Which happened to be here, but it couldn't be better. Right in the heart of London.' As he finished, he leant against the radiator and sprang off like a scalded cat.

'My God, it's full on! No wonder I'm sweating!'

'They're all on,' I said. 'Our small rooms are even hotter. And if you open the window you get covered in dust from the building site. Don't leave any books on your desk.'

'Good thing I haven't got any to leave, then.'

Gerry stood up, fiddled with the tap on the radiator, and shrugged his shoulders: 'Corroded. The system was probably installed by the Romans. I'll put a ring spanner on it tomorrow.'

'After you've fixed my car,' said Duggan. 'You're pretty handy then?'

'Alternatives, if I find I can't teach,' Gerry smiled. 'In any case, I shall probably need to moonlight, considering the current state of teachers' salaries.'

Duggan took some coins from his pocket and carefully counted them. 'I've got a bit of money left. Let's go to the pub, shall we? Probably our last chance before we succumb to the demands of educational philosophy.'

'Good idea,' said Gerry. 'The Barley Mow's our nearest. I shouldn't think it'll be very busy on a Monday night.'

He was wrong. The Barley Mow was not only the local for much of the neighbourhood, but every student in the college seemed to have descended on it after the buffet. Frantically waving a pound note in the air, Duggan was finally rewarded with three pints of warm lager and three packets of crisps. We managed to find a few inches of elbow room in a corner of the saloon bar.

'May it be the first of hundreds,' said Duggan, raising his glass and drinking a third of his pint with great enjoyment.

'So we're the first group to train for three years instead of two,' said Gerry. 'I can't see how they're going to fill the time.'

'Well, let's not complain,' Duggan replied. 'Think of the social side. Okay, so we've got some exams to pass, but we need to make full use of all the college facilities. The dances, the societies, the drunken pram races, the ladies from the neighbouring colleges. I reckon teaching should be the easy bit.'

'But teaching has changed a lot over the last few years,' I said. 'I wonder if the lecturers keep up to date with everything that's going on. Dr Bradley seemed to think they do.'

'You mean this business of the teacher not standing in front of the class and teaching any more? Yes, it has changed. In the primary school it's all topics, centres of interest, learning across the curriculum and so on.'

Duggan's mouth dropped open.

'Learning across the curriculum? So what's all that about?'

'All the curriculum subjects are integrated together. It's called a broad-based curriculum.'

'Is it? Well I've learnt something already. At my primary school we chanted our tables and divided our sentences into subject and predicate.'

'Table chanting is right out nowadays,' said Gerry. 'You're supposed to start at a level the child can understand and provide him with lots of practical activity to reinforce his number awareness. And reading schemes, well, they're definitely frowned upon.'

'Frowned on by whom?'

'The people who decide the latest fashions in education,' I said. 'The idea these days is that you surround children with books and they'll learn to read.'

'What, by osmosis?'

'We don't know that yet,' said Gerry. 'We've only read the theory.'

'Well, I can appreciate the theory. I mean, surround me with beer and I get pissed.'

Gerry nodded seriously. 'Nice analogy. And using the same principle, if I surrounded you with books, you'd learn to read. I just don't know how. No doubt the course will tell us.'

'Well, you lads have certainly put everything into perspective,' said Duggan. 'If only Mrs Brice had used that technique at my school. Perhaps she wouldn't have felt it necessary to keep digging me in the back with her finger. Anyway we'll worry about it all later. The dart board's free. Let's have a game.'

As we walked back to the college an hour later I looked forward to the new routines and pleasures of college life. I felt very lucky to be training in the heart of London and I intended to make full use of everything this great city had to offer. Three years, I felt, would pass all too quickly, and as I finished unpacking my case I anticipated the pleasure of teaching young, enthusiastic primary school children. The neon lighting on the buildings outside my window gleamed brightly across the night sky and there was a constant rumble of traffic from the main road. I sat down at my desk for a few minutes to write a brief letter home and then I climbed into bed, exhausted after the long day.

(iii)

It seemed I had only slept for minutes when I was awakened by a high-pitched whistling noise from the next room. I looked at my watch. I'd actually been asleep for more than two hours. Slipping on a dressing-gown, I crept into the corridor and knocked softly on the door.

'Come in, you old bastard!'

Startled, I turned the handle and put my head round the door, to be greeted by an apologetic voice.

'Oh! I beg your pardon, old boy… I thought it was Eric.'

Peering through sleep-blurred eyes, I felt I was surveying the last minutes of a jumble sale after hordes of aggressive bargain hunters had decided anything remotely worth having was already in their possession. Books lay everywhere, some half open, some in assorted piles, and several with notes scribbled in them. Many of them seemed to be about British birds. An additional socket had been pushed into the light fitting and three bulbs lit the room like a miniature film set. A purple vase on a stained coffee table in one corner contained a solitary, wilting plastic rose. Pieces of paper, covered with pictures of birds, mathematical equations and musical notation littered the floor. The ample bookshelf supported a glass fronted wooden box, containing a stuffed tawny owl and a piece of bread and butter, buttered side down.

The wardrobe inclined dangerously to one side. It was stuffed with magazines, clothes and a mud-covered trench coat. Two suitcases perched perilously on top. A box of balsa wood was on the desk, with a set of miniature wood carving tools, screwdrivers and a banjo with some of its strings missing.

Dudley Hornpipe sat heavily on the end of his bed, still wearing the long grey pullover he had worn at the introductory meeting, but no trousers. Instead, he wore a pair of football shorts, with a pipe thrust down each sock. Suddenly, he sprang up from the bed.

'What am I thinking of? Do come in, old boy.' He cleared a path for me through the clutter. 'Sit where you like. There's a spare cushion on the floor somewhere.'

I sat down obediently, like a patient in shock.

'Of course,' Dudley continued, poking various bits and pieces under the bed, 'you can lie down if you wish. Little sense in standing when you can sit, is there? And even less in sitting if you can lie.'

I nodded lamely. My eyes were still having difficulty adjusting to the light.

'I'm running a test, you see,' Dudley explained. 'If there is sufficient power for three light bulbs, then there's no reason why it shouldn't run my stereo. When the Normans built this place they neglected to put in a couple of wall sockets. I don't think we've met, have we? I'm Dudley. And you are?'

'Mike.'

'Excellent. Hello Mike. Is this a social visit or did you want to borrow something? If it's milk, I'm afraid you're out of luck.'

'Actually, I'm here because I was trying to sleep and I heard a noise from your room…'

'Really? You have my sympathy. I expect it's the plumbing. I think there's a packet of sleeping pills stuffed in here somewhere…' He thrust a large hand into his desk drawer and rummaged around for a moment.

'No thanks, that's the last thing I need. Do you realise the time? It's twenty past one.'

Dudley's eyebrows rose in astonishment. 'Good Lord! Is it really?'

'It is. And I've been trying to get some sleep, you see. I heard a noise…'

'A noise? Oh yes, of course, of course. I do apologise.' Dudley picked up a thin wooden pipe from the floor. 'I've just finished carving finger holes in this and I was trying it out. I've made quite a few but I'm not sure the pitch on this one is quite right. I prefer the banjo, but it's a second hand one and for some reason the damn strings keep breaking.'

'Yes, I noticed that,' I said.

'What, at the meeting, you mean? Bloody embarrassing. Still, we were invited to bring musical instruments if we wanted to, so I blame the good Doctor.'

He scratched his nose solemnly and gazed sadly at the instrument on the desk. 'I'll tell you something fascinating, though. I'm quite keen on nature study, birds mainly, and this pipe makes a sound incredibly similar to a red-backed shrike. Listen...' He blew a shrill noise on the pipe.

'So it does,' I said, with just the faintest hint of impatience.

'I told you! I suppose the real sound is more of a sharp '*shack-shack*', but there you are.' He made a curious honking sound in his throat, gagging with the effort. I wondered how many other people on the corridor had woken up and were wondering what was going on. Dudley didn't seem to have considered this.

'I fancy I'll be involving the children in this sort of work,' he said. 'Birds are fascinating. I've got a real passion for them. We'll build nesting boxes, analyse their songs, trace flight paths and so on. Do you know, it's possible to cover a large amount of the curriculum on a topic like this. I think it all depends...'

My eyes had closed and I began to slide off the chair. Dudley put his hand on my arm apologetically.

'Oh look, I'm terribly sorry... I really shouldn't be keeping you up. How about some coffee? There's some instant stuff under here somewhere...'

He searched under the desk, pulled out a battered biscuit tin and forced the lid open with a rusty spoon. 'Mind you, I imagine you'd rather have a beer, but Eric took the last two bottles of my home-brewed with him half an hour ago and I haven't seen him since. Probably shook it too much and blew himself through the bloody roof. I did warn him. Have you tried brewing it yourself?'

I shook my head. 'No, never tried it. I've tried sleeping, though, and I…'

Dudley swept on, untroubled by the sarcasm. 'You really should,' he said. 'It's remarkably cheap. I brewed two gallons to bring up here. Couldn't get any more in my car. Eric quaffed more than his fair share anyway, greedy sod.'

'I couldn't drink any more tonight anyway,' I said. 'I really just fancy a few hours sleep.'

'Black coffee it is, then. Unless you can find someone with a pint of milk to spare. I've got a boiled egg if you want one.'

I stood up hurriedly and groped for the door knob. 'Another day, perhaps. I'll look forward to it. Now, if you could just stop playing your penny whistle…'

'Of course! Of course! Well, do come again.'

He pumped my hand in a vice-like grip. 'Drop in whenever you feel like it, especially if you need help with your maths.' Picking up a piece of paper covered in numbers from the floor, he scanned it thoughtfully. 'Excellent. I thought I'd lost that. I must admit the idea of teaching mathematics appeals to me.' He sat down again and obviously expected me to do the same. 'It's a fascinating subject, like child psychology. Have you read this book?'

I took the thin orange volume he held out. 'No, I haven't,' I admitted, desperate for my bed and thinking I might have to tunnel out of the room to escape. 'It's not a set book, is it?'

'Haven't a clue, old boy. I haven't bought any of the set books, anyway. This one is fascinating. It contains a lot of stuff on children's sense of shape and perception. You know the sort of thing… if a child stares at the sky he'll notice the moon rather than a cloud, even if the cloud is equally bright.'

'I must admit I've never really considered it,' I muttered.

'Especially at this time of the morning, when sleep is what I need to be considering.'

'Take it, with pleasure. Read a bit of it before you go back to sleep. You can let me know what you think of it in the morning.'

Seizing the opportunity, I took the book, pointed out that morning had already arrived and hurried back to the sanctity of my room. As I drifted back to sleep, I wondered what children would make of Dudley. They'd probably find him fascinating. Or crucify him.

OCTOBER

THE PLUMBING, AND A FIRST TASTE OF FROSTBITE

Not daring to be late on my first morning, I hurried out of bed at seven o'clock, woken by the persistent ringing of my own alarm clock and those in the rooms around me. Grabbing my plastic ablutions bag, I staggered out of my room and along to the washroom at the end of the corridor, to find Dudley already there amongst several other students who were shuffling around aimlessly in their pyjamas. Dudley looked as if he hadn't been to bed at all, his condition reflected in the painful effort he was making to turn a tap on. The scene, I thought, resembled a committee meeting of zombies.

I braced myself, and muttered 'Good Morning' to nobody in particular. Dudley turned and smiled weakly, squinted at his beard in the large cracked mirror, and then padded out in his carpet slippers and dressing gown. 'I'll see you in a while, old boy,' he whispered. 'I'm never at my best this side of lunchtime.'

The washroom was desperately primitive, consisting of a stone-floored rectangular area with surface pipework that had so many joins I assumed the room must have been an apprentice site for plumbers. One tap had been twisted upside down. A row of ancient white sinks on each side of the room drained into a common trough, and the plasterwork was coming away from the wall, threatening to take the two end sinks with it.

Adding to the misery of this chilly morning, the hot water system seemed to have failed, and the water was ice cold. Some students had resigned themselves to scraping the shadow from their faces with soap and cold water; others entered the room, held a hand under a tap for a moment, and then muttered darkly before wandering back to their bedrooms. Several sinks were stained and cracked, and water dripped onto the stone floor from a noisy tap in one corner of the room. The drips were forming an ominous puddle that threatened to seep into the corridor, and I remarked that Milly must have a job mopping it up every day. Somebody near me laughed coldly.

'She never cleans anything up, mate. People have caught bubonic plague from the dirt on this corridor.'

'Frank doesn't like her,' explained a short, frail student wearing a pair of boxer shorts three sizes too large and a limp string vest. 'She never forgave him for the time he threw up in her washbucket. He didn't even tell her.'

'I did tell her, Dennis. You know that.'

'Not for two days you didn't.'

'Okay, I grant you that. But at least I did tell her. I just forgot, that's all.'

'She had a great time, scraping diced carrot off her mop, and...'

'Well, that couldn't have been me, then. I don't even like diced carrot.'

'No, nor did she. I...'

The conversation was interrupted by the strains of '*Tonight*' from *West Side Story* being sung in a Welsh dialect at an impossibly high pitch. The sound rang around the corridor and travelled towards the bathroom. 'Jesus, it's Dai,' moaned a student at the sink in the corner.

'Who's he?' I asked, finding an empty basin and filling it quickly.

'Dai Early,' said Frank.

'He's a second year,' said Dennis. 'Brilliant musician. Plays five instruments. Trouble is, the bugger sings all the time and if he sings any higher his testicles will be sucked inside his skinny frame. We don't need it first thing in the morning.'

'Which is why we call him Dai Early,' said Frank. 'And we keep our fingers crossed.'

A large, round, freckled face appeared at the door, wearing wire framed spectacles with a missing lens. A grin stretching from ear to ear took up most of the lower part of the face.

'Mornin' boyo's!'

'Morning, you Welsh sod!'

'Thank you for that friendly greetin', lads. I'm very pleased to see you too. Now then, what shall it be this mornin'?' Without waiting for a reply, he broke into the Soldiers' Chorus from Faust.

'Oh come on Dai,' pleaded Frank. 'Piss off, there's a good lad.'

Dai halted abruptly and wagged a loaded shaving brush at him.

'You see, boyo, that's your problem. You've got no culture. No culture at all. I give you the benefit of my singin' voice, and what sort of thanks do I get? None at all.'

'What do you expect at this time in the morning, you Welsh leek! What are you trying to do? Make me cut myself shaving?' He turned on a tap, and the pipes emitted a loud gurgling whine. 'Jesus, Dai, even the plumbing sings better than you,' he said sarcastically.

Dai took hold of Frank's arm, looked him gently in the eyes, and began to croon '*There'll be a Welcome in the Hillside*' at him. Frank looked faintly nauseated, and I concentrated on removing the morning shadow from my face as quickly as possible, making a mental note to get my electric shaver repaired. Duggan entered the washroom looking as if he hadn't slept for a fortnight.

'Would you mind if I purloined your soap?' he asked, taking the sink next to me before realising there wasn't a plug in it. 'I feel like I've eaten mine.'

'Here, boyo, have mine,' offered Dai. 'Smells like the Welsh valleys.'

'Christ!' Frank muttered.

Duggan accepted the soap gratefully and wandered around looking for a sink with a tap that worked.

'There's no hot water,' I said. You'll have to wash in cold.'

'Wonderful. I really need that. Still, I suppose it'll wake me up.'

The group gradually lapsed into silence. It seemed that in order to make the most of the washroom's inadequate facilities, it was best to arrive as early as possible. I later discovered that Gerry had risen at five thirty, washed before anybody else, and gone off for a twenty minute run.

Duggan and I were among the first few down to breakfast, a substantial meal with a good choice of food, and this at least made us feel more confident about tackling our brief for the morning, which was to meet our main subject lecturers. Gerry set off to put his name down for the geography course, while Duggan and I decided to track down the science department.

A map of the college had been pinned to a blackboard in the main corridor, and we studied it carefully. An hour later, after repeatedly meeting other first year students either in the boiler room or the basement lavatories instead of our intended destinations, we realised that the map had been craftily doctored. The third year students responsible for this were also getting a great deal of enjoyment from offering inaccurate directions to every lecture room in the college and then standing back to enjoy the confusion. It felt rather like an unsuccessful hour wandering around Hampton Court maze.

Eventually, we discovered one of the laboratories almost by accident. A note had been fastened to the door stating that new students should sit and wait on the chairs outside, and it had been signed by the head of the science department, Dr Frost. Nobody else was waiting, and I knocked gingerly on the door. There was no answer.

'He's gone home,' said Duggan.

'Perhaps he hasn't arrived yet.'

'Knock again. Perhaps he's deaf. Perhaps he's in the middle of an exciting experiment. Perhaps he's asleep.'

I knocked again. There was still no answer.

'Let's go and have a coffee,' Duggan suggested. 'We'll come back in half an hour.'

'We'd better wait for a minute at least.'

Three other students joined us, one dressed in a grey suit and immaculately knotted tie. They nodded briefly, and sat down on the row of chairs.

'Are you waiting to see Dr Frost?' the student in the suit asked.

'I don't think he's here,' said Duggan.

'Have you knocked?'

'Twice,' I said.

'Knock again,' urged Duggan. 'Loudly.'

I rapped my knuckles on the door and leapt away from it as a voice thundered from inside. 'Bloody well come in!'

'I think he might be in after all,' said Duggan, smiling encouragement. 'Your turn first.'

I stepped tentatively into the small laboratory and stood waiting for a further instruction from the man and woman confronting me.

'Well shut the door and sit down, lad,' said the man. 'There's a force nine gale whipping through this place every time the door opens and if we carry on this way we'll all be in bed with double pneumonia. Didn't you hear me calling you?'

'No. I knocked...'

'I know you knocked, lad. Half of London heard you. I even heard you the first time. God knows why you couldn't just knock and come in.'

I perched gingerly on the edge of the chair that had been placed strategically in front of a long, formica-topped table. Dr Frost was, I estimated, about forty years old, though his bushy grey eyebrows and furrowed forehead made him seem older. There was a meticulous neatness about his white-coated appearance that reflected a scientist's concern for detail.

Sitting next to him was a slightly built woman of similar age, dressed a little dowdily in a white blouse and grey skirt, who sat with her hands folded in her lap. She wore small tortoise shell spectacles and her hair was tied neatly in a bun. Though cautiously friendly, she seemed a little ill at ease in Dr Frost's presence. Despite its modest size, the laboratory was lined with shelves containing science books and apparatus, some of it damaged and labelled for urgent repair, and the window sill was filled with a variety of pot plants in various stages of flower.

'Right,' Dr Frost muttered irritably. 'Name?'

'Kent, Sir,' I offered, rather disorientated. 'Michael Kent, that is.'

'Make your mind up, lad. And which of the sciences did you wish to attempt?' His thick eyebrows raised questioningly as he glowered impatiently at me.

'All three,' I replied brightly. 'After my interview with Dr Bradley I decided I'd rather like to have a go at the combined course.'

He seemed acutely disappointed, and stared hard at me. 'Would you indeed, lad? Well, Miss Bottle does most of that.'

I turned briefly to Miss Bottle, who smiled encouragingly but said nothing. It was obvious that she disliked Dr Frost's manner but had grown accustomed to it, hoping that offering an occasional smile to a bewildered newcomer might ease things along a little.

'Well,' resumed Dr Frost bluntly, 'The course is a full one and there's a great deal of work to be done. That means you'll have to work like the devil to achieve anything at all, lad. Especially if you intend to produce reasonable results in three year's time. Three years might seem like an eternity to you, but some of the idiots who've left here without a smattering of physics in their addled brains have proved that it isn't. I lecture in physics, so you'll be seeing quite a lot of me.'

He smiled, a little desperately.

'Miss Bottle lectures in the other sciences, and you'll attend her classes twice a week. For the moment, anyway, until we've had a chance to find out whether you're any good or not. There are plenty of opportunities for extra study and you'll be expected to make full use of them. Three lectures a week are hardly enough and you'll have to do a lot on your own, lad. You've studied mathematics and physics to the advanced level of course?'

'I have chemistry,' I replied. 'And maths, but not at 'A' level.'

Dr Frost stared at me in disbelief.

'You haven't? What the devil is that supposed to mean?'

'Well, basically, it means I haven't passed maths at 'A' level.'

'But you do have ordinary level at maths?' whispered Miss Bottle. I nodded eagerly.

'You won't get far on ordinary level maths, lad!' Dr Frost exclaimed, his eyebrows pumping up and down in harmony. 'How on earth do you intend teaching in a school if you can't tell a square root from a bulbous one?' He turned and glowered at Miss Bottle, who sat bolt upright with fright.

'After all,' he continued, staring at the point of his pencil as if daring it to break, 'If you can't pass a simple 'A' level in maths, how do you expect to pass combined science? Mind you, ninety per cent of last year's lot probably had difficulty passing water.'

He stood up, rummaged through a cardboard box and pulled out a pencil sharpener. With meticulous precision, he proceeded to put a needle-sharp point on his pencil before he spoke again.

'And what have you been doing in the sixth form, lad? Anything?'

'Mr Kent has English and chemistry at the advanced level,' said Miss Bottle, helpfully. I gave her a mental gold star for at least doing a little research on her prospective students.

'Really?' grunted Dr Frost, unimpressed. 'Well it seems a damn funny combination to me. Have you thought of doing something else for your main, lad?'

'Yes,' I replied, a little testily. 'But I would prefer to do science.'

'Would you indeed? Well, I'd prefer to play golf all day, but I can't. This point is, are you actually any good at science? I can't have people deciding they want to pack it in halfway through the course. Damn sight better to find out now if you're going to keep up with me or collapse from exhaustion before we get to the laws of refraction.'

He got out of his seat and walked to the window. For a few moments he stared moodily out at the rain, and then seemed to relax a little.

'Oh, well, I suppose it doesn't matter provided you catch up in your spare time. Which course are you doing?'

'He's doing the course for teaching primary children,' smiled Miss Bottle.

'Hmm. Well, you won't have much opportunity for doing science with them, lad. All you'll do with seven year olds is potter about outside in a patch of dirt growing carrots, or try to make a broad bean grow in a test tube full of wet blotting paper. And there's a few who've passed out from here who'd even make a muck of that!' He snorted miserably, and Miss Bottle sprang to the attack.

'I really don't think that's quite true,' she interrupted severely. 'A great deal of scientific investigation is done in the best primary classrooms. It's becoming an important part of the primary curriculum. Why, I..'

'I rather doubt that,' interrupted Dr Frost, dismissing her view immediately. 'I can't say I've seen much worthwhile activity from some of the idiots I've visited on teaching practice. Not that you need a great deal of mental agility to grow a bloody broad bean.'

He turned from the window and took the lid from the teapot on the table, peering inside as if he half expected a chemical reaction to be taking place. The interview seemed to be growing into a private, and, I suspected, regularly aired argument.

'I wouldn't say that,' Miss Bottle objected. 'It's quite amazing what some of the younger children are doing. I've even seen Nursery children experimenting most interestingly with sinking and flotation, and...'

'I really can't see the point, Doris. Good God, you might at least wait until they're old enough to understand what they're doing.'

'I'm sorry, but they *do* understand what they're doing,' Miss Bottle insisted, clinging grimly to her end of the argument. 'That is the point, surely? They gather materials, experiment scientifically without knowing exactly why, and then question their results with the guidance of the teacher. Why, I..'

'I'm sorry Doris, I still don't see it. You've got to get a few basic facts into 'em before they can get anywhere…

'Not at all. There's no reason…'

'Oh come now, Doris. Don't give Kent this 'learning by discovery' stuff. We want him to start off with a reasonable chance of success. I mean, would he learn anything about electromagnetic waves if I stuck a transistor radio in front of him? You wouldn't learn a thing, would you Kent?' My head began to dodge to and fro between the two lecturers like a spectator at a Wimbledon final.

'Well, I don't know,' I said cautiously, realising a careful response was required. 'I think..'

'There you are!' retorted Dr Frost triumphantly, slapping the table with a meaty hand. 'He wouldn't learn a bloody thing!'

'But educational ideas and values change so rapidly' argued Miss Bottle, revealing a staying power I was rapidly coming to admire. 'I think you'd be quite amazed..'

'I am amazed,' he said. 'Each year I am amazed. I stood in a student's classroom last year and watched him take a lesson about heat with nine year olds. He'd hardly had time to tell 'em what heat was before they found out for themselves and set the bloody table alight.'

Miss Bottle, who had held her ground respectably up to now, sighed and declined from further argument, and Dr Frost suddenly seemed to remember there were others waiting outside to see him.

'Anyway, Kent,' he said, closing the folder in front of him, 'That will be all for now. There is a general lecture in the chemistry laboratory tomorrow morning at nine o'clock. It would be appreciated if you could actually manage to get here at nine, as well.'

I stood up to go. 'Have you got any text books?' he asked in a softer voice.

'I've bought the ones listed on the sheet I was sent before coming here.'

'Well, they're not much good. Years out of date, most of 'em. I make a new list every year and they still send the old one out. Waste of my time as usual. Here, you'd better have this. Make sure you get the first two before you come to any of my lectures, will you?' He passed me a typewritten sheet of paper, listing a completely different set of books.

'I suggest you try the Charing Cross Road if the college bookshop hasn't got 'em. Half the students never seem to buy the bloody things anyway, or if they do they use 'em for standing mugs of coffee on. And do a bit of reading before next week, will you? I don't want to spend my first lecture going over the scientific principles behind the workings of a wheelbarrow.'

Miss Bottle smiled apologetically at me. 'We'll see you bright and early tomorrow morning then, Mr Kent,' she said. 'Don't forget a note book, will you.'

'And don't slam the door,' said Dr Frost.

I closed the door as quietly as I could and motioned to Duggan, who was talking earnestly to the student in the grey suit.

'What's he like?' asked Duggan cautiously.

'Dreadful. He's like a wild bull. You'd better say you've got 'A' levels in everything. In fact, you'd better speak to him from a kneeling position.'

Duggan looked alarmed. 'Oh God, he won't exactly be carried away by my little lot, then. The bloke I've just been talking to over there knows more than Einstein. Honestly. Daines, I think his name was. Another bloke mentioned an LP he's just bought and Daines started talking about second harmonic peaks in loudspeakers. We'd better make sure he gets in our group. We can copy his work.'

'It's not going to be easy' I said miserably. 'Dr Frost seems to think this subject has the highest failure rate in the college.'

Duggan shrugged unhappily. 'Well I don't suppose I'll be doing much to alter that,' he said. 'I should have stuck to plasticine modelling. I was always good for the odd coil pot.'

'I'll go and put the kettle on. You'll need a strong coffee after the next fifteen minutes.'

'God, you make it sound like a dental extraction. I...'

The door of the laboratory burst open and Dr Frost glared at the row of chairs.

'Who's next?' he said sharply.

'I think I am,' Duggan replied.

'Well, are you coming in or not? I've got plenty to do without sitting in here all day. And I shouldn't stand around if I were you, Kent. You could have bought half the booklist by now. Go to it, lad!'

I took a deep breath, glanced in sympathy at Duggan, and then hurried out of the laboratory and back to corridor three. It seemed strangely quiet and I felt vaguely guilty, as if I was truanting from lessons and shouldn't have been there. I assumed the other inhabitants of the corridor were still making arrangements for the coming lectures which began in two days time. There was an hour and a half left until lunchtime, and I went to my room to fetch a towel, some soap and a flannel. After my experiences in the washroom earlier that morning, I decided I might be able to have a warm bath in reasonable comfort while nobody else was about.

The bathroom was opposite the washroom, and showed a family resemblance to it. There were two large cast iron baths with decorative feet, and the baths were separated by a thin dividing wall that had been patched with pieces of hardboard. I stepped into the small room and attempted to lock the door, but part of the lock had been broken off and I wedged it shut with a piece of paper. There was a sudden rustling behind me.

"Ello, love' said a husky, disembodied voice from the direction of the bath. I turned to find Milly propped up on a pillow and lying fully clothed in the empty bath.

'Just 'ad one of me funny turns,' she said, obviously feeling I deserved an explanation, 'It 'elps if I lay down in 'ere. I'd lay on one of your beds but I couldn't trust some of you saucy buggers!' She lurched into a sitting position, took some tobacco, papers and a rolling machine out of her apron pocket, and began to make a cigarette. 'I always roll 'em meself. They don't cost so much that way,' she said. 'Do you want me to roll you one?'

'It's very bad for you, Milly,' I said. 'Filling your lungs with that stuff.'

'Well they're my lungs, ain't they love? Got to 'ave a bit of enjoyment, 'aven't yer?'

Hunting in her overall pockets for some matches, she struck one and held the flame to the cigarette. Two thirds of the tiny tube disappeared immediately. She took a long draw from the remaining third, coughed earnestly and turned to me again.

"Ow are you findin' the work?'

'We haven't really got going yet. I don't suppose we'll do very much before Thursday.'

'Nobody does anythin' very much anyway, love. Not 'ere. Want to teach in London, do yer?'

'I haven't really thought about it.'

'I s'pose not. You've only just started. My Kathy goes to a school round 'ere. I don't understand 'alf the things they do these days. This new maths and all. Marvellous, the stuff these kids 'ave in school now. My Kathy loves it. Not like when I was at school. You got the bleedin' cane just for talkin'.

Her cigarette had gone out and she peeled it from her lower lip, inspecting it carefully as if she couldn't understand why it was so short when she'd only puffed on it once.

'Why don't you smoke ordinary ones?' I asked.

'Can't, love. They make me coff.'

'But you cough with those.'

'Not like I coff with the others. Coff me 'art up with them. Mind you, I should really pack it in. Bloke two doors up died of lung cancer last week, but my old man reckons it's the traffic smoke wot does it. Got an answer for everythin', 'e 'as. We've been tryin' to get the telly fixed for a week. At least when that's on we don't 'ave ter sit around listenin' to 'im carryin' on.'

She looked decidedly miserable and sat silently for a few moments. Then she wiped her nose on the duster and climbed out of the bath, groaning with every movement.

'Are you goin' to teach the little ones, love?'

'Oh yes. Wouldn't want to do anything else.'

'Much nicer,' she confided. 'Them older kids are awful these days. I watch 'em from me winder when they're comin' out of Strutton Road. A right school that is. Wonder they let 'em on the bus. Mind you, I don't think the teachers 'ave got much control.'

I sensed I was about to be treated to the general public's view of education again. 'I shouldn't imagine it's easy,' I interrupted quickly. 'Teaching the older ones, I mean.'

'Bloody right, love. Trouble is, the parents ain't got much control of 'em, neither. At least my Tracey never gave me any lip. Good girl, she was. Married now, o'course. Gone up north. 'Avin a rough time of it, too, what with the ceilin' and 'er poisoned bowel an' all.'

She gazed despondently at her duster.

'Oh well, love, I suppose I'd better do the floor before they all come back. Don't let me keep yer from the bath. I'll do yer room while you're in there. Unless you want yer back scrubbed?'

She manoeuvred herself out of the room and I turned the tap on. A trickle of rusty water ran out, which slowly developed into an intermittent flow. After two minutes, when the water showed no signs of even getting warm, I remembered that the hot water system had broken down. I abandoned the idea of a bath altogether, went into the kitchen area, and put the kettle on. As I was filling the teapot, Duggan and Gerry came up the stairs together.

'I'm changing my subject,' Duggan announced briefly, ushering both of us into his room. 'The man's impossible. I mean, I may not be the best qualified student he's ever had, but he seemed to take great delight in disagreeing with every word I said.'

'I know the feeling,' I said.

'Luckily he was called away, or I'd have been chewed up and spat out. Miss Bottle spent the rest of the time trying to calm me down. She doesn't seem to like him at all. She has my sympathy. I suppose we'll have to go and get some new books this afternoon. There's some biscuits in the cupboard. How was your morning then, Gerry?'

Gerry took his tea and perched on the armchair near the window, balancing his long legs on the edge of the bed.

'Well, not bad really. I've got a rather delightful old dear for geography. A Miss Pratt. Looks as if she's been chipped out of granite. She's in charge of all the visual aid equipment too. Cupboards full of projectors and slide tins. Might be able to use it sometime.'

'What for?'

'Well the college hasn't got a film society and I thought we might have a go at starting one. We might as well start something.'

'We might even have to start some work,' said Duggan, pouring fresh milk into his mug. 'I was going to have a pleasant afternoon pottering round the shops and now we've got to go charging around the second-hand bookshops looking for physics books. Here, have you read this?'

He lifted a paperback from his shelf and tossed it across to Gerry. 'It's about a guy who taught in a big comprehensive in Manchester. It makes you wonder if we should be here at all. He says it took him half the year to make his class sit down, and another six months to get them listening to him. Somehow they found out when his birthday was, and they gave him a present.'

'Well at least that shows some kind of feeling,' I said.

'Yes,' Duggan agreed. 'The present they gave him was a box of chalks nicked from his own stock cupboard. It wasn't even coloured chalk.'

'But they can't all be like that.'

'No,' Duggan admitted. 'Some are worse, of course. One of the final year students told me his kids chained his leg to the table one morning on teaching practice, and they had to fetch the schoolkeeper to get the padlock off.'

Gerry's pipe dropped several inches and he puffed nervously on it.

'Go on!' I said. 'I don't believe you.'

'I don't blame you.'

'It makes you think, though,' said Gerry, shifting his legs into a more comfortable position. 'I mean, just how do we cope with keeping order? The kids are bound to know we're students.'

'Psychology, mate. I read a book on classroom discipline by a bloke who's taught in some of the toughest schools. He listed about twenty different techniques for getting a class quiet.'

'Like what?' asked Gerry nervously.

'Well once, for instance, he put his waste bin on his desk and gradually peeled strips of paper into it from a note pad. The kids came in very noisily, and he took no notice. He just carried on peeling bits of paper into the bin.'

'And?'

'The kids gradually noticed him and became silent. They thought he'd flipped.'

'Well I suppose anything is worth trying,' said Gerry. 'I mean, you've got to have a few ideas in reserve.'

There was a tap at the door and Milly's head appeared.

'Hello treasure,' said Duggan, giving her a suggestive grin.

''Ello gorgeous. Do you want yer room done? I've finished all the others.'

'Do you want us out of the way?'

'No love,' said Milly cheerfully, easing a bucket through the door with her foot. 'Just cock yer legs up a bit while I get under the bed.'

'What do you want to get under there for?'

'The broom, darlin'. Not me.'

She thrust the broom violently between Gerry's legs and made a great deal of noise as she banged it about under the bed. ''Ere!' she exclaimed, straining to reach the hidden dust, 'You see that film up the Cameo this week? My old man says to me, 'Get yer coat on and I'll take you out. Course, 'e only says that when it's somethin' 'e wants ter see. Couldn't get the bugger near *The Sound Of Music*.'

'Don't blame him,' said Duggan.

'Well, this teacher kills 'er 'usband by drownin' 'im in the bath, and then the body disappears. Then in the end the body comes back in the bath again and tries to strangle the girl. Bleedin' scary, it was.'

'It sounds like '*Les Diaboliques*', said Gerry.

'You what, love?'

'A French film. *The Fiends*.'

'It bleedin' looked like 'em, an' all. 'Didn't dare look in the bath when I got 'ome.' She leant expertly on the end of the broom. It was obviously a position she was used to.

'You haven't found any in our bath, have you?' asked Duggan.

'Found any what, love?'

'Bodies.'

'Now don't you go sayin' that,' she said sternly. 'I wouldn't 'ave gone anyway if Sid 'adn't wanted to go. Don't worry, 'e said, I'll cheer you up afterwards.'

Gerry looked faintly disgusted.

'What did he do, then? Afterwards, I mean?' asked Duggan innocently.

Milly wiped her hands on her grimy overall. 'I wouldn't tell you, love,' she grinned. 'Not at your age. Where's your bucket?' Duggan slid the waste bin from under the desk with his foot.

'There's nothin' in it,' she said. 'It's not worth me emptyin' it.'

'We haven't done anything worth throwing away yet,' I said.

'That don't really surprise me, love. None of 'em do. Till it's too late.'

'Would you like a mug of tea, you gorgeous creature?' asked Duggan.

'Okay, love, but I can't sit down for more than a minute. If I get caught sittin' down again I'll get me cards.' Gerry held out the packet of custard creams.

'No thanks dear,' she said. 'They give me wind.'

She coaxed her ample body gently into the other easy chair, and sighed with relief. Carefully removing a liquorice paper from the battered packet she kept in her overalls pocket, she began to roll another cigarette. Long strands of tobacco hung limply from each end when she had finished.

"Ave you got a match, love?' she asked.

Duggan took a box from his desk drawer. 'I don't know how you can smoke that muck,' he said severely. 'Why don't you smoke a pipe, like Gerry here? Do you more good than those things you're smoking. At least you'd kipper your lungs more slowly.'

She lit a match and laughed.

'I'd get me cards, love. I 'ave enough stress coping with you buggers. It's a wonder I don't 'ave a bleedin' 'eart attack with what goes on up 'ere. One of 'em was runnin' round the corridor stark naked last term. Worried about 'is exams, 'e was.'

'He was probably after you, you gorgeous thing.' said Duggan. She gurgled with laughter, trying to avoid letting the cigarette fall from her mouth. "E's a saucy bugger, this one, ain't 'e?' she said to Gerry. He nodded seriously.

'So when do you think they'll get the hot water running properly?' he asked, anxious to change the subject quickly.

'It's usually a day or two love. It keeps breakin' down. Bin playin' up ever since I've bin 'ere. Well, taa for the cuppa. I'd better finish up now.' She sighed, put the mug on the table and stood up, shaking her duster outside the door. The dust scattered and hovered in the cold morning sunlight.

'If she spends as much time with everyone else along this corridor I'm not surprised she doesn't get much work done,' I said.

'Oh well, it's stopped us from doing any,' Duggan replied. 'It's gone twelve. Let's go and get some lunch, then Gerry can have a look at my radiator. Auntie Jean will give us a cup of tea and some cake, and then we'll go and buy some books. I'd like to have a sporting chance with Dr Frost before he puts me in a test tube.'

JANUARY

SO, WHO'LL BE THE FIRST VOLUNTEER?

'Right then,' said Dr Frost severely, 'Which of you gentlemen would care to be the first?'

He stepped down from the front bench, thrust his hands deep inside the pockets of his immaculate white laboratory coat, and walked with measured steps to the back of the room. This was a moment he always enjoyed, when he could really begin to assess the teaching potential of the students in his charge. After all, he reasoned, if they could stand up and teach a science lesson to their peers, while at the same time coping with his barrage of vitriolic asides, they could almost certainly cope on a teaching practice with twenty five bored teenagers in a London comprehensive.

There was a rumour that his own initial two years of teaching had been a baptism of fire, when his vision of imparting scientific knowledge to enthusiastic youngsters had rapidly receded, to be replaced by the cynical realisation that many of the children he taught didn't view physics as one of life's most desirable features. In his first year of teaching, his strong qualifications had earned him a class of 'A' stream boys, but after a few months he'd annoyed his head of department by stating that, if they were the cream of the year, it must have been clotted. His embittered approach, refined with more than a dash of sarcasm over the years, had been moulded like a shield to deal with all but the most troublesome youngsters. Once he'd found his feet, no class had ever given him trouble again, and he now treated his training college students with much of the contempt he'd once reserved for the teenagers in his classes.

His colleague, Doris Bottle, felt it almost immoral that he should be lecturing to students doing the primary school course when he had only ever taught secondary school children. The methods were totally different, she insisted. He descended even lower in her estimation when he refused to acknowledge any modern methods of teaching science to young children, basing his lecturing on the styles and techniques used when he had been trained himself. After all, he reasoned, he'd managed to get an honours without too much difficulty, so the methods he'd learned by couldn't be that bad, could they? Miss Bottle regularly argued the point with him but invariably backed down, partly because he acknowledged no other view, and partly because, in the final analysis, he did happen to be in charge of the department.

It seemed amazing that three months had passed already. We had investigated and joined a number of college societies, discovered a common love of chess which we played into the small hours at least twice a week, ploughed our way through books on education, and visited London cinemas, theatres and galleries as often as our grants would allow. The only blots on this new freedom were Dr Frost's lectures, which were organised like secondary school lessons. There was no opportunity to lose concentration for a moment. Dr Frost had an uncanny knack of knowing just when somebody had switched off, and he would bark a question or request a formula from anybody whose face showed even a momentary blankness.

During his first lecture to our group, he had given us a searching test to find out how much we knew about his subject. On the whole, the group's corporate knowledge was decidedly small by his standards. Since there were only ten students in this group, he had temporarily taken over Miss Bottle's sessions as well, with the intention of raising all the students to what he insisted was a minimum standard of acceptability. It wasn't long before he also discovered that six students in the group didn't have advanced level mathematics. Feeling that they needed an additional hour or two of maths cramming each week, he'd started a special booster group on Tuesday evenings. He was determined that the dismal results shown by last year's group wouldn't be repeated and woe betide any of the six who didn't turn up.

This seemed a reasonable idea at first, but working for two extra hours on Tuesdays, a particularly full lecture day anyway, had quickly dampened our initial enthusiasm. We also found it increasingly difficult to cope with the amount of work being set for our spare time, especially since he seemed unable to accept that we had much to do in other subjects as well. Ultimately, we felt that pointing this out would be taking a risk in which the odds were decidedly unfavourable. During his teaching career, Dr Frost had never had a problem with homework collection and he had brought the same rigid insistence to his training college lecturing. He was, in fact, the only lecturer in the college to be addressed as 'Sir' by all his students and some of the staff as well.

Gerry had quickly discovered that his geography lecturers took a similar outlook as far as the work schedule was concerned and, apart from a few hours at weekends, there was rarely any spare time. He coped with this more readily than most, since he had a great enthusiasm for anything related to a map or a piece of land. Where others might be seen reading a detective novel after lunch, he would be gaining intense pleasure from poring over an atlas or the latest National Geographic magazine.

When Dr Frost had suddenly announced that he was finishing one of his lectures half an hour earlier than usual, it had taken our group by surprise. Were we to get an early lunch? A breathing space? Was it a sign of a more relaxed approach to us? In fact, this was an annual and regular occurrence; the Doctor was merely allowing himself enough time at the end of the lecture to explain his method of assessing our teaching potential. He had prepared a list of scientific topics, from which each student had to select one and prepare a suitable lesson for thirteen year olds. The lesson was to be tried out on the rest of the group, who would act as the class for a forty minute period.

There were tentative murmurs of objection from the six of us who were intending to teach at a primary school, but on the few occasions that Dr Frost had actually been known to acknowledge the existence of children under twelve, he had simply stated there was no harm in them learning something with a bit of meat to it.

His announcement had meant sudden and hasty revision of work we had done in the early years of secondary school. After glumly scanning the list for ten minutes, Duggan opted to attempt a lesson on the properties of heat, and I decided that mirrors might be worth a try. Fortunately, the physics laboratory carried a good stock of equipment, managed by an efficient young Irish laboratory assistant named Patrick, who had watched many students undergo the rigours of this initial teaching experience. Always sympathetic, he did his best to ensure the necessary equipment was in the right place at the right time. He also revealed that Dr Frost had suffered from stomach ulcers, and this hadn't helped his temper or his patience. He had not been overjoyed when a member of last year's group, whom he had previously thought to be hard of hearing, had been caught listening to the test match through an earphone disguised as a hearing aid. His displeasure at this incident had apparently caused him to lecture until well after meal time.

'Well, gentlemen?' he glared. 'Not a single volunteer?'

All eyes looked towards Simon Daines, the student Duggan had first met while waiting for an initial interview with Dr Frost three months ago, and whose knowledge had impressed him even then. Though there were several talented and mildly eccentric students in the group... David Barton, a volatile student from Newcastle whose roughened hands were often oily because he enjoyed taking motor cycles to pieces and reassembling parts of them in his room, Samuel Charlton who had nine GCEs and collected telephone box numbers in his spare time... it was Daines who had rapidly come to be recognised as the cleverest of our group, probably accounting for seventy per cent of the group's overall knowledge of physics.

In only our second lecture, Simon had startled the Doctor, and astonished everybody else, by pointing out an error in a substitution equation, and the Doctor had stared intently at it for a full five minutes before coming to the reluctant conclusion that he had indeed made a mistake. Daines, the group felt, was destined for research rather than teaching, but his usefulness to the others extended in many directions, not the least of which was bribing him to check experimental conclusions before they were handed in for marking.

'Yes, I thought it might be you first,' Dr Frost said to Daines. 'The rest of 'em seem to be hiding behind each other. Oh well, bring your stuff to the front, lad.'

Daines picked up the mass of equipment that Patrick had assembled for him several days earlier, and walked purposefully towards the front demonstration bench.

'What do you intend to do, lad?' asked Dr Frost, waving his hand at an insect that had begun a circular tour of his head.

'Paths of light through a prism, Sir.'

'Jesus, that's a bit hard for thirteen year olds, isn't it?' breathed Duggan.

'Well, it's a bit above the age group I suggested,' Dr Frost commented, as if he had overheard. 'Still, it doesn't matter. The rest of you might learn something. Though looking at you this morning, I doubt it. Barton, sit up!'

'I am sitting up, Sir.'

'Really? Well sit up further. The lesson is beginning.'

'I'll try, Sir.'

'That's most kind of you, Barton.'

'Thank you very much, Sir.'

Daines cleaned the blackboard, selected a fresh stick of white chalk, and paused for a brief glance at his notes. Shutting his file, he turned to face the group, mentally converting them into a class of eager-minded children.

'Now then, this morning I'm going to start by telling you how we could study paths of light through a prism,' he began energetically. 'Please watch carefully.' He drew a large, equilateral triangle on the blackboard and turned round again, looking in Dr Frost's direction.

'Sir, I shall have to assume the class has already had some lessons on light, of course.'

'Well they have,' Dr Frost retorted. 'I've been talking about it for the last four weeks.'

'Yes Sir, I realise that, but I am assuming the things my class have done would be slightly different. This lesson is intended to follow earlier work.'

'Yes, yes. Just carry on.'

'Well, as I was saying, we will assume they have covered plane mirrors, real and apparent depth, curve by refraction and possibly paths of rays through a parallel sided block of glass. The lesson I'm going to do would naturally be what they would have covered next, so I...'

'I doubt if they would have,' Dr Frost interrupted.

'Doubt if they would have what, Sir?'

'I doubt if you'd have got much about refraction into 'em. You'd probably have spent most of the year getting the dafter ones to realise why they can see themselves in a mirror.'

'I'm assuming they would be a fairly intelligent class, Sir.'

Dr Frost sat forward on his stool at the back of the laboratory and cupped his chin in his hands.

'Why?' he barked.

'Because I've prepared...'

'You can't assume anything, lad. You're likely to have a class with half a dozen who know roughly which direction their heads are facing, and the rest whose brains are buried somewhere in their backsides. Mixed ability, I'm told, is the order of the day.'

'Yes, Sir, but I've prepared this lesson for a fairly intelligent class and...'

'I see, then we'll have to pretend that that's what they are.' He looked round at the group with an amused expression. 'You hear that, gentlemen? You are an intelligent class. Well, well. Carry on, Daines.'

'Thank you. Have you got some coloured chalk, Sir?'

'Coloured chalk? Good God, I'm not sure if this underfunded department can run to that kind of luxury, lad. There may be a stick of yellow by the tap on the bench if you're lucky.'

Turning to the blackboard again, Daines added some yellow lines to the diagram and labelled them. The group sat silently, watching him carefully.

'I realise I'm stopping you before you have hardly begun,' Dr Frost frowned, looking at his watch, 'But you'll have to watch this turning around to the board too much. Keep talking, or you'll find half of 'em have gone to sleep. Or disappeared from your classroom. And don't think that can't happen, lad. Give 'em an inch and they'll take the rest of the day.'

'I've got to get the diagram on the board somehow, though,' Daines objected.

'I know that, lad. But you could have drawn it on a sheet of paper beforehand, and pinned it on the board. Or drawn it on the board before the class came in.'

'I couldn't, Sir. I didn't know who was going to be chosen.'

'Yes yes, laddie, I appreciate that. I am merely pointing out what you should do when you have a real class.'

'But I would have, Sir, only...'

Dr Frost sighed. 'Look, don't bloody argue about it. Just get on with it.'

He blew his nose loudly, stuffed the handkerchief into his pocket, and picked up a pad and pencil from the bench behind him. Daines wavered momentarily, and then resumed his lesson.

'Now, this is intended to be a triangular slab of glass. A prism, in fact. Does anyone know what I mean by a prism?'

Several hands went up, but Dr Frost waved them down again.

'Don't ask too many questions, lad,' he warned. 'Especially simple ones like that. We haven't got time. Frankly, I'm frightened of the answers you might get. Half the class will probably tell you a prism is a place you keep criminals in.'

There was a ripple of sympathetic laughter and Daines smiled cautiously. 'Well,' he went on, 'If we place the block with one of its sides flat on a sheet of white paper, as I'll show you in a moment, and set up two pins here... and here...'

Duggan groaned and moved his stool behind a chemical balance at the end of the bench. 'I pity the poor sod who's got to follow this one,' he whispered. 'Perhaps he'll keep it going until lunchtime.'

'Don't worry. When he's finished, we'll ask a lot of questions.'

Duggan shook his head sadly. 'That just puts it off until another day. It's like bloody Russian roulette. If he's stopping Simon every five seconds I should think the rest of us will be hard pressed to get a syllable out.'

As the lesson progressed, Dr Frost rocked slowly to and fro on his stool, scribbling an occasional note on his pad. Despite his earlier interruptions, he was obviously pleased with the way the lesson was developing. Daines carefully constructed the experiment from the materials he had brought to the front bench, setting out a large sheet of white cartridge paper, some mapping pins and a triangular prism. Then he cleared the remaining bits and pieces from around the work area, and invited his 'class' to come and stand around the bench. The rest of the group moved cautiously forward, like battle-worn troops testing a minefield. Daines then resumed his explanation.

'Now then, I shall mark these pins as it will help you to understand the result of the experiment. Watch carefully. We'll call this pin 'X' and this pin 'Y'. Assuming that everything has been set up properly, we should see two pins in line with the images of X and Y. Then we take a pencil and a ruler… can somebody pass a ruler..'

'Well, I could if I'd eaten one, but it'ud be bloody painful,' said Barton cheerfully.

'What was that?' snapped Dr Frost, leaning forward on his stool.

'It was a joke, Sir,' said Barton. 'Daines asked if someone could pass a ruler. I said it would be painful, Sir.'

'Did you really? That's a joke is it?'

'It was certainly intended to be, yes Sir.'

'Well laddie, if you had been in my class and made a joke like that I'd have tied your testicles in a reef knot and torn up your work. That wouldn't have made you very happy, would it, Barton?'

'It certainly wouldn't, Sir.'

'Right, then unless you have a valid or pertinent comment to make, I suggest you contain your garrulous tongue between jaws of discretion.'

'Thank you Sir. I'll certainly try, Sir.'

'Now what was it you wanted, Daines?'

'I wanted someone to pass me a ruler, Sir.'

'Barton, pass him a ruler.'

Daines felt he had been given an object lesson in dealing caustically with a classroom wit, and he took the ruler gratefully.

'Thank you. If we join a line between these two points… and then take the prism away, you can see what I'm left with. You'll see even clearer when you do it for yourselves in a moment.' Dr Frost smiled one of his rare smiles and scribbled something on his pad

'Don't go too quickly, lad,' he advised. 'I can see what you're getting at but don't overestimate the ability of your class. Far too many students make a complete mess of their first teaching practice doing just that. Quite good so far, though. Go on.'

'Well,' Daines concluded 'You'll see we now have an angle between the incident and the emergent rays, which I'll mark as 'Y'. This is called… '

'Don't tell 'em what it's called,' said Dr Frost quickly. 'See if any of 'em know.'

Daines looked round at the small sea of worried faces in front of him. 'Does anyone know the name of the angle?'

'Fred?' suggested Barton.

'Thank you Barton,' retorted Dr Frost. 'You're a fool, lad. What are you?'

'I'm a fool, Sir.'

'Thank you. Is there anyone among this supposedly budding group of science teachers who actually knows what the angle is called?'

There was a painful silence. Daines hesitated, wondering whether he should continue, or whether Dr Frost was commandeering his lesson.

'No? I thought not. Tell 'em, Daines.'

'Well,' Daines concluded, 'The angle between the incident and the emergent rays is called the.. er.. angle of deviation. And that's about it, except that you can try it for yourselves. Has anyone got anything they want to ask? I think it's perfectly straightforward, though?'

Somebody at the front nodded vaguely, more in appreciation of the lesson than an understanding of it. A hollow cough sounded from the back of the laboratory, breaking the respectful silence. Daines looked round at the group, his confidence fully restored. 'Well, if there are no questions, you can do it for yourselves now. Then you'll see what I mean if you're not absolutely sure.'

He stepped down from the front bench and began to distribute sets of apparatus, placing in front of each pair of students two sheets of white cartridge paper, some pins, a drawing board and a block of glass. Duggan immediately began marking the first piece of paper with the ruler and pencil we had been given.

'Are you sure you know what you're doing?' I asked cautiously.

'Only partly, Mike. Only partly. That's why I'm measuring

everything in sight. When in doubt, look incredibly busy, especially if the good doctor moves in this direction. He did well though. Simon, I mean.'

'You understood it all, then?'

'I didn't say that. I just said I thought he did very well. I wouldn't have tried it myself.'

Daines moved from group to group, murmuring encouragement, suggesting slight alterations, and helping where necessary. He was already beginning to seem like an experienced teacher.

'All right?' he asked Duggan kindly.

'Yes thank you, Simon,' Duggan replied graciously, standing back to survey his results. 'We were just wondering whether to have a crack at this on our first teaching practice.'

'Will you have secondary children?'

'No. Lower juniors.'

Daines ignored the sarcasm and smiled benignly, secure in the knowledge that his own ordeal was over. He had given his lesson, it had gone well, and the Doctor was pleased. During the first part of the practical session, Dr Frost had wandered about the room, spending most of his time with the students at the front and confirming the accuracy of the experiment for himself before returning to his seat. Now he stood up slowly, scratched his nose, and looked at his watch before speaking.

'Yes, well, Daines. That's not bad at all for a first shot. Probably a bit above the heads of lower secondary, but you seem to know what you're talking about, which gives you a head start on some of us.'

Daines smiled self-consciously and drummed his fingers on the bench water tap nervously.

'One or two points I'd mention, though,' Dr Frost added quickly, as if he felt that his praise might have been too lavish. 'You tend to go too quickly, lad. I realise this is your first attempt, but we might as well get things straight from the start. There's enough for three lessons in the one you've done this morning. Don't be in too much of a hurry.

Remember you're supposed to be teaching them, not lecturing to them. Take it step by step.'

Daines looked a little bemused. 'But you said there wasn't time to ask many questions, Sir,' he objected.

'Yes, I realise that, lad,' replied Dr Frost, his voice rising irritably again. 'I am simply pointing out to you that many of the children in London are beyond learning, from what I've seen of 'em. At least if you go slowly you'll have an outside chance of getting something in their heads.'

For a moment, I wished that Miss Bottle had been in the room to take issue with this statement, or at least provide a visual reminder that not everyone shared his opinions.

'Anyway, lad, that's the most important point,' Dr Frost continued, looking at the notes he'd scribbled on his pad. 'The other point is one on which Miss Bottle and I have agreed to differ. She tells me that the children she visits in primary schools potter about with bulbs and batteries and pieces of wire trying to find out about electricity. No doubt they end up giving each other electric shocks. With older children you must make it blatantly obvious what you're supposed to be doing. Don't tell 'em what is supposed to happen. Not at first, anyway. Give 'em a sporting chance of using their addled brains before you give up and tell 'em what day of the week it is.'

Daines sat down, looking relieved and a little flushed.

'That's all,' Dr Frost concluded. 'Go more slowly next time. Never assume the blighters you're teaching know as much as you do.' He stared round the room again. 'Hmm,' he added, 'I suppose some of 'em might, at that. Now then, who's next?'

There was an almost imperceptible movement of every student in the laboratory towards whatever piece of bench apparatus offered the slightest chance of concealment. Only Simon Daines remained completely visible. Dr Frost sighed with exasperation.

'Well, dammit, come on. I don't intend to waste the rest of the morning. What about you, Phillips?'

Duggan was taken by surprise and looked at him in disbelief.

'Me, Sir?' he asked incredulously.

'And why not, lad? I imagine you've been kind enough to prepare something for us, haven't you?'

'Well yes, but..'

'Then come along, lad. Surprise us all.'

Duggan stood up, looked around hopelessly for a moment, and then sat down again. Several other faces were emerging cautiously, and with considerable relief, from behind flasks, bottles and balances.

'You've got to face the cretins sooner or later, you know,' Dr Frost growled. 'If you intend to make a mess of it you might as well do it this morning. You won't actually fail in here. You will only fail if you cock everything up on your teaching practice.'

He suddenly seemed very angry again. Duggan fumbled with the pieces of apparatus in front of him, gathered them together and walked slowly to the front bench. Placing his folder of notes on the lectern, he gazed nervously round the room. Several students gave him sympathetic looks, wondering how his lesson could possibly top, or even equal, the previous one. Simon Daines smiled at him happily. Barton was busily examining a metal tube used for expansion experiments and probably wondering if he could incorporate it into the tailpipe of his motor bike. Charlton was staring intently at the ceiling, his eyes narrowed in concentration. Duggan took a deep breath and began, wondering how long it would be before the Doctor cut him to ribbons.

'I'm going to give you a lesson on…er.. convection. That is..'

'Speak up then!' Dr Frost roared from the back. 'Let's hear what you've got to say. You never know, it might even be worthwhile. You're going to give a lesson on what?'

'Convection, Sir'.

'Are you? I shall look forward to it, laddie. Keep your voice up. Children won't sit as quietly as we are, you know. They'll be all over you if you give 'em half a chance. Or they'll be making very silly jokes like Barton, won't they Barton?'

'I suppose they might, Sir. Yes.'

'Well then. Start with a bang, lad, and keep up the pressure.'

Dr Frost had never forgiven Duggan for missing a physics lecture just before Christmas, on the pretext of being too ill to attend. As an excuse for missing one of his lectures, an illness had to be terminal, and in the best Sherlock Holmes tradition the Doctor had checked with Matron and found that Duggan hadn't reported sick. This wasn't surprising as he'd taken the afternoon off to see Hamlet on a matinee ticket bought for a pittance from a drama student who hadn't been able to go. Though he had never found out the true reason, Dr Frost had regarded Duggan with suspicion and monitored all his subsequent attendances very carefully indeed.

'Convection's a bit simple, isn't it?' he said, throwing his pad down on the bench with an ominous slap.

'Not really. I'm assuming this group is a class of ten year olds,' said Duggan quickly. 'Since I shall be teaching primary children and since it is highly likely that I shall be teaching a junior class on my first teaching practice, it seemed a reasonable idea to work out a lesson for that age group.'

'I see lad. All right, go on.' Dr Frost seemed, for the moment, to have lost a round.

'Right then. Well, I expect some of you have put a poker in the fire. If you put a poker in the fire...'

'It gets bloody hot!' retorted Dr Frost. 'That's conduction, not convection.'

'I know,' said Duggan. 'I was going to lead on to convection. I was just mentioning conduction because...'

'Don't bother. We'll graciously assume we have been taught that.'

'Right. Well then, when heat travels by convection the molecules don't stay in one place..'

'We're assuming we've been taught about molecules, are we?'

'Well yes, I...'

'We're assuming quite a lot, aren't we?'

'Well, we have to, really. Unless I start off a new topic, we have to assume certain things. Anyway, in convection the molecules don't all stay in one place. That is, they do in conduction, but not in convection. Almost, anyway.'

'Oh come on, lad,' groaned Dr Frost, gazing out of the window with a bored expression on his face. 'We've got fifteen minutes left and it would be nice if we learned something. Just get on with it.'

'Well, we can show convection quite easily by using a beaker of water like this to see the movement of the molecules. To do that, I'm going to use these purple crystals. Does anyone know what they're called?'

Three hands were raised in the air.

'I presume you wouldn't ask a class of ten year olds what they're called?' interrupted Dr Frost.

'I might do, Sir. It would depend…'

'There would be very little point, lad. They probably wouldn't recognise water, let alone crystals of potassium permanganate.'

Charlton's hand shot in the air and Duggan looked across at him and nodded.

'They're crystals of potassium permanganate,' Charlton said proudly.

'I know. Dr Frost has just mentioned that. I don't see why…'

'You asked us a question,' said Charlton. 'You asked us what the crystals were called.'

'I know, but Dr Frost has just answered it.'

'Has he? Oh.' Charlton looked distinctly disappointed.

'For God's sake listen to the lesson, Charlton,' rasped Dr Frost. 'Get on with it, Phillips.'

'Right. Well, first we wrap the crystals in a tiny piece of gauze and drop it carefully into a beakerful of water. If we heat the beaker, we'll soon see a sort of continuous motion. A tiny stream of purple, that is. It proves that firstly the molecules are moving and secondly that they move in a circle. We called this circle convection,' he added proudly.

He paused to glance at Dr Frost, who was absent-mindedly trimming his fingernails with a pair of dissecting scissors. Barton yawned. Daines looked at his watch, held it to his ear and then shook it vigorously. Duggan struggled self-consciously to the end of his lesson introduction.

'Well, that's the…er.. theory of convection in a nutshell, really. Of course, this principle is behind hot water systems, land and sea breezes at the seaside, and so on. Depending on whether it's night time. Or daytime, of course, as the case may be. I assume I would teach you that another day. Now we'll try the experiment…'

'That's it then, is it? asked Dr Frost in wonder.

'Well basically… yes. But there's the experiment to do. And the summing up. And we can…'

'We can't, laddie, we can't. The class would be in uproar by now. For heaven's sake put some enthusiasm into it. Do you seriously think they're going to know what you're talking about when you rabbit on about the continuous motion of molecules?'

'I suppose they might not,' Duggan agreed miserably.

'Then why mention it, lad? It just won't do at all. There's no point in waffling about the weather at the seaside while you're making pretty colours with a handful of magic crystals and a pot of water. Ask 'em a few questions first.'

'But you told Daines not to..'

'Never mind what I told Daines, lad. His lesson was longer than yours. If you're going to teach ten year olds some science you've got to do it properly. Make 'em sit up and listen. Once they know your crystals aren't going to blow up or make a disgusting smell they won't be interested. Now what's this experiment they're going to do?'

'Well actually, I couldn't get enough stuff for everybody to do the experiment,' Duggan apologised, sorting through the equipment he had in front of him. 'If you'd like to come round the front bench I'll demonstrate it to you instead.'

'Couldn't get enough stuff? What stuff?'

'Well, things like beakers and…'

'Beakers? There's plenty in the stock cupboard? How many do you want, for God's sake?'

'Well, I asked Pat…'

'Pat?'

'One of the lab technicians. I asked him…'

'When?'

'Yesterday. He hadn't got the right keys with him and he was a bit pushed for time.'

'Really? And is this how you're going to carry on in a school? Although I suggest it's highly unlikely, you might just have a future Newton or Boyle or Madame Curie gazing admiringly at you amongst the children you're teaching. Are you going to tell Newton or Boyle or Curie that they can't do any experiments today because Pat hasn't managed to get any equipment out? We might have to write this lesson off as one we'd all rather forget. At least, that's what I think. I wonder what the children think? Children, what do you think?'

He turned to the group and raised his eyebrows in question.

'I think it's quite interesting, actually,' said Barton. 'It's about my level.'

'Is it, Barton? Yes, well, I suppose it does require the sort of brain power you'd use for connecting a bulb to a battery. Who agrees with Barton?'

Hands lifted tentatively into the air. Dr Frost sighed and nodded. 'Very well, Phillips. The verdict is on your side. Go on, lad. I suppose you'd better show us your experiment.'

Duggan placed a flask in a wooden holder while everybody moved cautiously to the front. He tightened the screw, lit a Bunsen burner, and placed it carefully underneath the flask.

'Now then,' he said, 'We drop the crystals in here. I've wrapped them in a small piece of foil to stop them streaming too quickly, and…'

'One moment, lad,' said Dr Frost quickly. 'I'm sorry to interrupt again, but it's no good having them all grouped around you like that, or you'll find a few mischievous blighters behind you who don't give a damn about convection. Or you, for that matter.'

'Please Sir,' said Charlton loudly, 'I can't see what's happening to the water. The Bunsen flame isn't adjusted properly.'

'It's bubbling, Charlton,' Dr Frost replied. 'Liquids tend to do that when they're hot.'

'Thank you very much, Sir.'

Duggan looked down at the flask. A thin coating of soot from the Bunsen flame had covered the bottom of it, and he tore off a length of paper towel to wipe it away. The flask was hotter than he had expected, his trembling fingers jolted the stand, and the tripod lurched sideways. With a spectacular crash, the flask hit the bench and split in two, splashing its contents over everyone standing nearest the front. Duggan gazed at the expanding purple puddle enveloping his notebook and sighed deeply.

'Oh, for Christ's sake…' he muttered.

'I'm afraid he's unlikely to help you, Phillips,' said Dr Frost, gazing at his immaculate white laboratory coat now flecked with tiny purple spots. 'This really isn't your day, is it? You've broken a flask, wasted an expensive chemical, covered your notebook in purple and burned the children nearest you. Not to mention the danger of broken glass. On current form, you could give up the idea of teaching and start your own demolition firm instead.'

There was a murmur of activity outside the laboratory and Dr Frost glanced at the clock.

'Oh well, saved by the bell, Phillips. You'll be relieved to know it's now lunchtime. We'll leave it at that. Get the mess cleared up, will you?'

'There's a question I'd like to ask,' said Daines, like an embarrassing guest at a party. 'What you did.. or what you were going to do, is fairly simple. If you were going to do something about heating liquids, wouldn't it have been better to do something like Newton's Law of Cooling? Then we could all have drawn a very simple curve to illustrate it. It's only an idea, of course.'

'You seem to forget I'm doing the primary course,' said Duggan unhappily, picking up pieces of broken glass with a pair of tongs.

'Yes, I know, but...'

'I think he's had enough for one morning,' said Dr Frost in a softer voice. 'Never mind, Phillips. It's best to get these things settled before you actually get out on teaching practice. At least you'll know what to expect. It'll be a lot easier next time, but it's your own fault for not preparing properly.'

He removed his stained coat, looked at it sadly, and hung it on a peg by the door.

'At least you were original,' he continued. 'I've had flasks dropped by students shaking like leaves. I've had a transformer dropped on my foot. I've even had a fool who gave me an electric shock. But I have to admit I've never been sprayed with potassium permanganate before.'

Duggan reddened with embarrassment.

'Don't worry lad, I won't send you the dry cleaning bill. This time. Now go and get some lunch, all of you. Last one out shut the door. It's Tuesday and I've got to go home to feed the rottweiler. I think he gets better cuts of meat than I do. Damn dog is just like one of the family.'

We felt we knew which one.

FEBRUARY

HOPPING WITH THE FRESHERS

College dances at St James's were important events on the social calendar, and we discovered that at least two were held every term, ranging from the grand formality of the annual Christmas Ball, to the unfettered exuberance of the Freshers' Hops, which were essentially a guaranteed method for new students to meet partners of the opposite sex.

Admission was usually by ticket only, and since some of the dances weren't particularly well attended, members of the social committee were often bribed to sell tickets with the promise of free lager, the quantity being dependent on the number of tickets sold. Ticket sellers faced a hard task; making most students part with even a small proportion of their grants was like squeezing blood from a stone. Tickets were usually sold in the early evening, when most rooms would be occupied by students writing up lecture notes and there was a greater chance of a sale.

However, this time of day also caused an additional headache for the sellers. Since the rooms were so close together, it was possible to knock on one door and mistakenly be answered from at least three others. One unfortunate ticket seller had answered what he'd taken to be a welcoming invitation and then realised he'd entered the wrong room when he found the occupant partly clothed and in a compromising position with his girl friend. Apologising profusely, he'd offered two free tickets as compensation for disturbance at a critical moment, but the offer was turned down because the student had been unable to think of a handy place to store the tickets at that particular moment in time.

Bands were often a problem, too. Either they played so loudly it wasn't worth approaching a partner because she wouldn't hear you anyway, or they didn't play anything anybody could dance to. Sometimes, they even played out of tune, and this seemed dependent on how cheap they had been to hire, or how much they had drunk as the evening wore on.

The event Duggan and I were currently considering was known, a little optimistically, as the February Fun Frolic, held in the college gymnasium. Because the gymnasium was notoriously cold in the winter months we would not have considered attending under normal circumstances, but the offer of two very cheap tickets from Gerry was very tempting.

'You can have them at less than half price,' he offered graciously, tossing them onto Duggan's bed. 'I was going to bring Melanie but I can't be bothered to drag her up here and then get her back home again to Watford in this weather.'

'Why don't you let her sleep in your room?' Duggan suggested.

'You would think of that.'

'I think of that most of the time. Let her sleep in my room, then. She can kip in the armchair and I'll look the other way when she gets undressed.'

'She's not like that.'

'What, you mean she never undresses?'

'No, I mean she's just not like that.'

'Well what are you going out with her for?'

'To keep her away from sods like you.'

'How much do you want for the tickets?' I asked.

'Not much. Five bob each.'

Duggan sat bolt upright on the bed. 'Five bob? My God, who's coming? The Queen?'

'It's a fair offer. Almost half price. I paid seven and six each for them.'

'That was a bit silly, wasn't it?'

'Well, the band's expensive.'

'Who's playing, then?'

Gerry scratched his chin absent-mindedly. 'I'm not absolutely certain, but as far as I recall it's Tony and his Tijuana Six.'

Duggan groaned loudly. 'Well, who would have guessed. The motto of the social committee runs true to form. If you can't get a proper band, you can always get Italian Tony and his Tijuana Six. Even if every other band in the world is out on a gig, Tony and his Tijuana all-stars will be sitting and waiting for St James's to ring.'

'I don't think they've played here that often,' said Gerry.

'Who played at the Hoedown?'

'Well yes, they did play at that. I grant you that one.'

'Who played at the Firework Fiesta?'

'Okay. I think they did that..'

'Who played at the fancy dress thing?'

'Did they do that one? I didn't realise.'

'Who played at...'

'Do you want my tickets or not?'

'We'll give you half a crown each,' I offered.

'Four and six,' said Gerry firmly.

'Four bob.'

'Okay, Four bob. And I'm crippling myself to manage it.'

'I know, and we sympathise,' said Duggan. 'We're the ones who've got to suffer the Frolic, though.'

'I'm sure you'll have a great time.'

'Thank you. We're grateful for your optimism.'

On the Saturday morning of the dance, a small team of volunteers from the social committee had spent several hours decorating the gymnasium wallbars and apparatus with colourful streamers, balloons and banners as usual, until the chairman of the group had fallen off a ladder and injured his leg. This had caused a great deal of concern because he was not only the mastermind behind the hall decorations, but also due to play in a hockey match that afternoon. Since the team was desperately short of decent players, a hasty consultation with the hockey captain ended with a suggestion that the chairman could be propped up in the goal with a splint on his leg, until the moans from the invalid suggested this wasn't really a very practical idea.

As usual, a small room adjacent to the stage had been converted into a makeshift bar, with three trestle tables along its length for drinks, mugs and glasses. On all these occasions, tickets were posted to other colleges within a twenty five mile radius, partly to ensure a good balance of female company and partly to pay off a debt from the last event, when things had got a little out of hand and a table complete with a large number of hired glasses had been broken beyond repair.

Very early on in our college lives, Duggan, Gerry and I had discovered it was never worth going to a college dance until the thing was properly under way. Unfortunately, all the other new students had quickly realised that as well, and now, apart from the social calendar's major and important dances, everyone invariably turned up during the same twenty minutes. This placed enormous strain on the bar, and since it was normally the first port of call, new bar hands always had to be recruited on the spot. The only qualification for this work was the ability to empty a bottle into a glass, and during this hectic period a customer would often be given the wrong drink, or a glass filled from a variety of bottles by each obliging helper. At the most recent dance, the problem had been resolved by the president of the student union, a massive scrum-half, moving in swiftly and demanding an orderly queue. Duggan's room overlooked the hall, and he was in a good position to judge when the noise had reached a suitably inviting level.

'It doesn't sound too great at the moment. We'll give it another half hour,' he said, looking at his watch and then peering among the clothes in his wardrobe. 'At least until they get to the first hokey-cokey. We'll hear when they do.'

'What are you going to wear?' I asked.

'What I've got on, I suppose. I mean, it's not exactly a formal thing, is it? They only have those at Christmas. It's one of these come as you are things. I think I'm going as I am. Do you think it'll be cold down there?'

'Not if there are plenty of people in the hall and the heating is working properly.'

'Wouldn't it be wonderful if it was.' He pushed the window open and peered outside. A trickle of music seeped in on the night air.

'Well, it's all pretty feeble at present,' he said. 'Shall we go for a quick jar first? If we spend half an hour or so in the pub there should be a reasonable crowd down there by the time we get back. And it's bound to be warmer in the pub.'

The saloon bar of the Barley Mow was crowded with students and public when we arrived, and the air was thick with chatter and tobacco smoke. A group of women in their fifties were celebrating Saturday night with a jubilant chorus of 'The Lambeth Walk,' accompanied by a short, bearded pianist whose legs seemed to have difficulty in reaching the pedals. The darts board, not often in use during the week, was now the centre of a fierce argument between students and locals, each staking claim to use of the board. Eventually, one of the men, smaller than the others, threw a dart forcibly into the floor and sat down with the women in the corner, glowering fiercely. They took no notice of him at all.

'Mine's a scotch,' said Duggan, looking around in vain for empty seats. 'A double, if you can afford it. And a ham roll with lime pickle if they've got it, and French mustard if they haven't. Bloody hell, the tables are full again. We'd better park ourselves by the window sill.' I elbowed my way to the bar, and patiently waited until the barmaid was able to serve me.

'Two halves of bitter and two packets of cheese and onion crisps, please love.'

'Only plain crisps, dear. The firm's on strike.'

'Not even cheese and onion?'

'No love. Plain, plain or plain.'

'I'll have plain, then.'

'Bitter again?' Duggan grumbled as I put the glasses in front of him. 'Really, it's time our grants were doubled. How are we supposed to maintain our social standing on the money we get? The woman in the post office thinks I'm drawing my old age pension each week. And look at this. Not even cheese and onion crisps. Oh well, at least I won't be breathing onion all over whichever lucky young female is destined to receive my attentions this very evening.'

'Providing any women actually attend the dance. It's February. And it's bloody cold.'

'Oh come on Mike, they'll be arriving in coachloads. They always do. Don't spoil my Saturday evening before it's started.'

He broke open a packet of crisps and carefully selected a large one. A group of students from a Chelsea college came noisily into the bar and fed money into the cigarette machine.

'Now then,' said Duggan, 'I shall raise this glass to my lips and pretend it's Chivas Regal. We drink a lot of that in Solihull. At least, our fathers do. And we try to pinch a bit of it now and then. Cheers.'

'Well, pretending's good for you. In educational circles they call it creative role play.'

'Do they indeed? Obviously I still haven't read the right books. I tell you what though. When I was a kid I had a really miserable teacher in my final year at primary school. At Christmas, she told the class to bring stuff for the end of term party. Cakes, and so on. Anyway, some of the boys, including me, forgot to bring anything to drink...'

'So she got out a bottle of Chivas Regal and shared it with them?'

Duggan grinned. 'Surprisingly, no. She asked the ones who'd brought some lemonade to share it with their friends. This meant that some of us still didn't get any lemonade, so she poured some water into the empty glasses and told the poor sods who hadn't got any lemonade to sip it and pretend it was fizzy.'

'You're joking!'

'No, amazing, isn't it? I mean, there are a few dotty teachers about, but I reckon that takes an award. I wouldn't mind betting there are still a few like her knocking around, too. And probably, some of them are actually in charge of the schools.'

'Well, we'll soon know. It's not that long before we go out on teaching practice.'

An elderly couple on a table very close to us stood up and left. Several people standing made a move forward, but Duggan swiftly commandeered their chairs and motioned me to join him.

'Going out on teaching practice is all very well,' he continued, clearing a space for his glass, 'But we haven't actually learned much about practical teaching so far, have we? I mean, it's all very well filling us up with subjects we've already done at school, but I can't see that helping us much when we stand in front of a class wondering how the hell to get them down from the top of the cupboards. Having lectures about the educational welfare service and what happens at detention centres doesn't exactly help us much, does it?'

'But you can't really teach someone how to teach, can you?'

'No, but you can give 'em a few tips on how not to. I don't think some of our lecturers have been inside a school since they left school themselves. Look, we're on the primary course, for heaven's sake, and we've got lecturers like Dr Frost who virtually denies that small children exist. When do you think he last stepped inside a primary school classroom?'

'When he last supervised students on a teaching practice, I suppose.'

'If he ever did. I wouldn't mind betting he leaves that bit to Doris Bottle. Mind you, imagine getting Dr Frost as your tutor on teaching practice. He'd be interrupting every bloody second. And the college has to rely on what the tutors say. I mean, it's no good me saying, 'Well Dr Frost, I know the lesson you've just seen was a piece of rubbish, but I did a really good one yesterday when you weren't here to see it', is it?'

'Perhaps he'd be different in a classroom,' I said, rather unconvincingly.

'I bet he wouldn't. He'd end up taking the class himself. You'd think he'd make at least some attempt to keep us up to date with modern teaching techniques. But hardly any of the tutors seem to, do they? I bet they churn out the same old lectures year after year. Seems a nice easy number to me. If you can't teach, lecture about teaching instead.'

'That's probably a bit unfair. It's their job to raise our academic standards as well. Presumably we'll learn the practical aspects of the job when we actually go out and do it.'

'Then let's hope we get landed in good schools with good classes and capable teachers. Even that's a gamble, though. Some of the schools round here must be terrible.'

'Probably so, but the college is bound to be a bit selective. I don't imagine we'll have to do that much at our first schools anyway. It's only a four week teaching practice. It'll just about give us time to find out what works and what doesn't.'

'Oh God, let's have another drink.'

The bar was warm and comfortable, and another hour passed before we walked back up the road to the college. The dance had been in progress for some time and a few people were coming out already, their arms wrapped tightly round the waists of girls they were hoping to entice back to their rooms for a nightcap. At the door, Dai Early took our tickets and looked at us in surprise.

'You're late, aren't you boyos? Missed much of it, you 'ave.'

'We hope we've missed the boring bit,' said Duggan. 'We like to give these things a bit of time to warm up before gracing them with our presence.'

'Do you now. Well, I couldn't exactly say things were jivin' an' jumpin' just yet, boy. But give it time. Just give it time.'

'Who's playing, then?'

'Aw, lovely band, boy. Tony and his Tijuana Six. Bloody magic, man. You'll love it.'

'Tony and his Tijuana Six, eh?' asked Duggan seriously. 'Haven't heard of them before. With a name like that, they must be good.'

'Bloody magic, boy.'

Duggan leant forward, put his arm round Dai's shoulder, and spoke softly in his ear.

'Now come on Dai. Couldn't you get another band?'

'Okay, boyo, they're crap,' Dai admitted. 'But they're cheap crap. The only alternative we could afford is me singin'. Now, unless you want a chorus of '*Men Of Harlech*' you might as well go in.'

Inside the gym, all the lights had been dimmed and for a moment it was difficult to see the handful of shadowy figures moving around in the centre of the hall. It didn't look very encouraging. Winter bitten students and their girl friends were hugging the radiators, their faces waxen and distorted in the dull coloured glow from the painted lightbulbs.

Groups of people sat round the tables at the sides of the hall, trying desperately to pretend they were enjoying themselves. Each table had been provided with a tablecloth and two candles in painted saucers. Though it was all intended to be purely decorative, the candles were being used as a welcome source of warmth. Seven couples had summoned up the energy to dance, but their movements were half-hearted, as if they were going through the motions simply to keep warm. On the stage, red-shirted Tony and his Tijuana Six were playing with their usual gusto, attempting like failed Pied Pipers to lure couples out of their shadowy corners and onto the floor to dance. As the sound bounced off the walls, the group's lack of musical finesse was counterbalanced by the sheer volume of their delivery. Duggan grimaced, and covered his ears. We headed towards the bar in the small adjoining room, but it was almost as noisy in there.

'Two pints of bitter, mate,' Duggan shouted at the student serving behind the bar.

'Ten pints of bitter?' the student shouted back. 'Got a lot of friends, have you?'

'I said two pints. Mind you, at this rate we'll need ten pints to take our minds off the music. Where is everybody? There's usually loads more than this.'

'Eh?'

'Where is everybody?' Duggan yelled.

The barman put his mouth nearer to Duggan's ears. 'A lot have gone to a barn dance at St Matthew's, but it's been cancelled and they're on their way back. The hockey club hasn't arrived yet. They usually liven it up. Don't worry mate. Give it time.'

'That's what Dai Early said. I'm just wondering how much time I've got to give it.'

'Eh?'

'Don't worry. It doesn't matter.'

Disappointed, we carried our pints to the nearest unoccupied table in the hall. Even the beer seemed determined to freeze as quickly as possible. Duggan ran his finger slowly round the rim of the glass, tracing an icy pattern in the mist that had formed.

'Well,' he muttered, 'There's not much action here. I should have brought Stephanie down after all. She may not be Ginger Rogers but she could certainly show that lot a few moves. If things go on like this, you could end up being my dancing partner, Mike.'

'Well I tell you one thing. You won't get me back to your room afterwards.'

For several minutes, we sat and watched as a few more couples trickled into the hall, their faces startled by the sound level. The band suddenly stopped abruptly in the middle of the piece they were playing and lowered their instruments, making the unexpected silence seem strangely unnatural. Tony wandered among his group, and in a very loud voice demanded to know who had nicked page three of his music. All around the hall, people lowered their voices, suddenly aware of just how loud they had been shouting.

'God, I've been to better sixth form dances,' Duggan said. 'We had one just like this. Nobody went near anybody until the last ten minutes. The beer was better too. I think they've brewed this stuff themselves.'

The social events secretary suddenly appeared at our table and filled his tray with empty glasses and bottles.

'So when does the truckload of nubiles arrive, mate?' asked Duggan eagerly.

'What's the matter with the ones we've got?' he objected. 'There must be at least a dozen unattached females sitting out there in the darkness.'

'Well why are they still unattached, then? This thing's been on for nearly two hours.'

'We've been saving the best ones just for you,' he replied generously. 'So why don't you get out there and dance?'

'Because we've only just got here,' I said.

'That doesn't matter. Get up and show a bit of willing. We spend hours planning these things, booking top class bands...'

'Like Tony and his Tijuana Six?'

'They're great, aren't they.'

'They're crap.'

'Okay, they're crap. But they're cheap. And you won't notice how bad they are if you get up and shuffle around a bit. I'd dance with you myself but I don't think I've got your name on my card.'

He wiped the plastic tablecloth with a damp rag, emptied the ashtray and left some fresh beer mats on the table.

'He's right, you know,' said Duggan. 'We might as well get up and have a go. If we don't get up now I shall end up being too inebriated to move my legs. And if we're going to spend the rest of the night drinking we'd be better off doing it down the road. It's warmer in there.'

The band had started again after a shaky three chord introduction from the guitarist, and was now attempting what seemed to be a Tijuana waltz. Though more people continually came through the door, they still seemed reluctant to dance. And then suddenly, there seemed to be a disturbance around the entrance.

‘Well now,’ breathed Duggan. ‘What’s this then? Either the hockey club has returned, or a fight’s broken out. Or both.’

We peered through the darkness trying to identify the group by the door. There was a sudden crash, as the figure at the front of the group fell over one of the smaller stage blocks, followed by a cackle of unsympathetic laughter. A shadowy figure pulled himself unsteadily to his feet, and looked cautiously around for other stray obstacles. He was dressed in a long purple football jersey, muddy shorts that hung down over his knees, a jacket that didn’t fit, and a pair of football boots. He carried a banjo in one hand, and a bottle of ale in the other.

‘Good God!’ exclaimed Duggan. ‘It’s that bloke who lives next to you. The one we never see in the daytime.’

‘It can’t be. He’s…’

‘It bloody is. What’s his name?’

‘Dudley.’

‘That’s it. Dudley. It’s definitely him. I recognise the banjo.’

The figure began to wave the bottle of ale at the band, and for a moment it wasn’t clear whether he intended to conduct the next number, offer them musical support, or just provide them with refreshment. Tony, not understanding either, drew the musicians to a slurred halt and looked at him with a mixture of curiosity and annoyance. The figure hauled himself onto the stage, and lifted the banjo after him with loving care. Through the balaclava helmet he wore, it was just possible to identify Dudley’s beard and spectacles. Fascinated, everybody in the hall stopped to listen as Dudley held up his hands for silence.

‘Now look here, you sods. We, that is the social committee and myself, have gone to quite extraordinary lengths to organise this function, and I am sure… er… what?’

He stopped, swayed slightly, and stooped forward, hanging dangerously near the edge of the tiny stage while somebody whispered something to him. He nodded and lurched back into an upright position. 'Right. Now, as I was saying, they, that is, the social committee and myself, have requested that I should.'

'Nobly spoken!' shouted a voice from the middle of the hall, and three people applauded enthusiastically.

'There's more,' Dudley thundered, shaking a finger in the air and trying to focus more accurately on the microphone. 'They, that is, the social committee, have suggested I should get up here and... er... get up here and sort of...'

'Get things moving,' hissed his friend from the side of the stage.

'Exactly. Get things moving.' said Dudley. 'So... er... get moving and dance, you sods. And if you can't dance, drink. The beer profits are down.' He turned to the drummer and carefully handed him the bottle of Coke. The drummer handled it suspiciously, as if it might suddenly turn into a Molotov cocktail.

'Furthermore, hereunto and thereafter,' Dudley continued, 'We are obliged to shut this hall at the stroke of midnight, after which anyone remaining here will turn into a glass slipper. If a few more of you could.. er...shake about a bit with the admirable talent sitting around the edges of the hall, then the social committee and I would see our way clear to taking it as a great personal favour. Indeed. I thank you. I thank the social committee too, who have... er... generously laced this bottle with rum to assist me with this speech. I should inform you that I am now as pissed as a pirate.'

He staggered slightly and clutched at the microphone. Unfortunately, the stand had not been screwed to the floor, and Dudley, complete with microphone, keeled over in harmony. There was a round of rapturous applause, as he climbed to his feet and was supported in the small of the back by one of the drummer's sticks.

'One more thing,' he said, tapping the microphone to check its condition after the fall and setting up a howl of feedback, 'the least you can do is celerate... er... celebrate our glorious win this afternoon against... um...'

'St Agnes!' roared an appreciative hockey team.

'Indeed. St Agnes, bless her heart.' agreed Dudley, picking up his banjo and playing a loud chord on it. 'They played brilliantly, but we were more brilliantly… um… than they are. Or were. Thank you. It gives me great pleasure. And talking of great pleasure, any ladies who fancy a quick fiddle with my instrument, please form an orderly line in front of the stage. Thank you again.'

The band, feeling that this might be an opportunity to seize, quickly burst into a twelve bar blues. Instead of leaving the stage, Dudley began to remove his clothes, hurling his shirt, braces, boots and trousers into the middle of the dance floor, gyrating and gesticulating like a fading stripper. Then, having removed all but his shorts, he lumbered from the platform to thunderous applause and walked in a fairly straight line across the hall to where somebody was holding a change of clothing.

The effect of his speech was little short of miraculous. A generous cheer sounded from one corner of the hall and spread infectiously. The band changed the tune to an invigorating rag and couples hurried forward to take Dudley at his word, helped by the additional sudden appearance of the rugby club, also just back from an away match and eager to help drain the bar dry as quickly as possible.

'Well now,' breathed Duggan, 'It looks as if it might turn out to have been worth our money after all.'

The band changed gear again and moved into a different tempo on the same tune.

'It's supposed to be a waltz,' I said. 'We can do that one.'

'Right. We're off then'. He screwed up his eyes and peered round the shadowy extremities of the hall. 'From what I can make out, there's a small group of ladies over there who need me. They look bored stiff. I'll meet you back in the bar when they play something I can't do.'

Since I'd come with the intention of dancing too, I looked around for a partner. Although I'd tried hard to improve my dancing technique since my days in the sixth form, I was only willing to have a go when the floor was crowded. I glanced round the hall and then to the entrance, where a slim, attractive girl in a tartan coat was handing her ticket to Dai. I edged my way across the hall and asked her if she would like to dance.

'I'd love to,' she said in a soft, warm voice. 'I'll put my coat somewhere first, though.'

In a few minutes we were moving falteringly round the floor.

'I'm afraid I'm a dreadful dancer,' I apologised, trying desperately not to tread on her feet. 'I'll try not to cripple you.'

'Don't worry, I'm not that much better myself,' she smiled. 'My father paid for some lessons for me, and I was fine while I was dancing with the instructor, but pretty awful with anybody else. Then the instructor kept asking me out, so I stopped the lessons.' I wondered if this was a gentle hint that I should keep my distance.

'Anyway,' she continued. 'It's quite a change to meet somebody who can't dance very well. Most of the people who ask me to dance turn out to be undiscovered Fred Astaires.'

As I steered her into the light near the stage, I realised just how attractive she was. Her features were sharp, finely sculptured, with high cheek bones and almond-shaped hazel eyes. Her long blonde hair and pale complexion contrasted strongly with the warmth of her deep red dress. I noticed how little make-up she wore, and how unnecessary it would have been anyway. Deep inside, I congratulated myself on moving so swiftly.

'I'm sorry,' I apologised suddenly, moving her awkwardly to avoid the couple next to us. 'I wasn't concentrating. I was just thinking how attractive you are.'

On any other occasion, I would have groaned at such an obvious cliché. This time, however, I surprised myself because I really meant it. She smiled warmly, waiting for me to speak again.

'Which training college are you from?'

'I'm not a potential teacher, actually,' she admitted. 'I work in the library at the moment. Mostly the children's section. My parents own the delicatessen in Merton Road. Isn't it cold in here!'

'The only place where the radiators are working properly is on the top corridor. Well, not properly. Most of the thermostats are jammed. It's often like a furnace up there and I suppose we've just got used to it, but it was unbearable the first few days here. If you're too cold we'll go up there for some coffee.'

She laughed out loud and stopped dancing for a moment. 'Now hold on,' she said. 'I have heard *that* line before!' I reddened, feeling extremely angry with myself because I hadn't meant it to be interpreted in that way at all.

'I'm sorry,' I said. 'I honestly didn't mean...'

'I know. But you understand my caution. Come on, let's dance. You were doing well.'

We steered round a couple who had given up the waltz and were sitting on the floor staring at each other in mournful but mutual admiration. A few feet away, Dudley was dancing round in circles, his arms outstretched, either looking for a partner or oblivious to the fact that his most recent one had escaped in alarm. Somebody bumped into us and apologised in an extremely loud voice.

'I'm dreadfully sorry, mate. Not my fault at all, actually. It's Judith here. Tanked her up a bit too much. I can never get her bloody level right. Still,' he added, thrusting a beery face into mine and speaking in a stage whisper, 'We're off upstairs in a minute. Not sure if Judith's quite up to it though. Oh, hello Sam. I thought it was you. Where's David?'

I stopped dancing for a moment, not knowing quite how to handle the situation and wishing I had a few precious moments to think about it.

'Hello Derrick. He's sprained his ankle putting up these decorations.'

'Oh, tough. This is... er... Judith.'

Judith didn't seem in much of a state for introductions. With one arm thrown around Derrick's neck and her gingery hair looking like a wig that had been put on backwards, it seemed for a moment that she might sink to her knees and remain in that position until the dance ended.

'Well,' said Derrick, obviously disappointed, 'It looks as if the love of my life has had it for tonight. I'll...er... see you around, then.'

Taking a deep breath, he hoisted Judith to shoulder level and disappeared into the gloom. Samantha and I drifted towards the stage, but it was impossible to speak above the noise of the saxophonist, who was having trouble making himself heard above the drummer. The drummer, I noticed, had a wedge of cotton wool tightly screwed into each ear. The dance ended, and we waited for the next one.

'I'm sorry, I didn't even ask your name,' I said, anxious to speak while we could still be heard.

'That's all right. It's Samantha Baxter.'

'So you've been up here before?'

'Oh yes,' said Samantha. 'I often come to the dances, but they're usually better than this. The band's awful. I went with David to the Halloween Ball last year. Did you get to that?'

'No, I haven't been here long. It's my first year and we've only really just started. At least, we've only just started to do some work.'

'It's not that hard, is it?'

'Some of it.' A fleeting vision of Dr Frost flashed through my mind. 'We get a reasonable amount of time off, though.'

The band started up again minus the guitarist, who had taken the cover off his amplifier and was cautiously inspecting the inside. I moved Samantha gently back to the most populated part of the floor, where Dudley was involved with a group of three girls in what seemed a peculiar combination of dancing and stomping on each other's toes. Two of the girls were as drunk as he was. Samantha's eyes darted round the hall as she danced.

'Where is everybody?' she asked. 'There are usually more than this. The Halloween Ball was absolutely packed.'

'A lot of students have gone to another dance that's been cancelled. Quite a few haven't turned up because the band doesn't have much of a reputation. Others have gone home for a breather before teaching practice. And I think some have decided it's just too cold to come downstairs. Still, it's a lot better now than when we came in. There was hardly anybody here then.'

'What are you going to teach when you leave?'

'That's a long time away. Primary children, though. If you're teaching a whole range of subjects you don't have time to get bored with just one.'

'In London?'

'Probably. For the first couple of years at least. It's a bit too early to say, though. I'd like to stay down after college and rent a flat. Provided I pass, of course.'

'You're bound to, aren't you? They pass everybody, don't they? Aren't they desperately short of teachers at the moment.'

'I hope you're right.'

As we danced, I found myself concentrating on Samantha instead of the movement of my feet. She seemed to anticipate my movements and corrected me skilfully when my footwork drifted out of sync. She was, I realised, a much better dancer than she'd let on. As the band finished the number they were playing, Tony pulled the microphone towards him.

'And… a… now,' he cried in broken English, 'Issa the time for the ladies' turn. Ladies, find the man which you like and dance with him, yes? Now is your chance. Okay boys, one, two, three, four….'

Before I had time to suggest a drink, Derrick appeared at my side.

'Mind if I have this one, mate?' he said, grabbing Samantha.

'It's supposed to be her choice,' I objected.

'I know, old boy, but that's an incredibly sexist point of view, and we don't need to take any notice of that, do we? Had to leave Judith outside in the fresh air for a bit, I'm afraid. Fell asleep on me. You don't really mind, do you?'

I minded a great deal, but Derrick, well oiled and determined, whisked her away with steps that brilliantly outclassed my own.

Disappointed and annoyed, I moved towards the bar. With the sudden arrival of the coachload from the cancelled barn dance, the hall seemed to be getting more crowded by the moment, even though the event was officially due to end in an hour. Members of the rugby club were mostly dancing with each other in threes, ignoring any rhythm the band was trying to set. Hardly anybody sat at the tables now, and those who weren't joining in were wandering round the edges of the hall looking for partners to make the most of the remaining time. I turned to look for Duggan and almost fell into the arms of a well-built girl who grabbed me enthusiastically, flinging her arms around my waist and hurling me into action with the ease of a hammer thrower.

'Great!' she breathed. 'Great, great! Do you come here often?'

I gave a strangled cry as I tried to breathe.

'Gosh, sorry about that. Simply don't know my own strength,' she giggled happily. 'Marvellous. Super hop. Are you St. James's?'

I grunted agreement, freeing myself a little.

'I'm Joan of Arc.'

'Well,' I said, breathing more easily now, 'I should stay away from fires if I were you.'

'Sorry?'

'I said, if you're Joan of Arc, you should stay away from fires.'

'How do you mean?'

'It's a joke. You know, Joan of Arc was burned..'

'Oh I see. Rather poor taste. Never mind, I'll forgive you this time.' She spun me round in a wild pirouette, and the hall swam dizzily.

'Came up on a coach,' she said. 'We always come to your hops. Last one was better.'

'I didn't get to that,' I said, looking around wildly for help.

'No, thought I didn't see you. What's your main subject?'

'Science.'

'Science, eh? Mine's Religious Knowledge. Not that it means I'm a nun or anything.'

She chuckled and gave my right buttock an affectionate squeeze.

We swung round violently and careered into two other couples, ending up in a heaving pile of bodies that moaned and grunted. A girl who had the misfortune to be at the bottom of the pile screamed loudly, and sensing the opportunity for a swift getaway I moved discreetly backwards. I was suddenly gripped by the shoulders. 'For heaven's sake,' retorted a red-haired girl wearing enormous spectacles and a bowler hat, 'Do look where you're going.'

'I'm sorry,' I apologised, 'I didn't..,'

'Right, okay. That's all right. Shall we dance?'

She braced herself, swung her shoulders like an athlete limbering up, leant slightly backwards, and shook her head in time to the music. I found I could see right up her nose.

'What step are you supposed to be doing?'

'I'm just jigging about, really,' I said with a tired sigh. 'I'm not a very good dancer. Perhaps I ought to sit down and..,'

'That's all right. I'll lead and you follow. I taught half our girls to dance and I'm pretty bloody good at the male part. You don't mind, do you?'

'You mean you want me to do the girl's steps?'

'Mmm. Be a jolly sight easier for me. Just follow my feet. You'll soon get used to it. I'm Denise, by the way. Who are you?

'Mike.'

'Pleased to meet you Mike. Let's go.'

She was taller and a great deal heavier than me, and for a moment I considered standing on her feet and letting her manoeuvre me round in a tight circle. However, since she kept her feet a good distance apart, it was possible to stand almost stationary between them and simply apply a counteracting pressure to her waist each time she lunged forward. We moved to and fro with a sort of pumping action that kept both of us more or less rooted to the same spot.

'By the way,' said Denise earnestly, 'I might as well tell you right away I'm not going up to your room.'

I felt an intense sense of relief, and nodded fervently.

'Good,' she said. 'So long as we understand each other. I'm not a good time girl, you know.'

'Of course not. I didn't…'

'Well, we have to make sure. At one of your hops one of them told me he'd got some slides of Venice and I ended up ironing his shirts.' Keeping one hand clamped like a vice to my left shoulder, she swung the other one behind her and made a fluttering movement with her fingers. I thought she was trying to scratch the small of her back and I offered to help.

'No, leave it,' she urged. 'I'm signalling.'

'Sorry?'

'Signalling. I'm signalling to Jenny.'

A girl dancing with a member of the drama club caught her eye and waggled a finger in reply. I was at a loss to understand what was going on.

'We signal to each other,' Denise said, feeling I deserved an explanation. 'We come to each other's rescue if we get in a jam.'

'What sort of a jam?'

'If we're in danger of being dragged off to your rooms and we don't fancy it.'

'I hadn't even considered it,' I replied truthfully. 'What happens if you're both in trouble?'

'We signal to Melanie. She's over there holding the fort while we dance. We take turns.'

'Oh.'

She shifted into fourth gear and swivelled round to face Jenny, who waved encouragingly.

'If I'm going too fast, shout,' Denise urged.

'No, no, I'm fine,' I said feeling vaguely nauseous.

'Third year, are you?'

'No, first.'

'Oh. Hard luck!'

'Well I don't mind, really.'

'Hated my first year. Wanted to get out and see some action.'

'Which year are you?'

'Third. Soon be doing the finals. Murder. What are you doing tomorrow?'

'I don't know yet. Why?'

'You can come over to the hostel for tea if you like. Meet the rest of the gang.'

'Thanks, but...'

'That's all right. I'll come up here to you if you prefer'.

'I'm not sure if...'

'You can buy me a drink and we'll arrange it in the bar. Oh, they've stopped playing. Well, here we are then. I'll just go and tell Jenny. Don't move.'

She ground to a halt and I bumped against her chin. The pause in the music lasted only a moment, and feeling bruised and delicate I moved urgently amongst the largest group of students I could see, hoping to lose myself while I took stock of the situation. I couldn't see Samantha, and I was determined to conceal myself from Denise. The best plan, I thought, would be to dance with the closest unattached girl, and throwing caution to the wind, I swept one into my arms.

'Hello,' I said apologetically. 'Would you dance with me for a moment? There's someone I'm trying to avoid.'

There was no answer, and I suddenly realised that the rather pretty girl in my arms was crying bitterly. Embarrassed, I took a deep breath, pushed her head on my shoulder and plunged forward. The band was attempting a tango, and this made my discomfort even more acute.

'Come on,' I said, 'My dancing isn't that bad. What's wrong?'

'Everything,' she sobbed.

'Is there anything I can do?'

'No, nothing.'

I dragged her around desperately for several minutes, which made her cry even louder.

'Can't you really tell me what's wrong?' I urged, a little annoyed.

'It's Grahame,' she sniffed. 'He promised me he wouldn't dance with that cow. Done up like that, throwing it at him. He promised, the rotten bastard.'

She said this with such vehemence that the couple dancing next to us paused mid-step in astonishment, and the male half squinted at my partner.

'She's not talking to me, is she?' he said to me. 'I mean, we haven't even collided with you yet. What's the matter with her?'

I gestured helplessly.

'Well, I shouldn't drag her around like that, poor soul,' he said sympathetically. 'Yours, is she?'

'It's all very complicated. I just sort of got hold of her for a moment.'

'Well, I should just sort of let go of her again, chief,' he advised earnestly, whirling his partner away from us. The girl's sobs began to affect our dance steps, setting up a counter rhythm of their own.

'Would you like to sit down?' I asked hopefully, but the girl took no notice.

'It wasn't like that when we met,' she cried. 'When I found out about that bitch he promised to leave her alone and then last week I went to his room and he wasn't there and I waited and waited and he came in with a tin of baked beans and his shirt was all over the place and I *know* he'd been with her even though he said he'd only been out to buy a tin of baked beans because he thought we might get hungry, and I hate baked beans even more than I hate him.'

As she finished, her voice rose to an hysterical wail. I doubled our speed, muttered something about going to the lavatory, and thrust her into the arms of the first unattached male I saw.

'Cor, thanks mate,' he said gratefully. With great determination, I pushed my way back through the crowd to where Samantha was standing near the entrance of the bar.

'Hello,' she smiled. 'Where did you get to?'

'Don't ask! Quickly, let's have a drink. What would you like?'

‘Just a glass of white wine, I think.’

I carried the drinks back to where she was standing. Every seat had been taken and we crammed ourselves into a corner. I didn’t complain. The perfume Samantha was wearing was intoxicating and the heat from the bodies packed closely together had at least made the atmosphere warmer.

‘It’s livened up, anyway,’ Samantha smiled.

‘It certainly has. What happened to Derrick?’

‘I told him to go and make Judith some black coffee. He’s all bluff really. He can actually be quite nice. He’s very clever artistically and he and David planned the decorations for the Halloween Dance.’

‘So this David… is it serious?’ Though I’d only known her for a very short time, I felt a twinge of jealously when she mentioned his name. She smiled softly.

‘I’m not desperately serious about anything just yet. Anyway, let’s talk about you. When do you start your teaching practice?’ After the bizarre conversations on the dance floor, it was a relief to talk sanely again.

‘In a few weeks time. There’s a lot to do before then, though.’

‘I imagine you’re looking forward to it?’

‘With mixed feelings.’

‘Why?’

‘It’s the first time. I’ll probably make a mess of it.’

‘I’m sure you won’t. Any new job is difficult at first until you get used to it. Anyway, there’s no point in worrying about it.’

‘It’s not worry, really. It’s just the thought of the lecturers coming in to watch that puts me off.’

‘You’ll be fine. Let’s have another dance.’

Somebody burst into song a few feet away. A glass crashed to the floor and a girl gasped and jumped back, knocking into the bar which tottered on its wooden trestles. The chief bartender swiftly kicked the leg back into position, looked at it doubtfully, and slammed a crate of empty bottles against it. A cackle of laughter seemed to come from under one of the trestles, and one of the relief helpers, his white jacket stained and crumpled, peered inquisitively beneath the tablecloth. A face beamed out at him, and the helper pointed out the imminent possibility of the table collapsing if the student underneath didn't get out immediately. A third barman took no notice and continued slamming empty lemonade bottles into a cardboard box.

'Last orders!' he shouted ineffectually, not really expecting anyone to take any notice. A girl shouted out that she could undress herself, thank you, and would Roger kindly keep his hands round his beer mug unless he wanted a stiletto heel buried in his crutch, at which there was a roar of approval. Suddenly, there was a dry cough in my ear, and I turned to find Duggan trembling with emotion and wiping his face with a grimy handkerchief.

'Hide me,' he urged. 'Don't say anything. Just hide me. There's a girl from the Joan of Arc lot looking for me.'

I couldn't help laughing. 'Not Denise, by any chance?'

'I don't know her name. She nearly ripped my arm out. I'm lucky to be here with my trousers intact. Give me five bob and I'll creep to the bar and buy you both a drink.' He took the coins I held out and disappeared into the gloom.

'A friend of yours?' smiled Samantha. We seemed to be the only couple in the bar who were sober.

'I'll introduce you when he comes back,' I shouted, trying to make myself heard above the noise at the next table, where someone was screaming with laughter because her friend had accidently dropped a glassful of wine into her lap. 'I don't think you've met him at the best moment!'

Duggan dodged round the bar to get back to us, holding the drinks above his head to prevent them being spilled. I introduced him to Samantha.

'There you go,' he said, handing her a very full wine glass. 'It's rosé. They'd only got a tiny drop of white left so I topped it up with red. I should buy you another one before they run out of red as well.'

'No thanks,' she replied. 'I'll end up staggering round the library with a hangover on Monday.'

'You work there, then? I've never seen you in there.'

'I'm in the children's section at the moment.'

'I still should have seen you. I get most of my books from the children's section. My God, look out!'

He moved us to one side as a long line of dancers, each with a hand around the waist of the person in front, danced the Conga through the bar, under the largest trestle table, and out again. The first three in the line were trying to keep in time to the music, the middle group were merely hoping to keep in step, and the last few, their eyes tightly closed, had given up and were being dragged along by the others. A student in the middle wore only a towel, and the person immediately behind him was trying to thrust a hockey stick through the legs of the people in front of him, in an effort to make the towel fall to the ground, or, better still, collapse the entire line. Duggan watched them admiringly.

'Hey, things are really warming up now,' he said joyously. 'Fancy joining in?'

He looked from me to Samantha, his eyes only vaguely focusing.

'Oh well, perhaps not,' he said. 'Another jar first.' He turned to pick up his glass, but pointed instead to what looked like an untouched scotch on the table.

'Look at that,' he said. 'I thought it was supposed to be beer and wine only. Somebody's smuggling the hard stuff in. Unless it's cider.' He picked the glass up, sniffed it cautiously, and then took a gulp. 'It's scotch,' he said. 'I wonder who it belongs to.'

A huge student with a bandage round his head took a heavy stride forward and grabbed Duggan's lapel.

'Oi, you sod,' he shouted, 'Have you just swiped my drink?'

Several people looked round casually to see if the incident had any chance of developing into a fight.

'That's bloody twice that's happened,' he roared. Duggan looked visibly shaken.

‘I haven’t touched it, mate,’ he lied. ‘I’m teetotal.’

‘Well somebody bloody did. I go for a pee and the bloody thing disappears. Twice.’

‘Here, look,’ said Duggan, thrusting a pile of loose change into his hand. ‘Have another one on me.’

‘I should bloody well think so. Do that again and I’ll rip your arm out. Buy your own bloody drink next time.’ Duggan nodded eagerly, Samantha giggled, and I suggested we spend the last few minutes out in the main hall.

For its finale, the band was thumping out a Tijuana version of the Saints, and the caterpillar of Conga dancers spiralled in ever-decreasing circles to the centre of the hall until the column collapsed in an undignified heap. Around them, bodies leapt, shouted, stomped and shook to the music. Several people lay motionless on the floor, like scarred remnants on a battlefield. The balloons had been severed from their strings, and were being stamped on. Most of the lightbulbs had gone out altogether. Dudley, still standing upright but swaying dangerously, was on the stage conducting the band with a jock strap.

‘I think it’s time to go,’ I said to Samantha, who was looking increasingly worried. ‘It’s getting a bit uncivilised.’ She nodded quickly and fetched her coat.

‘You off already?’ shouted Duggan. ‘There’s a few more minutes yet.’

‘We’re not risking it.’

‘Really? They haven’t done the prize for the best ballroom dancer yet. Oh well, if you’re back upstairs before I get there put some coffee on.’

I edged Samantha to the door, hurrying out into the rain as quickly as possible.

‘I don’t think we’d have got out in one piece if we hadn’t come now,’ I said.

‘It wasn’t very good, was it. Never mind, they can’t all be perfect. And the rugby club seemed to be enjoying it.’ She stopped suddenly.

‘Oh damn,’ she groaned. ‘My bag, I’ve left it in the bar. It must have fallen out of my coat.’

I rushed back, wondering if the social secretary had rifled it to bolster up his funds. Amazingly, it was still lying at the end of one of the bar tables.

‘Left your handbag, mate?’ grinned the barman, trying to clear up the clutter around him. ‘Want me to see you home?’

A hand suddenly gripped my ankle. Dudley crawled from underneath the table like a giant insect and lunged to his feet. Recognising me, he grinned and started to speak.

‘Wonderful dance, eh Mike? Thoroughly enjoyed it. Wouldn’t have missed it for the world.’

Then he turned away, and was sick into one of the waste bins.

MARCH

LEAPING, LEARNING AND A DATE AT THE LIBRARY

The lecturing staff of St James's varied enormously in competence and ability, and this became increasingly obvious as our first teaching practice drew near. In general terms, the lecturers could be divided into three broad categories.

At the competent end of the spectrum were the enthusiastic tutors who had managed to keep in touch with rapidly changing ideas in primary education, and who paid regular visits to local schools to find out how successful these ideas actually were in the hands of the teachers who implemented them. This meant much extra work on their part, and few lecturers were prepared to commit themselves to anything like that extent. David Andrews, second in command of the geography department and one of Gerry's tutors, was a prime example of this group. He was highly qualified, talked at incredible speed, gave additional lectures whenever he felt they were needed, and knew an enormous amount about the geography of the world and the British Isles in particular. He was also in his early thirties, exceptionally handsome, and there were rumours that many eligible female lecturers had attempted to cultivate a relationship, although because he tended to move at the same speed as he talked, they could never keep up with him. When he marked a student's notes, he wrote at least one full page of constructive criticism, and nobody quite knew how he managed to fit everything into the twenty four hours available to him each day.

The second group, also small, included the pure academics, the tutors who knew their own subjects thoroughly, but whose knowledge of schools and the ways in which they currently worked was shaky enough for them to ignore it altogether. Nevertheless, they were reasonably proficient at offloading their specialist knowledge to the students in their charge, and by and large were interesting enough to listen to for an hour or so. Provided notes and essays were handed in at required intervals and attendance at lectures was regular, it wasn't difficult for their students to manage life at a comfortable pace.

The final group, far too large, consisted of lecturers who had completely forgotten what a school was and merely regurgitated identical lectures year after year until they eventually crumbled into retirement. Dr Williams, who lectured in English Literature and was one of the country's leading specialists in obscure medieval poetry, regularly bored his students rigid and often slid into sleep on warm Summer afternoons. His students then spent the rest of the lecture time in the college's well stocked library, seeking out the information they needed a great deal more efficiently.

Part of each week was set aside for a period known as 'professional studies', and this was intended to be an intensive session filled with hints and tips for successful classroom teaching. The success of these sessions was directly proportional to the ability of the tutors supervising them; David Andrews' practical geography sessions were exceptionally well organised and Gerry felt that primary education had probably lost one of its greatest exponents. Dr Williams, however, occupied these periods by making his students talk to the rest of the group about their hobbies, and Barton had kicked off by explaining how to take a motorbike to pieces. He'd become so involved in his talk that he'd overshot his time, and Dr Williams hadn't noticed because he'd fallen asleep. The rest of us sat wondering what possible relevance Barton's motorbike might have in the classroom.

Apart from the main and subsidiary subject each student was required to study, there were a number of essential areas to be studied by all students, the most important of these being the history, philosophy, and psychology of education. Depending on the skill of the lecturer, these sessions could develop into highly absorbing and relevant discussions, or tedious lists of dates and supposed historical milestones in philosophical thinking.

Finally, there was at least some acknowledgement that primary and secondary teaching techniques were rapidly changing and quite different from each other, and provision had to be made for this. Those students on the primary course were required to attend 'model' example lessons in basic curriculum, and Dr Bradley had originally intended to employ local primary teachers to help with this. Since problems with re-arranging local teachers' timetables and schedules proved to be insurmountable, the plan collapsed after a month, and the college lecturers once again had to fill the breach.

With our first teaching practice imminent, these sessions were well attended, though not always very useful. For lecturers like Professor Barnsley, who had organised maths in a large Suffolk primary for six years and then co-authored a popular mathematics scheme for schools, it wasn't difficult to organise the time extremely successfully. At the other end of the scale there was Ernest Benton, who had run a metalwork shop unsuccessfully in a failing Battersea comprehensive before escaping to a much more comfortable situation lecturing in practical workshop technique at St James's. Since he was also now required to demonstrate potted art and craft lessons on the run-up to teaching practice, he made his views on the subject perfectly clear; small children could neither paint nor craft, and giving any child much more than paper, cardboard and glue was a senseless extravagance and a downright waste of taxpayers' money. Even with these items, he maintained, the average child would only make a paper aeroplane to throw across the classroom, and giving children access to a pair of scissors merely constituted a license to kill.

Physical education was the only compulsory subject for both primary and secondary students, and a source of intense debate. The academic students loathed it, others tolerated it grudgingly, Gerry obliged enthusiastically and Duggan and I simply weren't very good at it. Nevertheless, since it was mandatory that a proportion of every primary child's day should be spent in some form of physical activity, it was essential that students knew how to teach it. They had also been told they would be required to do it on teaching practice.

The head of the physical education department at St. James's was Anthony Trainer, a slim, handsome and muscular tutor who rivalled David Andrews for energy and drive. In his first lesson he had stated that the building might be old and crumbling, but he certainly wasn't, and neither were his ideas. It was a view that Duggan and I rapidly came to endorse. The age of the building did frustrate his aims to some extent, however. On one occasion when a group of third year students specialising in PE had been warming up by playing leapfrog under Mr Trainer's lively direction, the heaviest of them had taken a flying dive over the back bent in front of him, misjudged his landing and slammed a foot right through a floorboard.

The other source of frustration for Mr Trainer was the group that Duggan and I were in, made up almost entirely of primary course students. Many of them hadn't enjoyed physical education at school, and they certainly weren't interested in it now. This saddened Mr Trainer, whose sensible and commendable belief was that a healthy body was the pathway to a healthy mind, and that the right and wrong ways of vaulting over a box were better practised than written about. He made quite sure that each of his groups did a great deal of running, jumping and very little standing still, the only excuse for non-participation being illness. Since he had never been ill in his life, even that was frowned upon unless Matron had endorsed it with a personally signed letter.

Much of his abundant energy came from a daily work out on the college trampoline, performing spectacular feats which drew gasps of admiration. He had played cricket for Sussex, won several swimming awards and even gained a black belt at Judo. When students became rowdy after final examinations, Mr Trainer was usually summoned and he squashed any trouble with the speed and precision of a Samurai warrior.

After coffee break each Monday morning, Duggan and I braced ourselves for a gruelling hour of physical stress, and crawled downstairs unhappily. Gerry was in an earlier group with secondary students, whose session was not only much shorter, but supervised by a different tutor whose approach to the subject was rather more relaxed.

'I shall refuse this time,' Duggan announced firmly.

'Refuse what?'

'To climb on the trampoline. I just can't take that kind of thing on a Monday morning. I can't take it most days, but especially not on a Monday morning.'

'You don't have to, you know. That bit's optional. He did say that at the beginning.'

'I know. But it's difficult to refuse, isn't it? With the rest of them all bouncing up and down like fleas on a mattress you'd feel an idiot if you told him you didn't feel like it. Anyway, I don't feel like it today, and I shall refuse. I shall tell him I've got a load of extra work on.'

'He won't believe it.'

Duggan thought about it carefully.

'No, I don't suppose he will. And if I just don't go, he'll be up to find out why I wasn't there. Why can't he just talk to us instead of making us all become seven year olds for an hour?'

'The other day you were grumbling that half the lecturers don't tell us how to teach,' I said. 'At least he's doing that.'

'I know. I realise that. I suppose I'll realise it even more when we get on teaching practice, but it's just the thought of leaping up and down like that on a Monday morning. Nobody civilised does that sort of thing on a Monday morning.'

Duggan was wearing the top half of a bright blue college tracksuit while I wore the trousers. By purchasing just one suit at the beginning of term, and wearing alternate halves each week, we had managed to convince Mr Trainer that we both had the full kit. Also, and more important as far as we were concerned, it had saved us several precious pounds.

We entered the hall by the back door, already a few minutes late. The hall was in constant use as a gymnasium, play rehearsal studio, indoor games area and scenery painting workshop, and it was usually in a disorderly state on Monday mornings. Some of the students were shifting props and artefacts to make enough room on the floor, and those intent on wasting a little time had discovered they could craftily shift artefacts and scenery to and fro several times. Mr Trainer beamed as we entered.

'Ah, Mr Kent and Mr Phillips. Come in quickly, gentlemen. We've only just started. Perhaps you would be kind enough to help Mr Whiting move that... um... railway thing.'

He pointed to a large piece of hardboard nailed to a framework leaning against the wallbars. Students from the drama group had painted part of a railway station buffet on it for their forthcoming Noel Coward production, and it wasn't until I gripped the top half that I realised it was thick with wet paint.

'I should... um... be a little careful with it, gentlemen,' Mr Trainer advised, watching as I searched for a piece of cloth. 'I'm not sure if it is...um... finished or whether it has only just been started.'

We pushed the board into a corner and joined the rest of our group. Only Dudley was missing, but this wasn't surprising as there had been an altercation with Mr Trainer earlier on in the term about the necessity of buying a tracksuit just to run about in for one period a week. To reinforce his view, Dudley had arrived the following week in pyjamas and a dressing gown, saying he thought they would serve just as well. He had also complained about being placed in a group for primary school trainees, and Mr Trainer had patiently explained that a number of secondary students had to be allocated to primary groups simply to even out the numbers.

All this had come to the attention of Dr Bradley, who said that if

Dudley wasn't prepared to attend the mandatory lectures, he could hardly be recommended as having completed the course. Dudley had pointed out that since he intended to specialise in teaching mathematics and botany to secondary school children, there didn't seem much point in learning how to shin up a rope. We presumed, from Dudley's continued absence, that no truce had yet been reached.

The students in our group were clearly defined personalities. In one corner, around the basket ball post, the secondary students were hurling a ball to each other in a manner that would have maimed anyone unfortunate enough to get in the way of it. All were impatient to begin the morning's work. In the centre of the hall stood Ian Billings, a brilliant history student who smoked five pipefuls of tobacco a day and was already a considerable authority on Tudor furniture. His interests were varied and wide, but PE wasn't among them. He was talking earnestly to David Barton, who occupied the room next to his and was beginning to annoy him with his fondness for leaving bits of motor cycle all over the corridor. Desperate for a second hand fuel tank he couldn't afford, Barton had spent the weekend asking the occupants of his corridor if they'd each lend him a small amount of money until next term's grant came through. Everybody had agreed not to ask for any money back, provided Barton agreed to have all his hair shaved off. He'd bought his fuel tank, and was now completely bald.

Another group of students sat patiently against the wallbars, waiting for the lecture to start. Two of them were frantically copying up lecture notes that should have been handed in several days previously. On top of the vaulting box, Ahmed Rashid sat scribbling musical notation on a tiny notepad. He was a talented guitarist, and in the process of forming a college group. Unfortunately, he was also short sighted, and had become disillusioned with Mr Trainer's lessons after breaking his spectacles twice. The second occasion had been particularly poignant, as he'd put them underneath a bench for safety and trodden on them two minutes later. Somebody had cruelly suggested he write a song about it.

The rest of the group stood or sat around the hall, tossing bean bags to each other, performing handstands against the wall, or just looking at the clock. They, too, were anxious for the lesson to begin, if only because time would pass more quickly that way. Mr Trainer finished marking the attendance register he meticulously kept, and turned to face the group.

'Now then, gentlemen,' he said softly, placing his hands on his hips and flexing his muscles, 'If you would be good enough to gather round, I'll outline the work for this morning.' Everybody moved forward and squatted around him on the floor. As usual, he was thoroughly prepared. One or two students picked up their notepads, but he smiled them away and said that notes could be written up afterwards.

'In the past few weeks, I have dealt mainly with the simple agilities that can be taught practically anywhere. By that, I mean in schools which have limited amounts of apparatus or space. Most of the primary schools we use for teaching practice purposes aren't lucky enough to have their own gymnasiums, and it's important you make good use of whatever facilities you do find.' He spoke lightly, but precisely, choosing his words carefully. His crystal-sharp eyes darted across the row of faces in front of him.

'In most local schools, you'll find the Southampton Cave apparatus fitted, though often in the school hall where the children have their lunch. The Southampton Cave apparatus is excellent if it is used properly, but not if you are the sort of teacher who tells the children just to get it out and get on it.'

'What is it?' asked Barton.

'What is what, Mr Barton?'

'The Southampton Cave Apparatus?'

'Ah. Well, I feel I have mentioned it several times before. Perhaps you were not with us on those occasions. The apparatus is permanently fixed to the wall, but it can be swung out and set up when you've completed the warm-up phase. Does that answer your question, Mr Barton?'

‘But what is it?’ Barton asked again.

‘Do you mean what does it actually consist of?’

‘Yes. What is it?’

‘Well, ah, it actually consists of a two-section set of wallbars, across which you can fix benches, balance beams and… um… hasn’t your *hair* been removed since the last time we met, Mr Barton?’

Barton grinned. ‘I’ve had it shortened, Sir.’

‘I see. I should.. um.. consider changing your hairdresser if I were you, Mr Barton.’

‘It makes it easier to wash, though. And I shouldn’t think I’ll catch head lice on teaching practice.’

‘Quite. Anyway gentlemen, as I was saying, daily physical education is vitally important for all young children. It gives them independence, agility, fitness, and an awareness of their own bodies.’

He pushed his hands into his tracksuit pockets, thought for a moment, and leaned forward almost confidentially.

‘I trust, gentlemen, you will not follow the example of a teacher I saw last year while I was supervising a student on TP. This teacher stood inside the classroom on cold mornings, wrapped a scarf around his neck, and sent the children out to run around the playground while he shouted instructions from the open window.’ Several students laughed heartily.

‘Oh, it’s quite true, gentlemen, I assure you,’ Mr Trainer said, freezing the laughter instantly. ‘Many teachers still avoid doing this subject in primary schools. At secondary level, of course, you don’t do it unless you are a specialist.’

He took his hands from his pockets and walked to the wallbars on the other side of the hall, gripping them for a moment as if testing either their strength, or his own. The group shuffled through ninety degrees to face him again. In order to be sure of undivided attention he frequently changed position, ensuring that the group turned as well. Mr Trainer was a man who rarely stood still, and it seemed to worry him when others did. He picked up his notes again.

'Very well, gentlemen,' he said, 'Let's waste no more time.' Several students looked distinctly disappointed.

'This morning we shall begin in the usual manner. I'll demonstrate some warming-up activities that use parts of the body to some... ahm... purpose, and then we'll go on to some work with hoops and balls. Practically every primary school has a good stock of hoops and balls, so you might find this lesson very helpful in three week's time.'

The group stood up, ready for what promised to be another withering test of fitness and endurance.

'Splendid!' Mr Trainer exclaimed, almost as if he was praising our ability to stand upright. 'Start by running round the gym, and each time you pass the basket ball ring, leap up and try to touch it. Like this.'

He gave an Olympian leap that suggested he could not only touch the ring, but also pass right through it if he felt like it.

'Run at your own speed,' he emphasised. 'And in your own time. I think that should warm us up a little.' Though he included himself in his remarks, he showed little need for warming up. As far as we could tell, he never strayed very far from boiling point.

For five minutes, the hall hummed with strenuous activity. Although instructed to go at their own pace, the students knew from bitter experience that this wasn't a viable proposition. Slowing down meant that the person behind, usually a towering six footer, hammered into you with the speed and weight of a rugby tackle, often leaving casualties groaning on the floor. After three minutes, two circles had formed; the outer reserved for the long distance runners who showed no signs of flagging, and the inner for those who'd quickly slowed to a less demanding jog. Barton, meanwhile, entered joyously into the spirit of things and pretended he was a motor bike, changing lanes recklessly. Rashid endured two fairly savage collisions before running off into a corner, holding his spectacles gingerly and inspecting his ribs for damage. Duggan, for a change, opted to stay with the outer circle but stopped after a failed attempt to touch the basket ball ring.

'How the hell does he do it?' he muttered hopelessly.

'Springs, man,' shouted Rashid above the pad of plimsolled feet, 'He's got springs on every foot.'

Mr Trainer, feeling it was time to change the activity, stepped lightly into the centre of the hall and blew a whistle.

'Stop now,' he called, bouncing up and down on the balls of his feet as if harnessing the desire to give one fabulously agile leap to the top of the wallbars. 'Sit down for a moment.' There was a group murmur of extreme gratitude.

'Fine, gentlemen,' he said, apparently unaware that many of his group were already on the verge of collapse. 'Now I want to continue with some simple movements that... um... stress the need for the child to think for himself. Or herself, of course. The idea is to give out a general instruction and then let the children work out how their bodies can best tackle the task. Remember, children vary greatly in ability. Your job is to bring out the best in each. Very well then, on your feet, gentlemen, please.'

The group stood up again, more slowly than before.

'I want you to curl up into a small bundle, tuck your elbows and feet in, and travel over the floor softly, but quickly... and as lightly as you can. My theme here is movement of the body's weight to different points...ahm... like this...'

He sprang into a crouching position and scuttled forward at lightning speed, like a crab roughly disturbed by an inquisitive child with a stick, shifting his body weight with precision and skill. We also scuttled forward like agitated crabs, rushing around frantically and groaning with the effort of it all. Billings scuttled and muttered, vowing never to smoke again; Duggan scuttled in cautious circles, and Barton managed to scuttle into a hiding position behind the vaulting box. Mr Trainer scuttled alongside everybody else, encouraging, goading, urging. After what seemed an eternity, he stood up and blew his whistle again.

'Excellent, gentlemen. Stop now, if you would.' No second invitation was needed, and everybody sat down.

'Good. Ahm, fine. Now remember, I emphasised that PE should be closely linked with other aspects of the curriculum. Especially drama, music, and movement. You could, for example, choose a theme such as... ahm... animals for your entire lesson. Or machinery, perhaps. Each child could explore the sounds and movement of machinery. There are hundreds of ideas, gentlemen. For this morning, I'll leave it to you. Choose an animate object and use your body to demonstrate it as accurately as you can.'

There was a pause as the group deliberated, and then bodies slowly moved into action. Duggan lay on his back pumping his arms one way, legs another. Billings stood quite still, stretched out his arms and fluttered his fingers. Rashid ran lightly round the hall, making a gurgling noise at the back of his throat.

'Move gentlemen, move,' urged Mr Trainer, 'Explore every position, concentrate on every action. Think, gentlemen. Move, Mr Billings. You don't seem to be moving very much. What are you?'

'I'm a tree.'

'A tree. Mmm. Then move those branches, Mr Billings, stretch them out towards the sun. A tree has roots. *Stretch* those roots, Mr Billings. Can you feel them stretching?'

'I can, Sir, definitely,' Billings replied, looking at him in pain.

'Splendid. Keep it up, gentlemen, keep it up. Now change to a different object.'

Billings suddenly hovered very close to Rashid, who was wobbling his legs and arms with spasmodic jerks.

'Watch it, Rashid,' cried Billings. 'I'm a big swooping eagle about to land, mate.'

Rashid turned round as swiftly as his sight would allow, and caught Billings neatly in the back of the neck with an outstretched hand, felling him instantly.

'I'm a lightning flash, man,' he replied triumphantly. 'And you've just been struck.'

'Well be more careful then. That hurt.'

‘It would do, man. I’m a million volts!’

Mr Trainer clapped his hands sharply, motioning the group around him again.

‘I realise,’ be began almost apologetically, ‘That you may feel our work this morning to be a little beneath you, especially the secondary trainees amongst us. But remember, you are learning by experience, gentlemen, and after all, that is what you are asking the children to do. I am sure we all feel a little... um... fitter as well?’

A few heads nodded. Mr Trainer glanced at his watch.

‘Good. We haven’t much time left, so we’ll go straight into the ball and hoop work. If you would all be kind enough to take a hoop and ball from the corner, I’ll give you an idea of the possibilities.’ Everybody walked slowly to the pile, and selected a hoop and ball. Mr Trainer also chose a hoop and stood bouncing it lightly in front of his body while he waited for his students to find an appropriate space on the floor.

‘It is most important, gentlemen,’ he emphasised, ‘to let the children discover for themselves what can be accomplished with a particular piece of apparatus. In this way, we encourage individual thought, self-expression and physical agility all at the same time. With the less able child you will need to offer more encouragement as he will tend to imitate his friends, but I think you will be rather surprised at the average child’s ingenuity with a hoop.’ He proceeded to spin one round his body in a spectacular feat of gyration, using his neck, arms, trunk, and finally his ankles.

‘Try these first of all,’ he suggested, neatly flipping himself free. For a moment, nobody moved. There was a stunned pause, like the moment before the final triumphant chord of a mighty symphony orchestra. Duggan turned to me and raised his eyebrows.

‘Well?’ he breathed, breaking the spell, ‘what are you waiting for? Let’s see you do a variation on that little lot.’

‘I thought you might like to go first.’

‘No fear, mate. I’m a less-able child. I’ll copy you.’

'You're not allowed to do that.'

'I'm telling my dad, then.'

It seemed as if everybody was waiting for somebody else to take the lead. Mr Trainer's eyes flashed quickly round the hall.

'Do carry on, gentlemen,' he said, not understanding the reason for the delay.

Self-consciously and slowly the hoops were raised into action, but any variation on such a performance seemed out of the question. I gave my hoop a lame little spin around my leg, and it clattered to the floor after two half-hearted turns. Billings contented himself with bowling the hoop across the floor, and Rashid, with a whoop of childish delight, leapt in the air and let it roll between his legs. Duggan seemed to be having more success than most. Having gyrated the hoop round his neck and waist, he became more adventurous, spun the hoop in the air, and then kept it moving with his body as it came down again.

'Good, good, Mr Phillips, an interesting development,' Mr Trainer said encouragingly. 'Now try to extend it.'

'Extend what, Sir?'

'The movement, Mr Phillips. Try to extend the movement even further.' Duggan looked at him briefly and then gave the hoop a flick with his wrist that sent it spinning. Pausing before he committed an action that might land him in hospital, he dived headlong through the centre of the hoop and landed in a neat crouch position. There was a ripple of applause. Mr Trainer picked the hoop up.

'Yes, very good indeed, Mr Phillips. Gentlemen, if you will stop for a moment, Mr Phillips will demonstrate this development.'

Duggan looked aghast. 'You mean you want me to do it again?' he asked.

'Of course. It is important to stop the class when somebody does a good action, so that everybody can enjoy it, and possibly learn from it. At the same time it is important not to make others feel inferior, of course.'

'But that was strictly a one-off, Sir,' Duggan pleaded. 'I don't really do encores.'

'Nonsense, Mr Phillips.'

'Honestly, Sir, I don't think I...'

'Just once more, please Mr Phillips.'

Realising objection was pointless, Duggan sent the hoop spinning again. With a carefully judged leap, he skimmed sideways through it and crashed into Rashid's legs. Rashid's spectacles, unable to cope with this sudden impetus, shot from his nose and flew high into the air. Two students rushed forward to catch them, collided with each other, and the spectacles dropped onto the end of a bench, splitting neatly into two parts. Rashid gave a strangulated cry, and for a moment Mr Trainer was lost for words.

'I... um... can only apologise, Mr Rashid,' he said at length.

'That doesn't help me, man,' moaned Rashid. 'I can't see without them.'

'Do you not... um... have a spare pair?'

'Can't afford it, man. I'm livin' on peanuts.'

Mr Trainer picked up the two halves and looked suitably sympathetic. 'I'll see what can be done, Mr Rashid. I'm sure we can find some money to pay for them to be mended. Meantime, I have... ahm... a roll of masking tape in my cupboard. Perhaps I can affect a temporary repair.'

Rashid groped his way to the side of the hall and sat down unhappily. Mr Trainer looked at his watch.

'Well gentlemen,' he said. 'I think this might be a suitable point to stop.' Feeling it was the least he could do, he picked up Rashid's hoop and bowled it expertly onto the pile in the corner.

'There's a lesson to be learned from every situation, of course,' he added. 'If children wear spectacles, they should be put in a safe place. Now then, anyone wishing to stay for some trampoline work may do so, of course. I... ahm...'

He stopped and listened. From the corner, behind the vaulting box, came a deep rumbling sound. Mr Trainer strode to the box and peered over the top.

'Incidentally, gentlemen,' he added, with just a trace of sarcasm in his voice, 'you will not benefit the children, or the school, if like Mr Barton, you fall asleep behind the apparatus...'

(ii)

The library was warm and inviting as I pushed the door open and took my books to the counter. Library facilities at the college were excellent, but the preparation of work for teaching practice had meant that the books most needed were constantly in demand, and the local public library was very useful during this period of intensive planning. As usual, my books were slightly overdue, and I counted out the fine to the woman at the counter. She glanced at me frostily.

'Other people want to use these books as well, you know,' she said severely. 'We have a waiting list for this one in particular.'

She pushed my coins into the fine box and they clattered to the bottom. I tried to think of a plausible excuse for keeping the books so long, but nothing remotely acceptable came to mind. The librarian squinted at me through her neat, tortoise shell spectacles.

'Are you from the college?'

'Yes, I'm afraid so.'

'I see. Well kindly return books on time, will you? Your people do this a little too often.'

She pushed my books into the returned pile, and I walked over to the first shelves of fiction. Samantha was stacking novels into an empty section and she looked up and smiled as I approached. Once again I was struck by how attractive she was.

'Hello. You look miserable. Been told off by Miss Ellis, have you?'

'Afraid so. I can't seem to get my books back on time.'

'Nor can half the college. That's why she gets so upset. I thought you might be in this week. The usual rush seems to be on. Where's Duggan? Not working, surely?'

I smiled. 'Hardly. The real panic hasn't hit him yet. He's gone to see some new French film that Gerry's raving about.'

'Oh, I thought he might still be laid up after that dreadful dance. Did he actually enjoy it?'

'I don't think he remembers that much about it.'

'I'm not surprised. It was pretty grim, wasn't it?'

'Well, it wouldn't be an event I'd have chosen to take a girl to. Now of course, if you *really* wanted a nice evening out…'

'Is this going to be a proposition?'

'No, I was just saying that… well, yes, it is actually. I'm asking you out. In fact, it is essential that you come out with me.'

'Really? Why's that?'

'Because.'

'Well, I'll have to accept, then.'

Miss Ellis glanced up from the desk and walked over to us.

'Is this person bothering you, Samantha?' she asked.

Samantha shook her head. 'No, it's all right. He was just trying to decide whether to choose a book on the theatre or a guide to local restaurants.'

'Really. We don't keep guides on local restaurants.'

'No, we ought to. I was saying it would be a good idea.'

'Well don't keep her long, young man. She's busy. She hasn't got time to waste.' Miss Ellis strode back to the counter and began checking through the reserved books.

'So it's a meal then?' I said quietly.

'Mmm. That would be lovely.'

'Saturday?'

'No, but Friday's okay.'

'Is Saturday David's day?'

'No. We're visiting relations. Actually, David didn't work out.' I felt a surge of excitement. I could hardly believe my good fortune.

'Any particular food?'

'Something spicy. Do you like Indian food?'

'Love it.'

'That's settled then. Now I'd better finish checking these books.'

'Well before you do, can you find me a good western for Duggan?'

'Going to read it to the class on teaching practice, is he? He ought to try a book of horror stories. I'm sure they'd enjoy that!'

'I wouldn't put it past him. Actually, I've decided to do a topic on the river Thames, so anything you've got on that would be helpful. I need some good art ideas too. And a book of short stories to read to them. Where do I look?'

'Go upstairs to the Children's Section. Somebody in there will help you. You should find lots of suitable books for your topic. I'll have a look later on, too. So whereabouts is your teaching practice school?'

'North London. Islington.'

'Really? That should be fun! Remember to confiscate their weapons first.'

'It's only a primary school. The lists went up on Tuesday and one of the second years who'd been to the school last year told me he'd got on quite well. Well, fairly well, anyway.'

'I'm sure you'll be fine,' she said warmly. 'I don't suppose they'd send you anywhere awful the first time anyway. Are you going on your own?'

'Yes. It's only a small school. Duggan's going with two others to a school in Greenwich. He sat up half the night trying to work out how he could maximise his travel expenses!'

'Now why doesn't that surprise me? Oh well, I'd better get on, or Cynthia will be over here again and she'll ban you from the library! I'll leave you to look around. The westerns are over there with the crime novels.'

'Thanks. See you Saturday. I'll pick you up about eight. Oh.. I'll need your address. And jot your phone number down for me. Just in case.'

'What, just in case you meet someone else by Saturday?'

I laughed. 'No, in case I want to propose to you over the phone.'

She fetched a piece of paper from the desk and quickly scribbled a number on it. Then she smiled and turned to help an elderly lady who had forgotten her reading glasses while I went upstairs to hunt through the children's shelves. Eventually, I found several books on the Thames, another on the story of rivers, and two books on art technique for young people. I also took a book of short stories, and a book of comic poetry written especially for children. Duggan, I decided, would have to come and fetch his own western. As I came back to the entrance, Miss Ellis looked at me in astonishment.

'You can't possibly have all those books,' she said sharply. 'Who let you have all those?'

'They're for my teaching practice.'

'I don't care what they're for, young man. You simply can't have them. How many have you got?'

'Seven.'

'Seven? Good heavens, you can take three but you certainly can't take seven. Choose three and take the rest back straight away.'

'Oh, don't worry,' said Samantha as I explained the problem. 'Put them in your bag. Just as long as you bring them back. Anyway, I shall keep a close check on you myself.'

I smiled pleasantly at Miss Ellis and placed three books in front of her for stamping.

'That's better. And I'd appreciate it if you brought them back on time.'

I carefully edged my way through the revolving door and out into the sunlight. I suddenly felt a great sense of elation. The planning for my teaching practice was going well. I was up to date with all my college work. Spring was on its way.

And on Saturday I was taking Samantha out.

APRIL

THE SECRET AGENT ARRIVES FOR TEACHING PRACTICE

The bus lurched to a halt at the traffic lights and I took stock of the situation. Ten to nine. Although I'd risen at seven and left myself plenty of time, I would never reach the school by nine. I prayed the school day didn't actually start until nine fifteen.

Most of the first year students had been up earlier than usual that morning, scratching round in drawers for extra file paper, hurriedly making last minute notes, borrowing books from each other and gulping down a hurried breakfast in the dining room. Few words were exchanged. Each person was too busy wondering if anything of vital importance had been forgotten. I had left Duggan hunting for a book of poetry he had put down somewhere in his room. Gerry had gone out almost as dawn broke, his pipe thrust between his teeth and a determined look on his face. Dudley had still been snoring next door as I'd left the corridor.

By the time I'd reached the underground, the trains were packed to capacity. Although there were only seven stops to the station I wanted, the train had broken down in the tunnel and after a delay of forty minutes, it had eventually crawled to the next platform. Tempers, already frayed by the pressure of tightly packed bodies, had begun to unravel in earnest, and I had left the stifling atmosphere of the tube and caught a bus instead. This, too, slowed to a crawl, and I now sat wondering whether if it would be better to walk the last part of the journey. After a moment's deliberation, I jumped off just before the lights changed.

Dodging between the people on the crowded pavements slowed me down again. Market stalls were being erected at the sides of the road and traders with tough, weather-beaten features were laying out vegetables, clothes, fruit, cheap crockery and jewellery. They exchanged few words; they had organised their stalls in the same manner for many years and there wasn't much to say. Men and women who had a little time to spare stopped by the stalls to pick up and examine items that had caught their eye. A number of children walked along the road to school, hurrying to keep up with their mothers who were pushing prams or clutching very young children in their arms.

The buildings in the main road seemed to span many decades. A tiny shoe-mender's shop, a watch maker and a few small newsagents appeared to be surviving alongside the encroaching, cut-price superstores. Outside almost every store, cardboard boxes filled with rubbish were piled high, awaiting the dustcart that would crush and dispose of them. From a tiny, gaudily painted transport cafe came the sound of a radio playing loudly. A dozen people sat inside, scanning newspaper headlines, sipping mugs of scalding tea, or chewing on thick wedges of breakfast bread and butter. A lollipop lady halted the traffic at the zebra crossing and I followed the growing stream of children across the road, gently easing my way through the crowd of mothers and prams waiting outside the entrance to the school. At the top of the high brick wall encircling the school, an orange board clung grimly to the wire netting over the gate, its fading white letters announcing that this was Briar Road Primary School, under the care of the Inner London Education Authority, Headteacher A.J.Reed, MA. BSc. The building behind the metal fencing looked just like a prison.

I watched as a mother finished a packet of crisps and tossed the empty bag on the ground near the gate, where it joined sweet papers and lolly sticks. A morning breeze occasionally attempted to rid the school entrance of its rubbish, but only succeeded in rearranging it and moving it a little further on. The sound of whirring lathes and metal being hammered drifted over the surrounding high wall, and a woman with her hair in curlers shouted at her child from a window in a block of flats, telling him to get out of the road right this minute. She shouted again, fighting a losing battle against the rumbling lorries on their journey north. The air was thick and heavy with disturbed dust and although there was a lollypop lady on the zebra crossing, I wondered how the children managed to cross such a busy road safely each day.

The school was extremely large, ugly, and built in three storeys. Probably, I thought, not long after Queen Victoria died. It made no pretence of being welcoming, nor presumably had the architect intended it to be. It had been designed merely to contain children of various ages for a good part of the day. So this was it, I thought. The beginning of my first day as an apprentice teacher. Looking at the screaming, fighting children who rushed frantically round the playground pushing and shoving each other, I certainly didn't feel like one. My only consolation was that I hadn't arrived late.

A fat drop of rain splashed into my face as a small boy dashed into the playground and hurried to the steps. Pulling up the collar of my raincoat and gripping my briefcase tightly, I went forward and stopped him.

'Yer?' said the child, panting heavily.

'Can you show me where the headmaster's office is?'

'If you want. We'll 'ave to 'urry up, though, 'cos I'm late.'

'No you're not,' I said. 'These other children are still in the playground.'

'They're infants,' he grunted, surprised at my lack of knowledge. 'You a noo teacher or somethin'?'

I bent down and spoke in a confidential whisper. 'No. Actually, I'm a secret agent. I have reason to believe our enemies may be using your school as a hide-out.'

The boy's mouth dropped open, the lateness temporarily forgotten. Then he grinned broadly.

'Get 'orf! You ain't no secret agent. Where's yer ID?'

'It's in my wallet.'

'Show us, then.'

'I don't know if I should. How do I know I can trust you?

'Course you can. Anyway, you ain't no secret agent. You're a noo teacher.'

'That's what I'm supposed to look like. It's a disguise.'

'That ain't no disguise. Where are they s'posed to be 'idin', then?'

'In the boiler room. That's where they hid their plans.'

'What plans?'

'The plans to kidnap your headteacher.'

'Well good luck to 'em then. We ain't got no boiler room, anyway. You're a noo teacher. You ain't no secret agent.'

The boy hurried ahead, and I followed him up the three flights of stone stairs that led to the top corridor. To my surprise, the inside of the building bore no relation to its dull exterior. The walls on each side of the staircase, painted in white above brown glazed tiles, had been filled with children's drawing and paintings. A beautifully made frieze of the Crimean War filled the entire space above the top flight of stairs, and a large painted portrait of Florence Nightingale had been pasted beside it, together with pieces of writing about her life. On the opposite wall, an Australian scene filled with animals and birds had been mounted. Further down the staircase, three dimensional prehistoric creatures made from corrugated card had been carefully positioned to create the maximum effect.

Reaching the top at last, the child, almost out of breath, narrowly avoided colliding with an extremely tall man whose head was thickly covered by a mass of closely cropped silver hair. He stood motionless on the last stair, his sunken grey eyes heightening the sour look on his face.

'Late again, Bristow!' he boomed, with a ferocity that made me jump. 'The third time in the last fortnight, isn't it? Kindly tell your mother to wake you up an hour earlier.'

The child looked up nervously.

'She can't, Sir', he faltered. 'She 'as to go ter work early.'

'So do lots of other mothers. So do I. That's no excuse.' The cold grey eyes turned to me.

'Excuse me,' I said cautiously, taken aback by this disagreeable start to the morning for Bristow. 'I'm looking for Mr Reed.'

'I am Mr Reed. Did you wish to see me?'

'I showed 'im up the stairs, Sir,' said Bristow brightly, as if this might compensate for being late. "E reckons 'e's a secret agent, Sir.'

'I beg your pardon, Bristow?'

'This bloke, Sir. 'E reckons 'e's a secret agent. 'E's looking for the boiler room, Sir. I told 'im we ain't got one.'

'Of course we've got a boiler room, Bristow. What are you talking about?'

I interrupted quickly. 'It's all right. I was just asking Bristow how to find you.'

'Then why is the boy babbling about boiler rooms and secret agents?'

'It was a joke. I told him I was a secret agent. It was just a joke.'

'Was it? I see.'

Mr Reed quite obviously didn't see at all. Bristow cowered and sped off to his classroom. I hastily explained who I was and Mr Reed eyed me suspiciously, as if wondering whether he ought to send for assistance. Eventually, deciding that I didn't actually represent a threat to the school, he ushered me along a short corridor lined with brightly painted bookcases and through some swing doors, now latched open to reveal the school hall at right angles to the corridor. Some of the classrooms were spaced between the hall and the staircase, and a constant drone of children's voices came from inside them, like bees in a thriving hive.

'Come in here, please,' Mr Reed gestured, throwing open the door of his study and waving me to a seat. The room was small and desperately neat. A comfortable chair had been placed, exactly, in front of the polished oak desk, on which stood IN and OUT trays, both tidily full. A tray with a steaming tea pot and a bone-china cup stood on the window sill. Opposite the desk were two smaller upright wooden chairs, and behind them new red curtains, drawn neatly back from the window. I sat down in the comfortable chair and tried to look reasonably cheerful. Mr Reed sat down precisely behind his desk, slamming the drawer of his filing cabinet shut as he did so. Through the wall, I could hear the sound of a typewriter.

'Yes, now then, Mr Kent,' Mr Reed began briskly. 'We'll overlook your unfortunate introduction to the school, but it would have been helpful if you could have been here on time.'

'I'm really sorry,' I apologised. 'The train broke down in the tunnel.'

'That's almost as weak an excuse as Bristow's. Never mind. There is just time for me to tell you a little bit about the school before we go into assembly. The rest you'll have to glean from studying the school handbook. You'll be having second year Juniors while you are here. It is four weeks, isn't it?'

I nodded.

'Then that gives you a reasonable period of time to get something worthwhile done. You'll be with Mrs Bridgewood. She is my Deputy Head, and an outstanding teacher. You will learn a lot from her. I understand your main subject is science. Growing mustard and cress and that sort of thing?'

'Well, a bit more than that, actually. I was hoping to do quite a lot of chemistry, and...'

'Were you? Well, we'll have to see about that. I can't take the risk of children burning or poisoning themselves.'

There was a knock on the door, and a neatly dressed secretary came in with a pile of letters.

'Oh I'm sorry, Mr Reed,' she said, 'I didn't realise you had someone with you. Would this be Mr Kent from St James's?'

'I think so, Mrs Jones,' Mr Reed replied. 'Though apparently there is a possibility of him belonging to the Secret Service.'

'Sorry?'

'It's a joke, Mrs Jones.'

The secretary looked completely bewildered.

'Oh, is it? I see. Do you want a school dinner, Mr Kent? There's pilchard salad or cauliflower cheese. You can pay me at the end of the week.' I humbly accepted a salad, and she closed the door softly. Mr Reed spoke again.

'As I was saying, the classes are quite large, but Briar Road is a very good school. I don't say that just because I am here, though you will come to realise that administration plays a very important role in school life. I administrate very well, Mr Kent.'

'I'm sure you do,' I said, feeling that some response, however slight, was called for.

'I also have a capable staff, of course. Efficient administration and a capable staff add up to a well run school. There are two hundred and eighteen children. The Infants occupy the ground floor, and the Juniors the other floors. If you turn out to be even one tenth as good as Mrs Bridgewood, I shall be more than satisfied.'

I smiled politely and moved my leg away from the small electric fire near his chair. It seemed to be threatening to initiate my first day at Briar Road by burning my ankle.

'Most of the children come from the flats surrounding the school,' Mr Reed continued, pouring a cup of tea for himself and sipping it delicately. 'This school, as you have probably noticed, is in an area of great social deprivation. Many of the children have difficult home lives and are not easy to cope with. You'll have no discipline problems if you keep them very busy. Be firm, Mr Kent, and don't give them an inch. When I started at a new school I always gave my new class half a dozen hymns to write out on a piece of paper. Then I'd make them cut out the words and put them together again. It kept them very busy, and they learned the hymns at the same time.'

He smiled briefly for the first time, but there was no humour in his eyes. I resisted the urge to tell him what I thought of his ridiculous idea, and I began to wonder if the college had sent me to the right school.

'I assume you have prepared topic work for the children, Mr Kent, and I should like to look at your file before you start teaching. You should find the school has all the equipment you need. Games equipment, tape recorders, slides, filmstrips. We have to make some concessions to modern thinking, whether we approve of it or not. I'd suggest you don't use that kind of thing at first, though. Discipline first, or you'll get nowhere.'

He paused to take a sheet of paper from his drawer, and as he bent down, I saw a child just outside the window behind him, apparently standing on thin air. Noticing my puzzled expression, Mr Reed swung round.

'Get off that scaffolding, boy!' he roared, making the window rattle. 'What the devil do you think you're doing? Get down and come here!'

The boy moved swiftly and was gone.

'We have painters and plumbers on site, Mr Kent, and they are a nuisance. The children climb on the scaffolding. If one of them falls off there'll be the devil to pay. Now, where was I?'

'You were telling me about the equipment.'

'Yes, well, I've told you about that. Watch 'em if they try to get on the scaffolding while you're on playground duty with Mrs Bridgewood, will you?'

I nodded wearily.

'Now, I've made out a timetable of the length of time I suggest you give to each subject, and I would recommend that you stick to it. I'll be coming in to see you several times while you are teaching.'

He wouldn't find me telling the children to cut up pieces of paper with hymns on, I thought. Mr Reed looked at his watch as a bell rang outside, and I could hear children coming out of their classrooms.

'I'll introduce you to Mrs Bridgewood after assembly,' he said.

'There isn't time now. Is there anything you want to ask me before we go into the hall? If so, say so quickly.'

There seemed a thousand things. I selected one quickly. 'Will there be any chance of taking the class on a visit? I was thinking of the Science Museum perhaps, to tie in with my topic on...'

'I doubt it,' Mr Reed interrupted. 'Remember, you're only here for a month, and you'll only have the class for parts of the day. There are also the risks. A fellow from your college once left two children going round and round on the Circle line until half past six. Neither of them could speak English, either. Another one fell in the Serpentine. I'm not having anything like that again.'

'What about books and paper?'

'There are plenty of text books, but Mrs Bridgewood does not use them a great deal. However, she is experienced enough to know what she is doing. I suggest you watch her carefully first'. He picked up a book from his desk, put his head outside the door and motioned to me.

'Right, we'll go in now. I've had a chair put at the back of the hall for you. There's a key on my desk. You'd better fetch it after assembly.'

I followed as Mr Reed strode outside, pushing his way through the last class now entering the hall. A number of children looked at me curiously, and I wondered if the secret agent story had spread that far already. All the children were eventually assembled in the hall, sitting on the floor and grouped in classes according to age. The class teachers, most of whom seemed quite young, sat alongside their children. Two fourth year boys were struggling to push the piano into a suitable position, while two others were putting out an overhead projector on a trolley, and a record player. I noticed that only the Junior classes seemed to be attending this assembly.

Mr Reed strode to the front and as I sat on the chair provided for me several teachers smiled a greeting, making me feel a little more comfortable. The noise level began to increase and Mr Reed stood watching the children for a moment, obviously expecting them to quieten and becoming increasingly angry when they did not. Suddenly, he held up his right hand and shouted.

'Right! That's quite enough! I realise it is Monday morning, but that doesn't mean you have to sit there squirming like a tin of maggots!'

I was startled by his abrupt manner and rudeness, and I looked across at the faces of the other teachers. They were expressionless. I wondered if they had just become used to this form of greeting.

'Perhaps I might be allowed to begin now,' Mr Reed continued. 'Good morning, school.'

'Good morning Mr Reed,' they chorused back.

'Because I happen to be a few minutes late for assembly I see no reason why you should make that kind of noise. I shall expect you to keep absolutely quiet for the rest of assembly. We have a new teacher with us this morning, and I hardly think he has been impressed by your behaviour. You will treat him just as you treat the rest of the staff.'

As I had no idea how the other teachers were treated, I wasn't sure if this was a good idea or not. All the children turned to look at me, and the chattering began again.

'That's quite enough. And that's the third time I've said it,' Mr Reed shouted. 'We shall now sing 'I Love God's Tiny Creatures.' He switched on an overhead projector and the words flashed onto a wallscreen. Then he strode to the piano, sat down, and played an introduction. The children stood up and began to sing, falteringly at first, and then heartily when they reached the last verse.

'Right, sit down,' he said, closing the lid of the piano afterwards and, strangely, locking it with a small key.

'Now then, the hymn we have just been singing told us how we should care for all God's tiny creatures, no matter how large or small they are. I am going to read about somebody who cared a great deal for God's creatures. Sit up, keep still, and listen quietly.'

Picking up his book from the table, he began to read the story of St Francis. It wasn't a version particularly suited to children, and they soon became restless and bored. Mr Reed had to look up sharply several times and wait for the murmuring to stop. At the end of the story, he clapped his hands again for silence, asked the children to stand, bow their heads and put their hands together, and then led them in the Lord's Prayer before ushering them to sit down again.

'It's a shame some of you can't be bothered to listen properly,' he said. 'There are several things I wish to say, so sit up and pay attention. I am sorry to hear that some children haven't been behaving properly at the swimming baths. It seems that some of you have been pushing others into the pool. Not all of you, of course. Just the few fools who think that sort of thing is funny. I understand the instructor was nearly pushed into the pool herself. If this sort of behaviour continues, I shall have all swimming cancelled for a month.'

There was absolute silence now.

'Right. I think I've made myself clear. I don't have to remind you...' The sound of hammers pounding on the wall outside threatened to blot out his words as he began to speak again. He raised his voice another octave.

'...I don't have to remind you that the builders are still here. I do not want to see stupid fools climbing the scaffolding. One fool was on the scaffolding outside my room this morning when he should have been in his classroom. If this nonsense continues I shall stop all playtimes as well. Are you listening to me, Bradley?'

A boy in the middle of the hall looked up and nodded seriously.

'Well it doesn't look like it to me, boy. You're wriggling like a maggot. And I don't want to see anyone touching tools belonging to the workman. You are neither plumbers nor carpenters and I don't intend allowing you to dismember each other. Right, sit up straight and get ready to go out.'

He walked to the table beside the piano, put on a record of brass band music, and stood with his arms folded while the children filed out with their teachers. I could hardly believe what I'd seen and heard. When the hall was practically empty, Mr Reed removed the record from the turntable and again motioned me to follow him back to his study, where he handed me a large iron key.

'Keep this until the day you leave,' he said. 'And please try not to lose it. I've had three cut in the last few months.'

'Surely I don't need a classroom key?' I asked. 'Doesn't Mrs Bridgewood have one?'

'It's not a classroom key, Mr Kent. It's a key to the gentlemen's lavatory. The plumbers are renewing the indoor ones and you'll have to use the original staff toilet in the playground, I'm afraid. Follow me now, please.'

In a state of mild shock I followed him once again through the hall and down the corridor along the other side. He opened a door near the staircase and ushered me inside.

'This is Mrs Bridgewood's classroom,' he announced. 'Now, where is she…'

The classroom was very large and surprisingly airy. Separated into groups and already occupied with various tasks were about twenty five children, busily comparing books and chattering softly to each other. A tall, attractive woman in her early forties wearing a neat blue overall was moving from group to group, marking work, offering spellings, discussing how best to tackle something new and giving help or advice to several children at once. She was crouching down with the children and their urgent discussions as they pored over their tasks showed they were completely absorbed in what they were doing.

On the wall at the back of the room was a huge map of the world, painted by the children. Numbers and pointers were dotted all over the map, each number corresponding to a country, and two girls were testing each other's knowledge of them. Above this was a display of masks, beautifully decorated and constructed with loving care. Five children in one corner wore headphones connected to a tape recorder and sat listening to a story, following the words in their books. Two girls were sketching some of the fish drifting peacefully in the fishtank near the window.

On a table at the side of the room were large models of Tudor houses, constructed from cardboard boxes and balsa wood. Above them, high on the wall, was an enormous painting of a Tudor street scene. The fourth wall was devoted entirely to mathematics, showing the wide range of practical topics the children had attempted. A boy at the front table looked up and saw us.

'Miss, Miss,' he called. 'Mr Reed's in 'ere…'

Mrs Bridgewood turned and stood up, pushing her apron back into place and wiping chalk dust from her hands. She beamed at me and shook my hand warmly.

'Hello, welcome, I'm Dorothy Bridgewood,' she smiled, after Mr Reed had left the room. 'Well, what did you think of our assembly?'

'A bit severe for a Monday morning,' I said cautiously.

She laughed out loud, and several children looked up and grinned, even though they couldn't hear the conversation.

'Wasn't it awful?' she said. 'I'm afraid our headmaster is a bit of an ogre. The children are quite frightened of him, but we don't see him much and he never bothers us, so we don't worry about it. Thank God he doesn't actually teach a class. Has he told you about his school at Tower Bridge?'

'He did mention something about cutting up hymn sheets.'

'Oh, he's got lots of stories like that. He's been here for sixteen years. How he got the headship we'll never know. Perhaps they were relieved to get him out of the classroom.'

'Doesn't it affect the children?' I asked. 'His attitude, I mean?'

'Most of the staff don't think so. I'm not so sure. Still, we do what we can to compensate. I'm afraid you came in at the wrong end of the day. His assemblies are the worst part. They don't involve the children at all and that's why they chatter. They're simply not interested. Who would be, if you're moaned at all the time?'

She stopped and spoke to a child who couldn't work out why the graph she was drawing didn't emerge as a straight line. I waited until it had been explained.

'They're doing maths now,' she said. 'Most of them, anyway, but I don't do it at the same time every day. In fact, you can use your time as you like. How long are you here for?'

'A month.'

'Mmm, I thought it would be. Well, that's fine. I'll give you a couple of days to get used to the children while we talk about what you want to do. You can wander round and have a chat to them in a minute. They'd like that.'

I gazed round the classroom in admiration. It was bright, colourful and extremely child-centred. The children seemed completely in control of their own learning.

'I've got them in groups at the moment, to finish off work they started a few days ago,' she continued. 'The lot over there are measuring themselves and then they'll go on to workcards using the measurements. I've got a couple out by the main gate doing a graph survey of the traffic. Very sensible ones, mind! Some of the others, like Julie over there, are doing some practical fraction work based on a story we had yesterday. And I think Jamie Dudmish is making a pair of calipers. He's a very clever boy. Another four are at the police station.'

'What on earth have they done?' I asked in astonishment.

She chuckled again. 'Nothing, I hope! The beat officer promised to show them how fingerprinting is done. They did a topic on police work last term.'

I took out the timetable Mr Reed had given to me, but she waved it away quickly.

'Oh Lord, don't take any notice of that, my dear! I don't think anybody here uses a timetable, apart from hall times for PE and things like that.'

'But how do you make sure all the children make progress.. and cover all the subjects?' I asked.

'You make lots of notes.. and you plan meticulously. The children in my class are allowed a fair bit of control over what they do and when they do it, but there must be an order to it, and I must know that they've covered a fair bit of ground in the space of a week. Sometimes, of course, one thing will last for quite a time. Those Tudor houses took quite a while.'

'They're really very good.'

'Yes, the children are very keen. They're not the brightest bunch I've taught, but they're very affectionate and you'll get a lot from them. Anyway, have a walk around and talk to them.'

Feeling greatly cheered by Mrs Bridgewood's enthusiasm, I stopped by a group of children playing what looked like mathematical bingo.

'Are you goin' to take us then, Sir?' asked a small snub nosed child with a shock of curly hair.

'Well, probably not today,' I smiled. 'I want to see what sort of things you do, first. What's your name?'

'Alan Badger, Sir. 'Ere, sit down fer a bit. You can 'ave me chair. I'll stand fer a bit.' The other children at the table nodded seriously in appreciation of this sacrifice.

'How do you play this game?' I asked, sitting on the chair and subjecting myself to intense scrutiny from five small faces.

'I'll show yer, Sir,' Badger offered. 'It's easy. You 'ave a card with the numbers on it, like this, and then Tracey asks a 'rithmetic sum like what's three eights and then if you got the answer on your bit o' card you cover it up. When you cover eight squares you win. You 'ave to watch it 'cos Fred 'ere cheats a bit. 'E ain't much good at 'rithmetic.'

'Why don't you 'ave a go?' Tracey suggested. 'Give 'im a card Wendy. We got lots over. You cover 'em up with these bits.'

One of the children, tinier than the rest, had been staring at me with half closed eyes and pursed lips. Eventually, he summoned the courage to speak.

'You're a stoodent Sir, ain't yer?'

I was momentarily taken aback.

‘We’ve ‘ad stoodents before,’ he added knowledgeably. ‘I didn’t like the last one much. ‘E kept shoutin’ at us. I don’t like it when they shout at us.’

‘Aw, shuttup, Fred,’ Tracey commanded. ‘Anyone ‘ud shout at you. Your mum shouts at you. ‘Cos you never listen, that’s why.’

Fred was silenced. I smiled and concentrated on playing the game. All the children showed great excitement when they were able to cover a square, and apart from Tracey occasionally checking Fred’s card, the game continued uneventfully. After several minutes, Badger dug me forcibly in the chest with his elbow.

‘There y’are!’ he shouted triumphantly. ‘You got eight squares, Sir. You’re s’posed to shout out. Jus’ beat me to it, an’ all! Cor, you’re good at tables, ain’t yer, Sir?’

He looked at my full card in deep appreciation.

‘I like this game, don’t you?’ said Tracey, collecting all the cards and scraps of paper together. ‘We ‘ave a shuffle round now an’ then someone else ‘as a turn at callin’.’

‘Do you like our Tudor ‘ouses what we made?’ asked Badger. ‘I saw you lookin’ at ‘em with Miss. We spent days on ‘em. I like makin’ models. I was gonna make my chimney out of fag packets but Miss don’t like us bringin’ fag packets to school.’

‘That’s ‘cos smokin’s bad for yer,’ said Tracey.

‘I know that. But we ain’t smokin’ the packets, are we? My Nan don’t ‘alf get through a few fags though. About five thousand a week, I reckon.’

‘What’s your name, Sir?’ asked another little girl at the table. She had a round, very pretty face with freckles and dark hair hanging down in plaits.

‘It’s Mr Kent.’

‘That’s a nice name. It’s my birthday the day after tomorrow. I’ll be nine. My dad’s getting me a bike.’

‘How are you getting on?’ asked Mrs Bridgewood, coming over to the table. I straightened up to talk to her.

'Fine at the moment. They seem very lively. And they're anything but shy.'

'Oh, they're lively all right. A bit too lively sometimes. They're a nice bunch, though.'

'How do you find time to hear them all read? Can they all read?'

'Most of them. There's an awful lot of work done with the Infant classes on reading. We try to make sure they can all read by the time they are seven. The children in the Infants are split up into reading groups for the first hour of the morning. It's a very intensive session on reading schemes, but it also means we don't have so much work to do on them in the Junior classes. You can concentrate on the ones who find it a real struggle.'

'But you still need to hear them all read, surely?'

'Sure. But you also rely on the parents to help. They sign a card saying they've listened to their child for fifteen minutes or so.'

'Do they all do it?'

'You'd be surprised at how many do. Parents aren't supposed to care much these days, and some teachers feel the general view of the public is that this job's a soft option. You know, you only work from nine till three and you have six weeks of Summer free. That's nonsense of course. Mind you, some of the children, like Hema over there, would sit and read all day if you let them. She's a sweet little thing. There aren't many terrors in this class. John Rouse over there can be a bit hard going. Brilliant footballer, though.'

'They all seem to be working hard at the moment.'

'Yes, they are. But they slow down towards the end of the day and one or two actually grind to a halt. Not children like Hema or Jamie Dudmish though. He's over there by the radiator. He'll work all day on his own. But then, his parents surround him with learning experiences, and it makes a difference. Brian had this class last year. You'll meet him at breaktime, but don't take him too seriously. He'll do his best to persuade you he's a tyrant.'

The children had become slightly noisier while they talked,

and she clapped her hands softly. Immediately, the noise fell to a completely acceptable level again.

'How soon can I have a try at teaching them?' I asked, eager to begin.

'As soon as you feel ready. Give yourself today at least to settle in, and have a go for an hour tomorrow if you like. Don't try to do masses of individual work on this practice. Just teach them as a class and get the feel of what it's like. You'll find them hard work, but they all enjoy being in school.'

'You seem to, as well.'

'Mmm. I love it. I couldn't do anything else. My husband thinks I'm crazy.'

A girl came out and offered her folder for marking, smiling shyly at me and twisting the hem of her skirt with her fingers. Mrs Bridgewood looked through the folder, murmured encouragement, and then turned to me again.

'Would you like to have a few for a while? I'll tell you what. Alan Badger made a super model of Big Ben last week, and he didn't believe it when he found out the big hand was over fourteen feet long. Why don't you take him down to the playground and measure it out with him. Take a few others, too.'

She looked round the classroom and clapped her hands. 'Alan, John, Darren Adams, come here please. Okay, you two girls as well.' The children hurried out to her.

'You remember we were talking about Alan's model of Big Ben last week? Well, Mr Kent is going to take you to the playground and you can do some measuring to show you exactly how long the hands of the clock are. You can stay until the bell rings, but behave down there, please. You'd better take some sticks of chalk. And some rulers and a yardstick.'

'Cor!' exclaimed one of the children, turning to his friend with excitement, 'We're 'avin' the stoodent!'

'What's a stoodent?' asked his friend.

''im. 'E's a stoodent. 'E ain't a real teacher. 'E's jus' learnin' the trade.'

The boy scurried across the classroom, collecting the equipment and sharing out plastic rulers amongst the group. The two little girls were wearing identical dresses, and they turned to each other and giggled each time I spoke. As they walked down the stairs, I asked the children about the paintings on the wall.

'Mr Glover's class did the one on the Middle Ages up there,' said one of the girls. 'We were in 'is class last year, an' we did the Middle Ages too. Lots of classes helped to do the other paintings. We did the one on Australia last term, with Miss. In 'istory, I think the Middle Ages is intrestin', don't you, Sir? They wasn't 'alf cruel, but it's intrestin', ain't it?'

'Very,' I agreed enthusiastically. 'What did you learn about the Middle Ages, then?'

'All sorts, really. We done about 'Enry the second and Becket and 'ow William come over to this country an' so on. I'll show you a folder I done about it when we get back to class, if you like.'

'Thank you. I'd like to see it very much.'

'The bit I liked best was when 'Arold got shot.' Badger butted in. ''E got shot in the eye, Sir.'

'Do you know how we know that?' I asked.

'Yeah, 'cos Mr Glover told us.'

'No, I mean it's all on a picture called the Bayeux Tapestry.'

'The what? Oh, you mean that carpet thing. Yeah, we made one of them. I done 'Arold gettin' it in the eye.'

'Shame someone don't get you in the eye,' cried the girl. 'Ain't 'e bloodthirsty, Sir.'

We'd reached the playground and I began to explain what I wanted them to do.

'Can anyone remember how long the hands of Big Ben are, apart from Alan?'

'Sir, Sir, I know, Sir,' cried one of the boys eagerly.

'What's your name?'

'John Rouse, Sir'

'Oh yes, the footballer.'

'Ow did you know that, Sir?'

'E's a teacher,' said one of the girls. "E knows everythin."

'Well 'e wouldn't know I like football, would 'e! 'E ain't bin 'ere more 'n five minutes.'

'Mrs Bridgewood told me,' I admitted.

''E is good, though, Sir. Steven Wheatley in the fourth year let's 'im play in 'is team. I don't like Wheatley.'

'You've changed, ain't yer?' cried the smallest boy. 'You was in love with 'im last week.'

'No I wasn't, see! I never loved 'im!'

'Yes you did. You used ter look through 'is classroom door at 'im.'

'No I never. That was Tracey.'

'I think we might be forgetting what we're here for,' I said firmly. 'John, you were going to tell me how long the hands were.'

'Oh yeah, I'd forgotten about that. I think it's about fourteen feet, ain't it, Sir? The big one, that is.'

'And the little one's nine,' Badger blurted out, determined to show at least a little of his knowledge.

'That's right,' I said. 'Now, give me one of the yard sticks for a moment...'

Rouse obliged. He was a tall boy for his age, with curly hair, a large round face, and two protruding front teeth that made him seem like a caricature from a comic. Badger had curly hair too, a mass of it that covered both ears. His nose was set slightly out of true, and both his bright red cheeks were smothered in freckles. Darren Adams, the smallest of the three, wore a grey hand-knitted pullover which hung almost to his knees, nearly covering his grey shorts. His hair stood on end as if he had just received an electric shock, and he wore a pair of tiny spectacles supported by full cheeks which looked as if they were permanently storing food, like a hamster's pouches.

'If you girls take your rulers and this yardstick into the smaller part of the playground to draw out the hands, and the boys do it round here, we'll see who's the most accurate,' I said. The two girls hesitated uncertainly for a moment.

'Sir, we ain't allowed round there just yet,' one of them said.

'Why not? Because of the workmen?'

'No. 'Cos someone's writ bum and stuff all over the wall,' offered Rouse seriously, savouring the words with intense enjoyment. 'Mr Reed says we 'ave ter wait till Mr Burrows can get round and clean it.'

'Really? Well, I hope it wasn't you, John.'

'No, it weren't me, Sir. I can't spell them words.' Adams and Badger giggled. One of the girls looked slightly embarrassed.

'Right, Well in that case you'd all better work round here. But don't copy each other. Boys go over by the wall. There's plenty of room there.'

They separated into two groups and began to measure, working quickly and urgently and telling each other how they thought it ought to be done. Rouse was the only child to stand still, apparently taking charge of his group and acting as technical adviser. After giving them a few minutes to work on their own, I walked over to the girls.

'Finished yet?'

'Cor, no Sir. Give us a chance!' the smaller girl exclaimed, rubbing out part of the line she had just drawn.

'I'm afraid I don't know either of your names yet.'

'We're both Susans, Sir. She's Susan Brennan and I'm Susan Davis. We live in them flats. She's my best friend, ain't yer, Sue?'

Susan Brennan was the quieter of the two, and, I suspected, might have been rather withdrawn without the friendship of her partner who questioned and chattered incessantly, as if she was anxious to know my opinion on everything she said.

'Ow long you goin' to be 'ere, Sir?' she asked, her nose twitching like a rabbit.

'Just for a few weeks. It wouldn't be worth stopping just for a day or two, would it? I wouldn't get to know you all.'

'Are you a real teacher, then?' asked Susan Brennan. 'Or have you just come to watch us, like?'

'Well, not exactly a teacher. I'm training to be a teacher. At college.'

'You'll like our class, Sir,' said Susan Davis. 'Roland's a naughty boy, but 'e's in 'ospital 'avin' 'is 'pendix out. Rousey's a nuisance too, and 'e ain't never away. 'E's cheeky, but quite lovable with it.'

'He's not lovable.' Susan Brennan interrupted. 'Just cheeky. Sometimes Miss gets mad with 'im. Not often, though. She's ever so nice, ain't she Sue? I like all the teachers, though, don't we, Sue?'

Her friend nodded vigorously as she completed the drawing of a huge clockface and stood up proudly to look at it.

'There, Sir, it's done. Is that alright? The line's a bit wobbly.'

'Cor, Sir, ain't them 'ands big,' breathed Susan Davis. 'It's a wonder they got 'em up there in the first place.' The boys also finished at that moment and came over for my verdict on their drawing.

'When you look up at the real 'ands they don't 'alf seem small, don't they, Sir?' said Adams. 'You wouldn't think they was that big, would yer?'

'No,' I replied. 'But if they were much smaller, you wouldn't see them at all from the ground.'

'Seems to me they must be 'eavy, though,' Adams added. 'What if they fell off? I bet they'd take yer 'ead clean off.'

'I don't really think they're likely to fall off,' I said quickly. 'Now then, I...'

'You never know though,' said Badger, inspecting the girls' drawing. 'They could do. My Gran knew a bloke once. 'E was a window cleaner and 'e was 'igh up cleanin' windows in one of them cradle things and the rope broke and 'e fell off. The ropes looked safe all right, but they wasn't. You can't tell. My Gran always goes over to the other side of the road when she sees one o' them cradle things. She says she don't fancy one fallin' on 'er 'ead.'

'Shame somethin' don't fall on yours,' sniffed Susan Davis. A bell rang inside and I looked at my watch.

'We'd better go upstairs now,' I said. 'That's the playtime bell, isn't it?'

'We'll miss our milk if we don't 'urry. And our biscuits,' cried Rouse.

The boys picked up the pieces of chalk and raced to the stairs ahead of me. Susan Davis shouted out to Rouse.

'Oi! What about the yardsticks?'

'You were usin' 'em,' Rouse shouted back at her. 'You bring 'em up!'

'You lazy sod! Ooops, sorry Sir! 'E is, though, ain't 'e?' I turned to call after Rouse, but the boy had already disappeared.

'Never mind,' I said. 'I'll make sure he does it next time.'

'Who's your favourite singer, Sir?' asked Susan Brennan.

'I like any sort of music if it's well played. I suppose I like classical music most of all.'

'What, orchestras and all that?' asked Susan Davis.

'I've got Swan Lake, Sir,' said Susan Brennan. 'Miss played it to us one dinner time and I really like it. My mum got it for me, 'cos I like dancing. You can borrow it if you want, Sir,' she added generously.

We reached the classroom just as the other children were going out to play. Rouse was hastily drinking a spare bottle of milk before anybody else laid a claim to it.

'You'd better hurry up and have your milk, or you'll miss your playtime,' I said to the girls.

'We don't mind,' said Susan Davis, putting the yardsticks back in their corner. 'We often stay in and put stuff out for Miss, anyway. Unless Mr Reed comes along and chucks us out when Miss ain't 'ere. I don't like 'im, do we Sue?'

'We tidy up the class as well,' said Susan Brennan quickly, thinking that her friend had been a little indiscreet. 'Honestly, Sir, some of the boys never clear up properly. We're always doing it for them. We like our classroom to be really tidy.'

Susan Davis began rearranging the chairs in the book corner, and Susan Brennan straightened the books. Dorothy was stacking some maths equipment into a cupboard.

'Hello,' she smiled. 'How did it go?'

'They were very good,' I said. 'I had an embarrassing moment about the chalking on the wall, though.'

She laughed. 'I bet! You'll get a lot worse than that once they've sounded you out properly. We don't really get much writing on the walls now though, especially inside, where all their pictures are. Sometimes somebody scribbles on a picture out of jealousy. We had a spate of extremely earthy words in the cloakroom last year, but as Brian said, at least the spelling was correct.'

'I don't suppose Mr Reed saw it that way?'

'Oh, he ranted and raved for half an hour in the hall and said he wasn't having filth written all over his school. He'd have done better just to ignore it. Whoever wrote it must have been tickled pink listening to him. Susan, can you put those other bottles in the crate, please.' She perched herself on the corner of a table for a moment and took a roll of strong mints from her bag.

'Here,' she said, 'have a mint. I gave up smoking a while ago and I'm a bit hooked on these. Susans, do you want a mint?'

'Cor, thanks Miss,' they said together.

'Once you've been here a little while these children are very little trouble,' Dorothy continued. 'It's amazing they're are as nice as they are, considering what some of them have to go through at home. I think you have to be absolutely straight with them, tell them exactly how you feel about something and never hedge their questions. They sense it if you do. They're incredibly loyal and they look on you as a friend as well as a teacher. And that's not a bad thing. They spend most of their day in school and you've got to put yourself out a bit. Teachers who don't rarely survive in a school like this.'

'But they're very mixed in ability...'

'Yes, they are, but you can cope with that. It's important to make sure the really clever ones like Jamie Dudmish actually inspire the others a bit, without losing out themselves. You haven't come across him yet. There's really no-one to compete with him in here, but I don't think his work suffers. In fact I know it doesn't.'

I grinned. 'It's all down to administration, then, is it?'

She laughed loudly. 'Oh, Mr Reed told you that, did he? He's never involved himself with the children, so he has to look for a reason to justify his existence. He ends up ordering masses of stock we've already got. Or lots of text books that are totally unsuitable because he never consults anybody on what they might need. I think quite a few people become headteachers just to get out of the classroom. It's certainly not for me.'

'Really?'

'Well, I'd do it differently, put it that way. Susan, I should wet that duster if I were you. You'll get your dress filthy.'

'Okay, Miss,' Susan agreed, moistening the duster under the tap. 'What are we doin' after play, Miss?'

'Making you write your tables out, I think.'

'Aw, Miss!' said Susan, wrinkling her nose.

'Actually, there's a TV programme about Australian wild life, and I thought I'd show them that,' she said to me. 'They had a smashing talk by an Australian teacher a couple of weeks ago and now she's gone back they've started writing letters to her class. Anyway, let's go and get some coffee before the children come in again.'

The staffroom was a small converted mezzanine room at the top of a tiny staircase, and nine battered easy chairs were grouped around two tables smothered with leaflets, newspapers and educational circulars. A pile of plastic hockey sticks and balls stood in one corner, and bookshelves occupied another. On a small table by the sink an urn steamed frantically, watched suspiciously by a teacher with tidily cut hair, steel rimmed glasses and a small, neatly trimmed beard. I noticed that all the other staff in the room were women. Dorothy introduced me briefly.

‘This urn is ludicrous,’ said the bearded teacher angrily. ‘It breaks down, it overheats, it breaks down again. Dorothy, can’t you get him to buy a couple of decent kettles? I mean, we are in the age of the electric kettle, for God’s sake.’

‘It packs up because you keep shouting at it,’ said a slightly overweight woman with dyed auburn hair and piercing dark eyes.

‘Look, Deidre, all I want is a cup of tea. I’ve been trying for an hour to get subtraction into Emily Bennett’s thick head and I reckon I deserve a bottle of gin, let alone a cup of tea. It’s alright for you Infant teachers. You only have to teach ‘em how to fill a bucket up with sand…’

‘You cheeky bugger,’ Deidre laughed, and hurled her newspaper at him.

‘You see what I have to put up with from these women?’ said Brian, turning to me. ‘Thank God you’ve arrived. Now, do you want the badly chipped cup, or the even more badly chipped cup?’

‘Oh Brian, give him a decent one,’ said a slim woman on the other side of the room. ‘It’s his first day. Give him one of the china cups.’

‘Are you trying to get me into trouble, Janice? You know the bone china is reserved for the school governors. And as the elected teacher representative, I must put it to you…’

‘Oh just give him a cup of tea,’ said Janice. ‘God, the fuss you make. You only have to make it once a week.’ I took the cup offered to me and went to sit in a chair by the window.

‘I shouldn’t sit there, Mike,’ said Brian immediately.

‘Take no notice,’ said Dorothy. ‘sit where you like.’

‘Well, don’t say I haven’t warned you. That’s Alice’s seat. She’s ripped people’s heads off when they’ve sat in her chair. You’re for it now, Mike.’

‘Don’t be silly, it’s not her chair,’ said Deidre. ‘It’s a school chair, for heavens sake.’

Brian drew a deep breath through pursed lips. ‘Well, you’re a braver man than me,’ he said.

'Oh leave the poor bloke alone,' said Janice. 'You'll turn him into a nervous wreck before he's even started. Who's got the spoon?'

'There we are, you see,' said Brian. '*The* spoon. We'll be borrowing each other's cup of tea next. I think the kids knock the spoons off and flog 'em down the market. Unless they haven't got any at home, which wouldn't surprise me.'

'At least Rousey has stopped taking the school milk,' said Dorothy. 'It took a while to cure him of that. I'm sure his mother put him up to it.'

'I thought gin was more her line,' said Janice.

'I wonder what he's nicking now,' said Brian. 'He's probably got his eye on Dorothy's Mini. So what do you think of 'em, Mike? Dorothy's class, I mean, not Minis.'

'They seem very pleasant,' I said. 'I don't know them very well yet, though.'

'Yes, they're not too bad. Rousey's good on Euclid, and Susan Davis knows her Russian novelists. I should watch Fred though. He's a bit weak on his Latin.'

'Honestly, Brian, you'll put him off for life,' laughed Janice.

'Come off it, Jan, you know they don't actually learn anything until they get to me. All that creative muck you and Dorothy do just gets their clothes in a mess. I did painting last Friday, so that takes care of my creative work for this term. Andrew Kearns actually spoke, too. Mind you, I made him stand on a desk with a paint pot on his head for an hour, so that shut him up.'

'You're a bugger, you really are,' said Deidre.

'Don't take any notice of him,' said Dorothy.

'Does anybody?' said Janice.

'Heaven knows what the kids see in him,' said Deidre.

'Now come on girls,' said Brian, pulling a broken chair towards him and putting his feet on it. 'You know my presence in the staffroom is a constant joy to you all. Hello, look, Wilson's on the scaffolding again. I wonder if he'll fall off...'

‘Oh God, I hope Mr Reed doesn’t see him,’ said Deidre. ‘That boy is fearless. You have to admire his climbing skills.’

‘Now there you are, you see,’ said Brian, ‘You child-centred teachers should be harnessing his interest in it and using it across the curriculum. He should be climbing it, measuring it, painting it, and writing about it.’

‘Mr Reed said there hasn’t been an accident for a long time,’ I said. There was a burst of laughter from the other side of the room.

‘He’s never here when there is one, that’s why,’ said Deidre. ‘He’d be a lot happier if he could spend all his time going to conferences. Dorothy should have his job. She’s the one who organises everything in this place.’

‘And me, of course,’ said Brian. ‘I keep you all happy and contented. What would you do without me?’

A short, well built woman in a track suit looked up from the athletics magazine she was reading and spoke for the first time. ‘What have we done to deserve this on a Monday morning?’

‘Look Shirley, I was just putting Mike here on the right tracks,’ said Brian. ‘He’s a student. I want him to succeed. If he tries all that creative stuff they’ll crucify him before he’s had a chance to find out their names.’

The door opened, and a frail, nervous woman with a scarf covering her hair put her head hesitantly into the room. ‘Oh, um… has anyone seen the key to the PE cupboard?’ she asked tentatively. ‘I need some bats and balls. They are kept in the… um… aren’t they?’

‘Do you want the big ones or the small ones?’ asked Shirley.

‘Oh. I don’t know which would be the best. I just…’

‘Wait a minute Liz and I’ll get them for you,’ Brian offered. ‘Don’t you want any tea?’

‘I don’t think I’ve got time. I’ve been in a bit of a muddle with the biscuit money. There are so many things to add up on Mondays…’

‘Have a cup of tea.’

‘You’re pushing it a bit,’ said Janice. ‘Have you put something in it?’

'No. I'm just a very considerate man. When I make the tea, I like everybody to appreciate it. Would anybody like to sit on my knee and drink it? Deidre? Liz? Dorothy? Mike?'

The bell rang for the end of break and with a soft gasp Elizabeth's head disappeared from the doorway. Brian looked at the clock on the wall.

'Hey, that's a bit quick, isn't it? Who's on duty?'

'Alice,' said Dorothy. 'And it is time. That clock's slow.'

'Well, she'll have to watch it, then. That's two weeks running she's rung it on time. I think I'll have a teacher's benevolent lesson and let them fling a few balls about in the hall.'

'You can't,' said Deidre. 'Elizabeth's in there. Then I am.'

'Oh, well, that's that then. Another burst of inspiration bites the dust. We'll have to do silent reading, then.'

Dorothy smiled, took my cup and washed it quickly under the tap. 'Will you look after them for a moment?' she asked. 'I left some pictures I need in the car. I'll only be a few minutes.'

She had left the classroom unlocked and most of the children were already sitting down continuing with their work. A few were taking turns at peering through a microscope in the science corner, and the two Susans were turning a giant plastic globe on its axis and asking each other questions.

'Come and help us, Sir,' said Susan Brennan, taking my hand and pulling me over to the globe. 'We're finding the places on here that we've got on our wall map. Susan and me like doin' this.'

'Cor, Sir!' cried Susan Davis, 'You want to see what Rousey's got under the microscope. 'E's got an ant, Sir. It's still alive and you can see its legs movin'. They're really hairy.'

'Like yours then, ain't they,' called Badger.

'You shut up, Badgerbrain,' said Susan Brennan.''Oo's talking' to you?'

'Miss lets us put a lot of things under the microscope,' Susan Davis continued. 'She showed us some of Fred's blood the other day, when 'e hurt 'imself in PE. You could see them corsle things.. what are they, Sue?'

'Corpuscles,' answered Susan Brennan.

'That's it, them. We could see 'em Sir. There are white ones and red ones in your blood an' if you get too many white ones you die. Or is it red ones? I'm not sure, are we Sue? Oh look, Sir, I've found Tasmania. It's down 'ere.'

I left them turning the globe and went round the classroom to see what sort of books the children were reading. The choice of material was wide ranging, but there seemed to be something at an appropriate level for everyone. I asked Rouse what he was reading.

''E can't read,' Badger offered. Rouse slammed his book shut. 'Oh yes I can. 'E weren't askin' you, anyway.'

'You can't read. You jus' look at the pictures. You was readin' that book about dinosaurs for months an' when Miss asked you about it you never knew nothin' about it.'

'Yes I did. You watch it!'

'What was it about, then? Tell us somethin' about dinosaurs.'

'I wouldn't tell you nothin', mate.'

'That's 'cos you don't know nothin'.'

'I do, though.'

'Well tell us somethin', then. You don't even know the name of a dinosaur.'

'Tyrannosaurus Rex.'

Badger sniffed with contempt. 'Well, we all know that one, don't we! Even my little brother knows that one. Even my pet 'amster knows that one.'

Rouse stood up, and took a deep breath. 'D'you want your 'ed smashed in?' he asked.

'Oo by? You?'

'Why are you standing up and looking like that, Master Rouse?' called Dorothy, walking briskly into the room. 'And Alan Badger, why are you being a nuisance?'

'I'm not, Miss. I was just sayin' Rousey can't read.'

'That's being a nuisance. And you're wrong then, because he can read. Almost as well as you, when he tries. It would have been nice if I'd found you helping him instead of being mean.'

'I was only sayin'...'

'I can imagine. Funny how these 'only sayings' always end up with you half killing each other, isn't it.'

'Sorry Miss. Are we going to watch a film?'

'Only if you're good. Children, line up by the door quietly. We're going to the Audio Visual Room.'

'Can I help you connect the TV, Miss?' asked Rouse eagerly.

'No thank you. John. I can manage that bit myself.'

'Aw Miss,' Rouse grumbled. 'Me dad lets me change all the fuses in our house.'

'Well that's your dad's responsibility. I'm not prepared to take the chance.'

'You could get sued, couldn't yer, Miss?,' said Adams thoughtfully, unravelling a thread at the end of his pullover. 'If 'e got a shock you could get sued.'

'I'd probably get a reward,' said Dorothy. 'Now come on, or we won't have any time left.'

They filed down the stairs to a converted classroom on the next corridor. The floor of the room was completely carpeted, and there were thick curtains at the windows which doubled as blackouts. The tables under the windows contained an assortment of musical instruments, and two tape decks had been set up with a microphone to record children using them. Badger tentatively struck a xylophone, withered under Dorothy's all-seeing gaze, and then turned to his friends, still eager to continue the previous conversation.

'I knew a bloke once wot shoved a screwdriver in the mains,' he said with grim delight. 'It melted the screwdriver right down to the 'andle. 'E was dead lucky though, 'cos the 'andle was made o' some thick plastic, and...'

'What difference 'ud that make?' asked Rouse.

'Course it 'ud make a difference.'

'Like what?'

'It's an insulator,' said Dudmish, speaking for the first time in a soft Scottish accent. 'The electricity can't get through. It's like rubber.'

Badger paused for a moment, and then made a determined effort to retrieve his audience.

'Jamie's right,' he said seriously. 'Anyway, this bloke could 'ave 'ad 'is 'and taken right orf.'

'E's off!' cried Susan Davis. "Ere 'e goes again!'

'I think we'll all have to go if you don't sit quietly now,' said Dorothy. 'And I'm not going to start until everybody's absolutely ready.'

She switched the television on and the screen flickered into life. The class settled immediately, turning their full attention to the programme. After it was over Dorothy talked about the programme and showed pictures of Australia and its animals, adding pieces of information, filling in details she thought had been missed, and relating it to the talk they had been given by the visiting teacher. I noticed that she held the children's attention with almost deceptive ease.

'That was great, Miss,' said Fred with intense enthusiasm as the programme ended.

'Yes, I thought you'd like it. It's almost time for lunch. Don't forget to wash your hands before you go into the hall. And make sure you're back right on time this afternoon. The group by the door go first.'

The children stood up and went out quietly as the bell rang, and Dorothy closed the doors on the television stand.

'Well they certainly liked that,' I said when the last child had gone.

Dorothy smiled. 'Yes, they seemed to. Mind you, they're always interested in watching a television. A lot of them haven't got one at home. They do forget easily, though. I have to try and set an average pace for the class when I'm doing something with them all. It isn't easy, because you've got to cope for the Freds as well as the Dudmishes. That's why individual work or group work wins hands down every time. You'll see. They have to go at their own pace.'

'Dudmish doesn't say a lot.'

'No, he watches everything, though. And he listens intently. Mind you, even children like John Rouse have their talents. You might not believe it, but he's pretty surprising with anything scientific. He had an old transistor radio to bits in the hall a few days ago and Brian bet him a pound he couldn't put it back together again. Brian actually lost. Rousey's father drinks a lot, unfortunately. John wouldn't take a school guitar home to practise just in case his Dad broke it when he was drunk. He's got a little brother in Deidre's class. He's much more withdrawn than John.'

'What's their mother like?'

'She fools you at first. She seems to dote over them both. She's quite reasonable to talk to, until you realise some of the things she does. The other night, for instance. Dad went out with her, for a change, and they left both the boys in bed. They didn't come back until half past eleven. When they did get back, both boys were waiting for them on the pavement. Mum couldn't understand it at all. Said she thought John was quite capable of looking after his brother for a few hours. It's been reported to their social worker, but I don't think anything much will be done.'

'That's awful.'

'I know. That's what I mean when I say it's amazing the children grow up as well as they do. Little Julie, who sits in the corner. You've probably not noticed her yet. She's being brought up by someone she calls her Nan, who really does her best but can't afford to buy her very much. Mum walked out when Julie was very young and nobody's quite sure who the father is. There's a rumour that Julie was conceived on the back seat of a coach, coming home from a factory outing to Blackpool. She's quiet, but a delight to talk to on her own. Poor little love! The others are very good to her, though. Even Rousey.'

She took a pile of books from a cupboard and put them down on a table. 'Anyway, no more case histories for the moment. You'd better go and get your lunch, before Brian eats it for you! They serve the food in the Infant hall. I'll see you in the staffroom.'

Lunches were served at two separate sittings by a line of white-coated kitchen staff standing beside trays of food at one end of the hall. The selection of food was good, and I was surprised at how much mealtimes had changed since I'd been at Junior school myself. All the teachers ate with the children, and they sat at a different table each day. Although the children chattered excitedly to each other, the noise was reasonable and Mr Reed patrolled the hall slowly and grimly, hands tightly clasped behind his back like a policemen who hated his job but still possessed a sense of duty. I collected my salad, smiled cautiously at Mr Reed, and sat down on the nearest vacant seat. Immediately, a beaming face looked up at me.

'Ere, it's the secret agent,' said Bristow.

'Oo?' asked another boy at the table.

'The bloke wot reckons 'e's a secret agent.'

'Oo told you?'

'E did.'

'Well you be careful and don't gobble your food down so fast,' I said. 'Or I won't show you my cards.'

'You ain't got none,' said Bristow. 'You're a noo teacher. I seen you in Mrs Bridgewood's class.'

'I'm gathering information to take back to headquarters. And you're likely to gather a stomach ache.'

'We don't get stomach aches,' said a girl with an adenoidal voice and an extremely runny nose at the end of the table. 'Only Kim 'ere. She's the one what should eat slow. She's usually sick after she's 'ad 'er dinner.'

A large dewdrop fell from her nose and splashed onto her potato. She pulled a small damp hanky from her sleeve, and blew her nose noisily. Then she thrust the whole potato into her mouth and sat chewing it open mouthed.

Tomorrow, I decided, I'd choose my table with a little more care.

Quite unexpectedly, I had the chance of teaching the class the following afternoon. Alice Ridgewell, who taught the third years, had developed a migraine and gone home at lunch time.

'I suppose we'll have to split her class up again,' said Shirley, in the staffroom at lunch time. 'You can bet your life Reedy won't teach them. He's bound to have some other pressing engagement.'

'That's the third migraine in a month,' said Brian, 'Or was it asthma last time? She ought to pack up smoking. Fancy smoking twenty fags a day when you've got athsma. You can hardly cut through the smoke in here sometimes.'

His eyes turned to me, and he suddenly sat forward in his chair. 'Wait a minute,' he said, 'Why doesn't Mike have them for the afternoon?'

'That's unfair', said Deidre. 'You can't expect him to do that.'

'Of course we can. He wouldn't mind at all, would you, Mike?'

'No, not at all,' I said, hoping I sounded more confident than I felt.

'Look, I'll tell you what,' said Dorothy, 'if Mike has my class I'll have Alice's. At least Mike knows mine. I'd better go and clear it with our dear headmaster though.'

'He won't mind. Anything to avoid taking them himself,' said Brian. 'That's settled, then. Now who wants to take mine for the afternoon?'

My mind raced. I didn't want to start on my Thames topic because my lesson plans and the work I'd prepared were at college. It would be better if I did something short and simple. I wasn't sure if I could even handle the class yet, and they'd been fairly lively during the morning. Dorothy had put it down to being a windy day, saying that a change in the weather always made them more unsettled. With a flash of inspiration, I thought of the large and carefully tended aquarium in the classroom. My father had kept fish, and I knew quite a lot about them. For the remainder of the lunch break, I went into the small school library to draw a large, colourful picture and find a few suitable books.

After lunch, when the children came into the classroom, Dorothy explained what was happening. An expectant murmur of anticipation buzzed round the classroom as she went out and closed the door quietly behind her.

'What we gonna do, Sir?' asked Fred. 'Can I do some drawin'?'

'No,' I said. 'And I'm just like Mrs Bridgewood.'

'No you ain't,' said Rouse. 'You're a bloke.'

'I mean,' I replied slowly and deliberately, 'I'm not going to start until you're all absolutely quiet.'

The chatter died down and they turned attentively to me. I was very aware that at any moment during the afternoon Mr Reed could walk into the room, and I was determined that if he did, things should be perfectly under control.

'Now then, put your hands up if you've got a goldfish at home.' A dozen hands immediately shot into the air.

'Tell me about yours.'

I pointed to Julie, sitting at the back of the room with her hand partly raised, as if she was unsure of answering. Her face reddened and she put her fingers to her lips.

'Let me tell you 'bout mine, Sir,' cried Rouse, waving an outstretched finger three inches away from my nose.

'Wait a minute,' I said firmly. 'I'll ask you about yours in a moment.'

Rouse turned round and grinned at his friends.

'Well Julie?' She was still hesitant.

'Imagine I'd never seen a goldfish before. How would you describe it to me?'

'It's a sort of golden colour,' she replied in a faint, gruff voice. 'And it's got fins at each side and it gets fed once a day...' She stopped abruptly, and Rouse immediately began waving his hand in the air again.

'Alright then,' I said. 'Tell me about yours.'

'Well come ter think of it, I can't really, Sir.'

'Why not? Surely you can think of something that Julie hasn't told us.'

'Well the thing is,' he said innocently, 'I can't, because me cat et it larst night.' He turned to his friends again and a fit of giggling broke out. Adams chewed the end of his ruler, his eyes cautiously watching to see how I would react. Badger sat very still, arms tightly folded.

'Oh shut up, Rousey,' shouted Susan Davis.

"Oo you talkin' to?'

'You. We don't wanna listen to you all afternoon.'

'You watch it, Davis!'

'Don't you threaten me, Rousey. I ain't scared of you, mate!'

This was obviously going to be one of Rouse's less co-operative afternoons. He had been mildly difficult during the morning, and Dorothy had assumed there had been some trouble at home, though he had settled down quickly once she had sorted out his work for the morning. Now he seemed to sense an opportunity for finding out just how much I would tolerate. I ignored his remarks and turned to the rest of the class.

'Goldfish are quite amazing creatures,' I said. 'Most people think they are only small, but they can grow to around fourteen inches long. Show me fourteen inches with your fingers...'

The children's hands opened to reveal distances that were surprisingly accurate. Fred looked distinctly unsure and parted his fingers for several inches. Then he looked round at Susan Brennan and with a cautious glance in my direction hastily adjusted his estimation.

'Of course,' I continued, 'Not many grow to that length. They have to be properly looked after in a pond. It sometimes takes them twenty five years to grow that long.'

'Cor, same age as my mum,' said Badger cheerfully.

'Is that all?' said Susan Davis. 'Your mum looks older 'n that, don't she?'

'That's what my Dad says,' Badger agreed.

'Come on, we're getting off the subject,' I said, moving to a different position in the classroom and watching their eyes follow me. 'Now, goldfish were first bred by Chinese people…'

'What's 'bred' mean?' asked Fred.

'It's stuff you eat, stoopid,' cried Rouse.

'You're the one what's stoopid,' called Susan Davis. "E don't mean that kind of bread. 'E means like raisin' babies.'

'Propagating,' called Jamie Dudmish. 'It's the same as propagating.'

'Proper what?' called Rouse, turning round to Dudmish.

'Proper Charlie, that's what you are, mate,' retorted Susan Davis.

'Anyway,' I said loudly, 'They were bred by Chinese people. Here's China on your map of the world, look. There are lots of different kinds of goldfish, too. They're not all yellowy gold. Some have even got patches of black and blue on.'

'What, where they've bin bumpin' into each other?' asked Fred.

'Of course not, stoopid. Sir means there are different kinds of fish, don't yer Sir?' said Susan Davis helpfully.

'Thank you Susan. Now, the ordinary goldfish is the easiest one to keep as a pet. Can anyone describe its shape to me?

'It's oval,' said Badger, moving his chair back and putting his knees on the table. 'And it's got a pointed 'ed.'

'Like yours,' said Rouse quickly.

'You'll get a pointed 'ed in a minute. It gets through the water easily 'cos it's got a pointed 'ed…

'Well, sort of. Actually, there's something shaped very much like a fish, only man-made. Does anyone know what I'm thinking of? It can rise and sink in the water?'

'Me dad, when 'e's 'ad a few,' Rouse retorted. "E lays down in the barf. 'E don't rise, though, 'e jus' sinks!'

There was a chuckle of approval at his joke. I turned to him sharply but again decided to ignore his remark. It would be fine, I thought, if Mr Reed decided to wander in when Rouse was in this sort of mood.

'Sir,' called Dudmish, looking rather bored, 'It's like a submarine. That's man-made. They built it in the shape of a fish so it would go through the water easily.'

'Well done Jamie,' I said warmly, wishing there were ten children like him in the class. 'Now what was it that Julie said helps the fish move along in the water?'

'Fins!' chorused half a dozen voices.

'Wings!' shouted Rouse.

'You're almost right, John', I said, turning and giving him a gentle pat on the head. 'Not quite, though. Most young goldfish now have miniature propellers on each side and they're wound up each day by the mother fish. You may have seen her doing what is known as the inversion movement to wind them up. Of course, once the fish has learned to swim properly it doesn't need the propellers any more. We call this 'shedding the propellers', John.'

Rouse's mouth dropped open and he stared at me carefully. Then his mouth creased into a grin.

'Cor!', he exclaimed. 'For 'alf a minute I thought you was serious. For a minute I didn't think you was 'avin' me on.'

The class laughed, their sympathies shifting back to me again. I felt as if I was walking a tightrope and I realised I wasn't going to get through anything I had planned at this rate. I drew the children's attention to the large picture I'd drawn during the lunch break.

'Now, Julie said that the fish swims with its fins, and you'd be surprised just how many fins it has. If you've got a goldfish at home have a good look at it tonight and see. This one's called the pectoral fin, and there's one of those at each side. They act like brakes when the fish moves through the water. This one's the pelvic fin, and it keeps the fish steady. And this one is a very important fin, called the dorsal. It's thin and it helps the fish move quickly. Now, I'll show you how the tail fin works...'

I took a piece of paper from the cupboard, cut it roughly into the shape of a fin and held it up in front of the class. The children turned to watch.

'Sir, I know,' called Dudmish, pleased that the lesson at last seemed to me making some sort of headway. 'It flicks from side to side, and that's what pushes it forward. It moves a bit forward when its tail goes straight after each flick, then the dorsal fin steadies it up again.'

He stood up and moved his hands in the air to demonstrate exactly what he meant.

'Good boy,' I said encouragingly. 'You're quite right. Now, I wonder if anybody knows how it breathes?'

Hema, the tiny Asian girl, raised her hand tentatively. 'He opens his mouth in the water. He gulps in the water. He breathes the water,' she said precisely.

'Well, it doesn't actually breathe the water,' I said. 'It takes in some water and...'

'My Auntie Jean nearly drowned once,' said Badger. 'We was at Eastbourne, and she'd gone in for a dip and she went out too far.' Interest swung round onto Badger and he sensed an attentive audience. 'She 'ad about five pints o' water in 'er lungs an' they 'ad ter pump it all out. My Uncle Den said it was the first thing 'e'd known what'd kept 'er quiet for a few hours.'

'Oo rescued her, then? You?' asked Rouse.

'Nah. Me Uncle Den. 'E swum out when 'e saw 'er strugglin' in the water.'

'She was lucky. A shark could've got 'er.'

''Course it couldn't,' Adams interrupted. 'You don't get sharks at Eastbourne.'

'Course you do. You can get sharks anywhere it's 'ot. Can't you, Sir?'

'I don't think you'd find many at Eastbourne,' I said cautiously, thinking it might be best not to deny it completely in case it gave rise to an argument I couldn't keep in check. 'Anyway, I was asking if you knew how a fish breathes. Do you know what we breathe?'

'That's easy,' said Susan Brennan. 'We breathe air.'

'No we don't, we breathe in oxygen,' Jamie Dudmish corrected her.

'You're both partly right,' I said. 'There is oxygen in air, and we breathe that. But a goldfish breathes oxygen, too.'

'Ow, Sir?' asked Susan Davis. 'It's got its 'ed stuck in the water all the time.'

'Sir, I know,' called Dudmish again. 'Sometimes it comes to the top of the water and gets the oxygen. And sometimes it takes the oxygen out of the water. It takes a big gulp of water and uses up the oxygen in it. Then it gets rid of the water and does the same thing again.'

'That's why you 'ave to use a big tank,' said Adams. 'Them glass bowls ain't s'posed to be very good for 'em because...'

'The surface area is too small,' Dudmish interrupted. 'The water can't get enough oxygen to it.'

'How does the fish get rid o' the water then?' asked Badger.

'Ow d'yer think?' retorted Rouse. 'Through its willy, same as everybody else.'

'Don't be stoopid. A fish ain't got a willy.'

'Course it 'as. If it didn't 'ave a willy, it'd get so full up with water it'd burst.'

'Well my dad goes fishin' an' I've looked at 'is fish, and none of 'em 'ad a willy,' said Badger, conclusively. The two Susans giggled uncontrollably.

'They've got gills,' said Dudmish impatiently, determined to bring things back to sanity. 'They use the oxygen they need, and then get rid of the water through their gills.'

'Oh yeah,' agreed Fred. 'E's right. I've seen 'em do that.'

'Shall I bring mine in termorrer, Sir?' called Susan Davis. 'I won 'em at the fair.'

'They shouldn't really be given away at fairs', I said. 'It's very unkind, and they don't tend to live long if they've been cooped up in a little plastic bag.'

'I 'ad one a little while ago,' said Badger. The class turned to listen, knowing that another gruesome morsel was about to be delivered. 'Me brother took it out of the bowl to see 'ow long it 'ud live. It only lasted a few minutes. I...'

'You cruel sod!' shouted Susan Davis. 'Ow'd you like it if someone took you out of your bowl to see 'ow long you'd last?'

'I don't live in a bowl, do I!'

'Well you ought to, mate. Then you'd see what it's like. Shame you don't live in a bowl, in my opinion.'

'I ain't int'rested in your opinion.'

'Well tough luck, mate, 'cos you're gettin it.'

'Sir,' asked Susan Brennan, taking no notice of Badger. ''Ave you got any fish at home?'

'No, but I had several when I was your age.'

'Ow old are yer, then, Sir?' asked Rouse with interest, gazing at my face as if he was seeing it for the first time. 'Pretty young, I'd say. Alan reckons about forty, but I don't reckon much over thirty five. Are yer, Sir?'

'Well John,' I replied, wondering how Dorothy ever managed to teach the class anything at all, 'since it is obviously causing you both some concern, you're both wrong. I'm nearly eighty, but keep it to yourselves. People often ask me how I manage to look so young.'

'If you was eighty, you wouldn't be teachin' 'ere', grinned Rouse.

'E ain't teachin' 'ere, 'e's a stoodent,' Adams reminded him.

A child at the back of the class yawned loudly. Julie looked up at the clock, and Dudmish opened a book.

'Please Sir,' he pleaded, 'can't we just get on?'

'Yeah,' agreed Susan Davis, springing into the attack again. 'Sir's trying to teach us a lesson. 'Ow's 'e goin' to be a real teacher if you don't let 'im do any teachin'?'

'E'd 'ave an 'ard job teachin' you anythin'', grinned Fred, putting a hand underneath his shirt and scratching his chest earnestly.

'You watch it,' she retorted. 'I know more'n you, anyway. You can't even spell 'Europe', mate!'

Fred conceded the point sheepishly, and I started to fasten my pictures to the wall with masking tape.

'Right, that's enough now,' I said. 'It's time for you to do something.'

'We 'ave bin doin' somethin',' Adams objected. 'We've bin answerin' your questions.'

'Well you haven't answered many,' I retorted. 'Anyway, I don't mean that sort of work. I mean doing something to prove to Mrs Bridgewood you haven't been wasting time this afternoon.'

'Can I draw a picture of a goldfish?' asked Julie.

'Well, you can,' I said, 'But I've got a better idea. I'm going to give out some large pieces of card and you can cut the shape of an aquarium out of it, a bit like the classroom one. Then you can decorate it with strips of blue and green tissue paper to make it look like water.'

'Cor, that's a good idea, Sir. Ain't that a good idea, Sue?' said Susan Davis admiringly.

'Thank you Susan. I'm glad you like it. When you've done the background, you can cut out some of the different kinds of goldfish, colour them, and then stick them on the background. I've got some books here which show all the different kinds of goldfish. Have a look at them. Then you could do some pieces of writing to go with them.'

' I thought we'd get to that bit,' said Rouse.

'What bit?'

'The writin' bit. I thought we'd get to that. I dunno if I'll 'ave time for that.'

'Can we draw our own fish?' asked Adams, putting on a small pair of spectacles and adjusting them with infinite precision. 'Instead of copying the ones in the books, I mean?'

'I shouldn't let 'im, Sir,' Susan Davis advised. "E can't draw.'

'What you talkin' about, I can't draw?' Adams retorted.

'You can't draw. What about that cow you was drawin' for Miss the other day. You 'ad its legs all up one end.'

'I never.'

'You did. All the legs was up one end, Sir.'

'They never was. That was the angle I was drawing it at.'

'You can't draw, mate, that's your trouble.'

'I wouldn't like to tell you what yours is, then. I wouldn't...'

'I think that's quite enough!' I shouted angrily. 'If you want to copy the ones in the book, do so. If you don't, draw your own. And when you do your writing, you could also mention the things a goldfish eats.'

'You ain't told us that,' Adams objected.

'It's ant's eggs,' said Susan Brennan. 'Now you know. You should've known that anyway.'

''E don't know nothin',' said Susan Davis. ''E certainly can't draw nothin'.'

'And mention the importance of things like cleaning the tank properly,' I said, struggling on grimly. 'And how snails can help keep the water clean. And anything else you want to mention.'

Fred looked up at the ceiling as if searching for inspiration. 'If you never gave the fish any food, I wonder if they'd 'ave a go at the snails,' he said at length.

'Don't be daft,' said Susan Brennan disdainfully, looking up from her work. ''Course it wouldn't. They only eat ants' eggs.'

'Yeah, she's right,' agreed Badger generously. 'Tell you what, though. My uncle what works in the docks knew a bloke once what got bit by one o' them trianchula spiders. 'E was unloadin' these bananas, and 'e stuck 'is 'and in the crate, and this trianchula ran right up 'is arm..'

'I think you've gone right off the point,' I snapped. 'Kindly do the work first and then tell us about it afterwards. I'll gladly give up the whole of playtime to listen to it.'

'Okay,' he agreed affably.

'Can we say about some of the diseases goldfish get?' asked Dudmish. 'My cousin keeps fish and he knows about them. Like white fungus, Sir?'

'That's an important fact,' I said. 'Tell us what you know.'

Since most of the class were fascinated by anything to do with the abnormal, they listened attentively while Dudmish outlined the diseases that had affected his cousin's fish. While he was talking, I gave out materials for making the background and water effect.

'You can do the writing afterwards, on the white paper you normally use,' I said.

'We ain't got none,' said Rouse, looking inside the paper cupboard.

'You mean we haven't any,' I corrected him.

'Yeah, I know. That's what I just said. We ain't got none.'

'We used it up yesterday,' said Susan Brennan, going over to the cupboard and looking on each shelf. 'Miss said she was going to get another lot from Mr Reed but I think she must've forgotten.'

'I'll fetch some for yer, Sir,' Adams offered, quickly taking off his spectacles and packing them back into the case. Adams wandering round the building for half an hour asking all the teachers if they had any spare paper didn't seem a good idea and I decided to ask Mr Reed myself. At least it would prove I was doing something.

'I'll just go and fetch some,' I said to the class. 'I'll be back in a moment.'

'Shall I write their names on the board if they muck about?' asked Rouse.

'That won't be necessary,' I said. 'I'm sure everybody can behave for two minutes.'

Leaving the class working reasonably quietly, I hurried along the corridor and knocked on Mr Reed's door. He was sitting behind his desk finishing the last of a pile of cucumber sandwiches. As he looked up, a piece of cucumber fell limply onto his lap, and he picked it up gingerly, like a child lifting an insect and trying not to crush it between his fingers. 'I had to go out for a while during the lunch hour,' he grunted in explanation.

'I need some white writing paper,' I said. 'We seem to have run out. I'm in the middle of a lesson and I…'

'Really? I thought you weren't teaching them until Thursday?'

'I wasn't. Mrs Bridgewood is taking Miss Ridgewell's and...'

Mr Reed thought for a moment until everything slotted into focus. 'Oh yes, that's right. Can't you make do for now? As you can see, from no fault of my own I'm in the middle of a hurried lunch, and stock day is Mondays. Mrs Walton does the stock. If she keeps running to the stock cupboard every half hour she'd never get anything else done. You're actually taking the class at this moment, are you?'

I suddenly became very weary. The children had been tiresome, and now the headmaster seemed reluctant to give me a few pieces of paper.

'Yes, I am,' I said irritably. 'And unless the children write on the walls, I don't see what else I'm supposed to use.'

'The children write on the walls anyway, Mr Kent,' Mr Reed said dismissively. 'How much paper do you want, exactly?'

The telephone on the desk rang suddenly. Mr Reed lifted the receiver and began a heated conversation with somebody in the local education office. Since the likelihood of getting any paper from Mr Reed was now becoming extremely remote, I hurried down to Brian's classroom on the next corridor instead.

'Hello!' Brian greeted me cheerfully, almost as if I'd been expected. 'Paper, paint, cardboard, balsa wood, chalk, atlases, benzedrine...'

'Writing paper. We've run out.'

'Stock day, Mr Kent, is Monday, and I shall have to inform you that I can't...'

'Don't tell me,' I groaned 'I've just had all that.'

'Sorry. Well, it's not unusual to run out of stock. You get used to it after you've been here for a while. Sometimes we even have to pool our stuff to help each other out. It took Dorothy ages before she could get him to dish it out once a week, let alone when you want it. It's bloody ridiculous. Like trying to smuggle gold out of Fort Knox.' He asked one of his girls to fetch a packet of writing paper from the cupboard, and he tossed it across to me.

'That should keep you going for a while,' he said. 'I usually wait until he's unlocked the stock cupboard and then get one of my kids to lure him away on an urgent errand. Like telling him there's an inspector here or something. Dorothy's got a spare key, by the way. Come to that, so has the cleaner. You can always get stock after school, when he's gone. He's always the first off the premises, so you don't have to wait for very long. Got 'em tamed, then, have you?'

'Not really. It's not going very well at all.'

'Well, don't worry about it. It's playtime in ten minutes. You'll be okay. We've all had problems at first.'

I looked round Brian's classroom, wondering if I'd ever reach this state of expertise. The room was almost as attractive as Dorothy's and the children were working carefully and enthusiastically on a bewildering range of topics. I wondered how long it had taken Brian to get the room looking so attractive.

'Don't worry, it comes after a while,' Brian said, noticing my expression. 'It's just like anything else. It takes a while to know what it's all about. You'll get there.'

'From the way you talk in the staffroom, I expected it to be all chalk and talk in here,' I said.

Brian laughed. 'I enjoy that,' he said. 'It get's 'em all going, doesn't it! Anyway, you'd better get going too. The kids won't sit quietly if there's nobody around.'

I hurried back to my classroom with the paper. Many of the children had finished pasting the tissue paper onto their backgrounds, and were cutting out fish ready to decorate, talking in very loud voices. Three children were arguing in the corner and Susan Davis ran to me as soon as I entered the room.

'Sir,' she said angrily, 'Rouse 'as got me pen, Sir.'

'E's bin tryin' to kiss 'er, Sir,' explained Adams mildly.

'No I weren't.'

'Yes you was! You was tryin' ter kiss 'er. We all saw yer.'

'No you never!'

'Where's your work?' I snapped at Rouse, suddenly tired of his behaviour and depressed with my ruined lesson. Rouse had done nothing since I'd left the room, and most of his paper had fallen to the floor underneath his table. A large footprint covered the drawing he had attempted and then abandoned.

'I ain't no good at drawin',' he muttered darkly.

'That doesn't mean you can't at least try, does it? Where's Susan's pen?'

'I dunno. I never took it. I ain't even seen 'er pen.'

''E 'as, Sir,' shouted Susan. 'Look in 'is tray. It was a handwritin' pen what my Nan gave me. I bet it's in 'is tray.'

'No it ain't. I never touched it. Oo'd want your pen, anyway.'

'Let's 'ave a look then. You was over 'ere.'

''E was tryin ter kiss 'er' Adams persisted.

'John Rouse, take your tray from under your desk and let me have a look. Right now,' I demanded as calmly as possible. If I were a betting man, I thought, I'd lay a month's wages on Mr Reed walking into the room right at this moment.

'Why should I get me tray out?' Rouse demanded aggressively. 'I wasn't the only one over 'ere.'

'You was over 'ere most of the time,' shouted Susan Davis angrily, 'so let's 'ave a look!'

'All right,' I said wearily, 'Everybody take their trays out and put them on top of the tables.'

There was a groan of annoyance as the children fetched their belongings from under the tables. Pencils and rulers clattered to the floor. There was no sign of a handwriting pen in any of the trays and I felt embarrassed and unhappy rummaging through the children's personal property. I couldn't prove that Rouse had taken the pen and I had no wish to accuse him wrongly. What would Mrs Bridgewater do in this situation? Should I search their pockets? Or even their shoes and socks? The possible hiding places were endless. The bell suddenly sounded for playtime.

'Leave your work,' I said bluntly. 'You can finish it after play. Susan

Davis and Susan Brennan, please look for the pen. Rouse, you stay here. The rest of you go outside.'

'He took some money the other day,' said Badger.

'It doesn't concern you,' I snapped. 'Go outside.'

'I always get the blame for takin' stuff,' Rouse mumbled. 'I was only goin' over to see 'ow much she'd done. I only wanted to borrow 'er felt tips.'

'Well, you can see what happens when you leave your own table, can't you. Did you see Susan's pen while you were over there?'

'No. I dunno 'oo's got it. I never took it. I ain't taken nobody's stuff.'

Susan Brennan suddenly gave a shout and climbed from underneath her table. 'Sir, it's alright! I've found the pen. It was under here. It rolled into the corner. I've got it, Sir.'

Susan Davis, silenced now, went very red and turned her head in embarrassment. I rounded on her angrily.

'I think you'd better say you're sorry. Right this instant, young lady.' Susan muttered an apology. Rouse stood still, hands clenched and his face white and sullen.

'Can I go now?' he asked gruffly. I nodded, and he walked out of the room moodily. Feeling guilty and miserable, Susan Davis followed at a discreet distance behind him. I watched them go, wondering whether I should abandon the idea of being a teacher and look for an easier option instead. Thoroughly depressed, I closed the door and climbed the narrow stairs to the staffroom.

'Something wrong?' asked Dorothy tactfully. 'Anything I can do?'

I sat down heavily on a chair by the window. 'It's Rouse,' I said. 'He's been on top form today. But none of them have exactly been easy going. I've made a right balls of the lesson.' I described the lesson, and my visit to Mr Reed.

'And then Susan Davis accused Rouse of taking her handwriting pen.'

'And had he taken it?'

'No. Susan Brennan found it on the floor. The trouble is, I was angry anyway, and I was quite ready to believe he'd taken it.'

'Well, at least you found out where it was,' said Brian. 'That's pretty good, for a start.'

'His brother was working a fiddle last month,' said Janice. 'Helping to sell biscuits at playtime and then stealing some of the money from our school fund tin. I trusted him. I suppose it was just too much of an opportunity. It was my own fault, and he got a good telling off. They really get to you sometimes, but you have to keep on. Then at the end of the year you realise you've changed them a little bit, and it feels good.'

'Yes, come on Mike, it's only your first lesson,' said Brian kindly, handing me a cup of tea. 'It gets easier all the time. They like you to prove yourself a little bit. It keeps you on your toes.'

'Most people's first lesson is the same,' added Dorothy. 'We all felt that way when we started. You'll find John's forgotten all about it by tomorrow. I'll have a word with him, if you like.'

'I'd rather you didn't,' I said. 'We're not very good friends at the moment. It was a lousy lesson anyway.'

'Noble sentiments,' smiled Janice. 'Don't let it get to you, though.'

I finished my lukewarm tea in gloomy silence.

I called to her across Cambridge Circus. She smiled in recognition and I hurried across the road, dodging a fast moving taxi determined to get its passengers to the theatre on time.

'You're late,' she said. 'Unforgiveable sin!'

'I know. I'm sorry. I've had a really dreadful afternoon.'

'Why? What happened?'

'I had Dorothy's class. One of the other teachers went home ill. I thought I'd be able to teach them just like she does. I should have known.'

'Oh dear. Were they very difficult, then?'

'No, not really. They're just very lively kids. I didn't realise just how much skill Dorothy has.'

Samantha put her arm round my waist and hugged me.

'Anyway,' I said admiringly, 'I couldn't have missed you. You look lovely.'

'No time for that,' she laughed. 'And we'd better hurry. The play starts in twenty minutes.'

We had arranged to meet in town so that Samantha could take advantage of late night closing to buy some clothes, and I hadn't anticipated any problems in getting to our meeting place on time, but after the disappointing afternoon things hadn't improved back at college. The hot water system had broken down again, and there had been a problem in the kitchen, causing the evening meal to be half an hour late. Since I hated unpunctuality, I'd almost resigned myself to Samantha watching the play on her own. I took her hand and we crossed over the road towards Shaftesbury Avenue, dodging between the traffic and the late night shoppers.

'What did you buy?' I asked, taking the large green carrier bag she was carrying.

'Oh, lots of odds and ends. It's Dad's birthday next week, so I bought him Dvorak's seventh. It's the only Dvorak symphony he hasn't got. And I bought some shoes. And a jumper. Look, what do you think?' She stopped abruptly in the middle of the road and held a black polo neck pullover against herself.

'How about that, then? Do you think it suits me?'

A cab driver leaned out of his cab window. 'It's beautiful, darling,' he called. 'You won't be wearin' it long if you cross the road like that, though.'

She turned and grinned and then hurried across to the pavement. 'I think he liked it,' she said.

'You're really beautiful, you know,' I said. 'You'd look lovely even if you were wearing a sack cloth.'

'We'll see. You can buy me one for Christmas. So, what have you been up to this afternoon?'

'Thinking of giving up teaching.'

Her face became serious for a moment. 'You're not regretting it already, surely?'

'No, not really. I'm sure I'll get plenty more days like today. It's so tiring, though. I was worn out after teaching them this afternoon. If things go on like this, I'll be going to bed at half past nine each night.'

'Really?' she laughed. 'Who with?'

'Ah, well now...'

'Don't tell me. The headmaster's wife says he doesn't understand her...'

'He probably doesn't. He certainly doesn't understand children.'

We turned behind the Garrick theatre and hurried into St Martin's Lane. It was choked with a line of cars trying to squeeze past an elderly Morris Minor that had stalled in the middle of the road. Somebody began to hoot at the back of the queue, not understanding the reason for the delay, and a man in his early twenties got out of the car and tried to edge it onto the pavement.

'Good thing I didn't suggest you brought me up here in your Rolls Royce,' said Samantha. 'We'd never have found a place to park.'

The owner of the Morris lifted the bonnet and peered cautiously underneath. A puff of steam escaped and he waved it away with his hand. Other drivers moved past as discretely as possible, their faces set straight ahead, not having time to stop and help. I felt vaguely guilty as we hurried past too and I rummaged through my pockets for the tickets.

'I bet you've forgotten them,' said Samantha. 'Now then, what's the line? 'I'm terribly sorry and all that, but never mind, we could go back to my room and discuss the psychological implications of dealing with disturbed children from a difficult social environment...''

'My God, you sound just like one of my lecturers.'

'I know. It's because students keep coming into the library and asking for books with that sort of stuff in them. Or else they ask me out.'

'Well I can't blame them for that. I'd probably do that myself. Oh look, the tickets are here in my wallet, so it looks as if we'll have to see the play instead.'

'Where are we sitting? Nothing less than the front row, I hope?'

'Afraid not. Student grants only run to the upper circle. And the English Department doesn't really sponsor trips to 'The Mousetrap'.'

'Really? You'll have to get something done about that. I would have thought it was a landmark in English drama.'

We reached the theatre and climbed the stairs at the side entrance. I bought two programmes while Samantha looked for the seat numbers at the front of the circle, hung her coat over the balcony, and sat down.

'It's amazing how this play still packs the theatre every night,' she said as I returned. 'I wouldn't have thought there was anybody left in London who hadn't seen it.'

'I'm surprised you haven't,' I replied.

'So am I. It's one of those things we keep meaning to do, and then don't get around to. We did book once. We couldn't go because mum was ill. I'm really looking forward to it.'

'If you get frightened, you can always grip my thigh firmly.'

'Really? Well, thank heavens for that!'

A programme attendant leaned over and pointed out that coats weren't allowed on the balcony in case something was stolen from them, which was our problem, or in case they fell onto the unsuspecting heads of those fortunate enough to be sitting in the front stalls, which was his. His condescending attitude seemed well in keeping with the way the day had gone so far. Samantha folded her coat across her lap and studied the programme.

'For the next couple of hours you're to forget school and enjoy the play,' she said. 'That's an order.'

'Yes Miss. I've forgotten school completely.'

'Good. Oh, I forgot. Have a chocolate. I've only had them about a month.'

'That's all right. If we don't like them we can always flick them over the balcony.'

'Mmm. I bet that's what your kids would do if they were here.'

'I thought we'd forgotten about school?'

'Oh yes. Sorry.'

The lights dimmed. I slipped my hand into Samantha's lap and settled back in my seat. The play had been running for a while, and though I'd seen it before, several members of the cast had changed and I followed the first act closely, interested to see how the new actors would interpret their characters. But after an hour my familiarity with the play caused my mind to wander back to the classroom, and the inspection visit in a week's time by one of my lecturers. Suppose I couldn't get good control of the children by then? How would they react in the presence of a visitor? Would Rouse interrupt every few minutes, and if he did, would the class take my side or his? There was always Jamie Dudmish, of course. He could always be relied on to give an intelligent answer. It wasn't that important, but I wanted this first teaching practice to go well. If I worked hard with the children on the Thames project for the next week or so, I should...

'Hey,' said Samantha, squeezing my hand as the lights went up for the interval. 'Aren't you enjoying it? You've been miles away for the last ten minutes. You're not still thinking about the children, are you?'

'They had crossed my mind.'

'Well for heaven's sake stop it. And cheer up. Here, I'll even buy you an ice cream.'

'I'm sorry. I'm being really terrible company.'

'Don't be daft. You can pour your troubles out over a cup of coffee afterwards. Just forget them now, that's all. Anyway, if you go and fetch the ice cream, I'll pay.'

The thought of the classroom receded as Samantha considered the motives each character might have had for committing the murder. By the time the lights dimmed for the second act, she had convinced herself she knew the identity of the guilty person, and since I knew the ending, I enjoyed watching how the play had been constructed so that suspicion wouldn't fall on the real murderer.

'Well fancy that!' Samantha said softly as the members of the cast took their final bow and the curtain fell for the last time. 'Who'd have guessed? I certainly didn't.'

'Nor did I when I first saw it. Clever, isn't it?'

'Mmm. It was really enjoyable. Thank you. You looked happier in the second half, too. It takes you a long time to warm up, doesn't it?'

'Not normally. I'll prove it to you one evening.'

'I'm sure you will. Meantime, let's see if our combined funds can run to a cup of coffee, shall we?'

The night air was colder now, and we walked quickly to avoid the threatening rain. The sky was strangely light above the city and grubby clouds scurried urgently above the office blocks pushing amongst familiar landmarks, like giant invaders from a land of stone and glass. Cranes towered in black outline, sleeping symbols of the rapidly changing skyline. We edged through the crowds and walked towards the embankment, finding a small, brightly lit coffee house near the river. It was almost empty, and we took a seat near the window.

'I love the city,' said Samantha, staring out into the street as fat drops of rain began to make passers-by turn their collars and move faster. 'We've been here eight years now. Dad doesn't like it much, though. I think he'd be happy to move to the west country. Dorset, or somewhere, but at least he can always get to a concert when he wants to.'

'What will you do?'

'I'm not sure. I'll probably stay at the library for a while. I think I'd love to work in a really interesting library… the British Museum, that kind of place. Or do some research into history or something. You're lucky. At least you know what you want to do.'

'I thought I did.'

'Oh come on, one miserable afternoon doesn't mean you're going to be a total failure. Do you mind if I have a burger? I'm starving!'

The waitress took our order and returned a few minutes later with the burgers and two steaming cups of coffee. Samantha sipped hers carefully.

'I think I know half the college from working in the library,' she said. 'But David was the only one I went out with seriously. Then he got depressed about the end of year exams and played Mahler all day. I mean, I like Mahler too, but not to the exclusion of everything else.' She opened the bun and injected a generous measure of tomato sauce.

'He took me round the college, once. It's pretty ancient, isn't it? Attractive, though. I bet they pull it down before long. They seem to be pulling everything with a bit of character down.'

'If it doesn't fall down by itself. Even the cleaner matches the building. I think she's been there since it opened. The first day I arrived she told me how the previous student in my room had committed suicide.'

She grimaced. 'Charming! Did he have a bad time on his teaching practice too?'

'No. He failed his finals.'

'That's awful. You're very lucky, though. At least your college is in an ideal place. What if you'd been stuck out in the country, or something? There's always lots of things to do in London.'

'On a student allowance?'

'Ah, you're going to give me the lecture on how impoverished students are. There are loads of places to go even if you haven't any money.'

'And we don't get much time,' I added. 'Think of how hard we have to work.'

'Oh, I can imagine,' she said, her hazel eyes smiling in mock sympathy. 'Well, look on the positive side. St. James's Park is only round the corner from you. You can go there for free and take your books to study. Anyway you're not going to tell me they overwork you, surely? When David wasn't listening to Mahler he was usually in the pottery room using up a year's supply of clay just because he liked the feel of it. I'll change places with you.'

'I'm sure you'd be welcomed with open arms. Literally.'

'Yes, I don't doubt that,' she laughed. 'Anyway, think of all the places you can take the children to if you teach in London. Are you going to do any visits with the class you've got now?'

'Hopefully. Once I get this topic of the Thames under way I'll try to fit a couple of visits in. It all depends on the headmaster, unfortunately.'

'Really? Why?'

'He doesn't think the children should get out of their seats, let alone go wandering all over London.'

'That's silly. There's so much they could do. The Science Museum, the Commonwealth Institute, the Tate. A ride down the river to Greenwich. The Cutty Sark. Or the zoo, even. There, and I'm not even a teacher.' She sipped her coffee thoughtfully and I smiled, feeling certain she could persuade Mr Reed to let her take a class of children anywhere.

'They went to the zoo with the last student,' I said. 'They came back absolutely filthy because it had been raining all day. And one of the kids got into trouble because he tried persuading an elephant to eat his mother's bread and butter pudding. Somehow Mr Reed got to hear of it and threatened to consult his invisible chart.'

'His what?'

'His invisible chart. If children get into trouble he drags them into his room and gazes at the wall. He tells them he's looking at his invisible chart to see how many strokes of the cane to administer.'

'That's incredible! I don't believe it.'

'Neither did I. But it's true.'

'I thought caning was virtually abolished these days. I thought you had to give them a gentle talking to instead.'

'He doesn't tell the kids that. He doesn't actually nail children to the wall, but he comes pretty close to it sometimes, and he isn't above giving them a clout.'

'That's unbelievable! I didn't think that sort of thing went on any more. I thought everything had to be wildly creative and progressive.'

'It does. At least, as far as all but two of the staff are concerned. Still, it's his school and nobody can force him to change his ideas. The staff just hope he'll retire. Or get run over or something.'

'Well it's certainly not fair on his staff. Or the children, come to that.'

'Or even the students,' I added miserably.

'Poor you,' she laughed. 'Come on, I'll buy you another coffee.'

The room had filled up quickly as we'd talked, mostly with people anxious to escape the rain that was lashing against the pavement outside. A boat carrying trippers chugged into its mooring by the embankment and the passengers spilled ashore, covering their heads with umbrellas, coats, or just newspapers in an effort to avoid a soaking. A woman hurriedly helped a group of teenage girls in school uniform from the swaying boat and gathered them around her urgently. She counted them hastily, and then urged them swiftly in the direction of the nearest bus shelter.

'There's devotion to duty for you,' Samantha smiled, watching the woman admiringly. 'Still at it at this time of night. You've got all that to look forward to, Mike. How's Duggan getting on at his school?'

'Fine, as far as I can tell. He's got some crazy headmistress...'

'Not another one?'

'Ah, but this one's the opposite of mine. Anything goes, according to Duggan. He comes back to college with the most astonishing stories...'

'What, more astonishing than yours?'

'Almost. His headmistress spends so much time with the children she never gets round to ordering any stock. I think she wishes she was back in the classroom. Gerry's doing well, though. He's in a secondary school doing a massive project on the history of the cinema. Apart from geography, that's his main passion in life. He loves it. He took a group of kids to the projection box of the local Odeon and they spent the morning operating the curtains, projecting a Kung Fu film and playing with the equipment.'

'It sounds as if somebody should do a thorough investigation of headteachers. Aren't there special training courses for them, or something?'

'Apparently not. Dorothy says Mr Reed doesn't even let his teachers go on courses very often. He says they only come back with ideas!'

Samantha burst out laughing, disturbing the quiet chatter of the room. 'You're joking. I don't believe a word of it!

'Sadly, I'm not. Still, it gives the staff something to laugh about. If they took him seriously they'd all get so depressed they'd leave. And that would be a tragedy for the kids. People like Dorothy are so dedicated. I've got quite a difficult boy in my class, John Rouse, but she seems to get so much from him. I just hope he's away when my tutor comes round.'

'Can't you hide him in the chalk cupboard or something?'

'I'm sure he'd love that. I can't really think of an educational reason to justify it, though.'

'When's your tutor coming in?'

'End of next week. I don't know how long they'll stay. All morning, I suppose. They've only got me to see.'

'Well, if it's a woman, do that nice smile of yours and offer to take her to the theatre. Or perhaps John Rouse will put a nip of gin in her tea for you. Anyway, it'll be alright. You worry too much about it.'

'I suppose so. Do you want any more coffee?'

'No, honestly. We ought to get back. My Dad worries.'

I paid the bill, and helped Samantha put her coat on. The rain had stopped now, and the lights along the embankment were reflected brokenly in the huge puddles along the pavement.

'Mmm,' she said, breathing the dampness of the night air and snuggling up to me. 'It's been such a lovely evening. It really has.'

'You've made it so.'

I gently pulled her close to me and kissed her deeply, feeling the soft warmth of her body against mine. A boat sounded its horn in the night air as it chugged its way upriver, breaking the reflections of the embankment lights on the water. I suddenly felt completely at peace with the world.

'You're so beautiful,' I whispered softly. Samantha's head snuggled onto my shoulder, and for several minutes we stood still and watched the river, neither of us feeling the need to speak. I felt warm and comfortable inside. It had been such a lovely evening, and I wouldn't give up the idea of teaching.

Not just yet, anyway.

MAY

A VISITOR, TROUBLE AT THE TOWER, AND MRS GARRETT

The day after my evening with Samantha I'd been relieved to learn that Miss Bottle would be supervising my teaching practice. I thought a lot of Miss Bottle. Her science lectures were practical and interesting, she tried very hard to relate everything she did to primary classroom practice, and she also managed to maintain a high academic standard, her kindly disposition concealing a capable and determined nature. I'd considered using the River Thames as the theme for my teaching practice after she had given several lectures on water.

The topic had certainly gone well with the children. Dorothy had stripped the back wall of the room to give me a lot of display space and together the children and I had created a huge painted frieze of the Thames, showing its beginnings high in the Cotswolds and its journey down to the sea. The children had found out about the Thames through the ages, written poems and stories about the great ships that bring cargoes along it, painted pictures of the docks and wharves, constructed bridges from boxes and balsa wood, experimented with techniques for purifying muddy water and then learned how Thames water was being made suitable for the return of some wildlife.

As I became increasingly enthusiastic about the work, so did the children. I still found them a challenging class to teach, but they were certainly more co-operative now. Dorothy and Brian had given constant encouragement, watching my progress with interest, but taking care never to undermine my confidence. Even Rouse had become enthusiastic; after an initial remark about 'not seein" much point in learnin' about a load of water', he had subsequently made one of the best models in the class.

On the morning Miss Bottle was due to arrive, I was in school an hour earlier than usual to make sure everything was just right. I'd planned the children's work for the morning with meticulous care, so that I'd have time to talk to Miss Bottle and discuss the work I'd done, while ensuring the children were quiet and absorbed. As Samantha had said, it wasn't essential to receive an outstanding report from this practice, especially as it was my first. Nevertheless, if I was going to be a teacher I intended to be a good one, and Dorothy had already set me a high standard. As I stood in front of the class at register time, I wondered how much I should tell the children about Miss Bottle. Then I just decided to say they would be having a visitor.

'I'd like you all to be especially good today,' I said. 'There's an important lady coming to see you, but I'm not sure what time she'll arrive.'

Rouse looked up with interest. 'Is it the queen?' he asked.

'No, not exactly. But she's still very important and I've told her you're the best class I've ever taught.' 'Cor,' exclaimed Susan Davis. 'You ain't 'alf nice, ain't yer, Sir.'

'Only if you behave. And especially this morning. But I'm sure you will.'

'Sounds like a bribe to me,' Badger commented suspiciously. 'I don't like the sound of it. 'Oo's this visitor, anyway?'

'Tell us, Sir?' Adams pleaded, his voice rapidly joined by the voices of the other children. 'Then we'll know 'ow good we 'ave to be. I mean, if it's just your auntie we don't 'ave to be as good as if it was the Prime Minister or someone.'

'You'll just have to ask her, won't you?' I replied, immediately realising this might not be a very good idea. 'Anyway, she'll probably tell you herself when she gets here.'

‘Well, if it’s the queen, we’ll recognise ‘er,’ said Rouse. ‘I’ve seen the queen.’

Eyes turned to him in interest at this latest development.

‘Don’t tell me you’ve been knighted, John?’ I said.

‘Eh?’

‘I wondered if I might be addressing Sir John Rouse?’

Rouse screwed up his face in puzzlement and looked at me. ‘What d’yer mean?’

‘It doesn’t matter. Anyway, let’s get on and finish what we were doing yesterday. We want the classroom to look really interesting by the time she comes. I’m proud of your work, and I want her to like it too.’

But the time had passed and Miss Bottle had not appeared. I was annoyed because I was desperately tired, and the work schedule I’d planned for the morning was likely to be wasted. I also felt disappointed for the children because I wanted their topic to be seen and admired. After all, I thought, even Mr Reed had visited the classroom the day before and been mildly impressed.

When the bell rang for lunch, my disappointment changed to annoyance. I finished my teaching practice in a week’s time, and now it looked as if nobody was going to come at all.

‘Well, she ain’t turned up, ‘as she, Sir?’ said Adams, stuffing his work into his tray. ‘P’raps she couldn’t find the school or somethin.’’

‘It looks like it,’ I said. ‘Put your things away everyone. Susan, you’ve dripped paint under your table. Can you clear it up before you go?’

‘Yes Sir,’ she said. ‘Can Susan Brennan ‘elp me, Sir?’

‘I suppose so. But don’t be late down.’

The children went out slowly, disappointed at losing the opportunity to show off what they had created. Rouse hovered by the front table and waited for me to put the topic folders in a pile.

‘That story you’re readin’ us,’ he said. ‘Is it in the library?’

‘Not the school one, no. At least, I don’t think so. Why?’

'I'd jus' like ter read it, that's all.'

'You can't read that. It's too 'ard,' jeered Susan Davis.

'Oo asked you? I ain't talkin' ter you.'

'Well, you can't.'

'I could 'ave a try. What's it ter do with you? Anyway, 'ow d'yer join the other library?'

'Just go round after school and ask at the desk,' I replied, pleased that Rouse liked the story so much he wanted to read it for himself, even though I knew it would be too difficult for him. 'The assistant will give you a card that your parents have to sign. Then you take it back and the assistant will give you a plastic card you use each time you go and choose books.'

His face clouded over.

'Oh. It's a bit of a bother then, ain't it? I thought it 'ud be a bit easier than that. Me mum 'ud say she ain't got the time and me dad 'ud say what do you want to join for anyway. 'E can't read much 'imself, so it ain't much good askin' 'im.'

'Fetch the card and I'll sign it, then,' I said.

'Nah. I don't think I'll bother.'

'Don't be silly. It's not difficult.'

'I don't like ter go down there on me own,' he said, thrusting his hands in his pockets in the characteristic gesture he showed when he was frustrated about something.

'I'll go with yer,' Susan Davis offered. 'I'm going tonight. You can come round there with me if you want.' Rouse turned away shyly.

'Well, there you are,' I smiled. 'If you want to join, it's up to you now. And you couldn't have a nicer young lady to go with.'

'What, 'er?' he retorted incredulously.

'Aw Sir,' cried Susan, 'You would 'ave to say that. Anyway Rousey, you comin' tonight or what?'

'I might.'

'I think it's very kind of Susan,' I said. 'Anyway, finish now and have your lunch.'

I followed them into the corridor and almost collided with Mr Reed.

'Ah, Mr Kent,' he said briskly, 'I was just coming in to have a word with you. I've had a telephone call from your college. Rather inconvenient I have to say, because I'd just locked my room up. Miss... ahm... Bottle was unable to see you today because she's been asked to cover another tutor's lecture. She sends her apologies, but she has made arrangements for a Dr Williams to come and see you this afternoon instead. He'll be here by two o'clock.' He looked vaguely down the corridor in the direction of the stairs for a moment, and then strode off to do lunch duty.

My mind reeled with the news. I hadn't planned to teach the class at all in the afternoon, but now I'd have to. And showing Dr Williams what I'd been doing didn't appeal to me at all. Being one of the college's ancients, short sighted and hopelessly out of date with primary education, he would probably tread on the children's models, or fall asleep at the back of the classroom. Nevertheless, something had to be attempted. Not a lesson on goldfish, that was for sure.

I ate my corned beef salad gloomily, gradually piecing the afternoon together in my mind. I could use the lesson I'd planned for the next morning, and talk about the link boys who'd worked on the river bank in Tudor times. I'd already prepared some effective worksheets describing them, with plenty of follow-up ideas for the children to do afterwards. Feeling more relaxed I finished my chocolate pudding and lumpy custard and went back to the classroom to fetch the sheets from my bag. Only the master sheets were in the bag and with a sinking feeling I remembered that the worksheets I'd carefully duplicated were still on my desk at college. Determined not to panic, there was still time to duplicate another set in the staffroom. After all, I only needed twenty five copies.

When I reached the staffroom I saw that the copying machine was in several pieces on the table. A service mechanic was poring over it, adjusting a metal plate with a screwdriver and spanner.

'Is this going to take long?' I asked, a slight desperation in my voice.

'No idea, chum,' said the mechanic cheerfully. 'You can never tell. It looks as if somebody's been feeding the wrong kind of paper into it. It's not built for that thickness.' He thrust a pair of tweezers underneath the roller, tweaked out some crumpled paper, and dropped it into the bucket.

There was no time to waste. I could just about get to college and back if Dorothy had the class for the first half hour after lunch. I scribbled a note, asked the first child I found to go and give it to her, and hurried out of the school gate. A lunchtime helper supervising the children in the playground looked at me suspiciously, as if I was leaving the premises without permission. A train drew into the platform just as I arrived at the station and I hurried onto it, running over the lesson possibilities in my mind. I'd talk for ten minutes or so… not too long because it was never easy with another adult in the classroom. Then I'd ask a few questions, and the children could work on the sheets while a group of them showed Dr Williams round the Thames topic. The train rumbled into a station, and the doors clattered open. I looked at my watch. Three stations to go. It would be terrible if I wasn't back to school by two.

The top corridor of the college was deserted. A trickle of jazz piano filtered from an open door at the end of the corridor, the only sign that anybody else was around. I fumbled with my keys, stumbled into the room, and hurried to the desk. The work I'd spent so much time on was not there either. I stood still for a moment, not quite sure what I should do next. There was nothing for it, I'd just have to teach another lesson; perhaps read them a story, but Dr Williams would hardly be able to assess my teaching skills on that. In a panic, I hurried back to the station, tired, hot and very angry. How could the worksheets just disappear like that? Unless Rousey had been down my bag and sabotaged the lot. No, that was unfair; he'd been so much better since he'd built that model of Tower Bridge.

When I arrived back at school, I recognised the battered Austin Cambridge that belonged to Dr Williams parked at the side of the road. So he was here already. There wasn't even going to be enough time to browse in the library for five minutes and gather a few thoughts together. The bell rang as I entered the gate, and I rushed up the stairs ahead of the children. Mr Reed was waiting outside Dorothy's classroom, red-faced and tapping his foot on the floor with irritation.

'Where the devil have you been?' he snapped. 'You realise, I suppose, that your tutor is already here? I would have thought you could at least have made yourself available in the lunch hour. Mrs Bridgewood has kindly agreed to look after your tutor while you at least gather your wits together. This really isn't very satisfactory, is it?' There was nothing I could say. I stormed into the classroom as the children followed behind me noisily.

'Get your reading books out,' I snapped. 'I'm going to do something in a moment. Meanwhile, it would be helpful if you kept quiet.'

'Are you having us this afternoon then, Sir?' asked Dudmish, wiping the dust from his face with a dirty handkerchief after playing football.

'Yes,' I said forcefully. 'Why, did you wish to make a formal objection or something?'

His mouth dropped open. 'Pardon, Sir?' he asked politely.

'Is there some reason why I shouldn't be taking you this afternoon?'

'No Sir. But Mrs Bridgewood said...'

'Well then, read!'

'Sir,' said Rouse loudly, waving his hand under my nose. 'Can I go to the lav?'

'What?'

Rouse sensed that this might not be the best moment to leave his seat.

''Er... nothin',' he said. 'I'll wait. I'll 'old it.'

There was silence, broken only by the sound of pages being

turned. Eyes occasionally lifted from books to see if I was still angry, and several minutes later the door swung open and Dorothy came in.

'My, they're quiet,' she said approvingly. 'What have you done, put sleeping pills in their pudding?'

''E ain't 'alf mad with us, Miss,' said Susan Davis. 'Dunno why.'

'I bet I can guess, though,' said Dorothy. 'Look, Mike, don't worry. She's...'

'She?'

'Yes. Miss Bottle. You were expecting her this morning?'

'But I thought she couldn't get here. I thought Dr Williams...'

'Well, I don't know who Dr Williams is, but a very smartly dressed lady calling herself Doris Bottle has been sitting in the staffroom for the best part of half an hour being entertained by Brian. And Brian thinks she's delightful. She's gone down to look at his classroom and then she's coming in here. She seems very sweet.'

I could hardly believe what I was hearing. I was certain Miss Bottle would be sympathetic to what had happened and I breathed a sigh of relief. She was bound to understand.

'I'll go,' whispered Dorothy. 'I don't like to disturb the peace in here. Have you got something ready?'

'I'll think of something. It's a long story. I'll tell you at playtime.'

I turned to the children, now busily chatting to each other, sensing the danger was over.

'What are we going to do then, Sir?' asked Rouse politely. 'Can we get on and finish our river work?'

'You still look a bit worried, Sir,' said Badger kindly. 'And a bit off colour, too. I knew a bloke once...'

'Gawd, 'ere we go,' moaned Susan Davis, and there was a chorus of sympathy. I groped for an idea to start the lesson, and with inspiration born from desperation I launched a sudden idea.

'This afternoon,' I said, 'we'll have a debate. Now, listen carefully...

'A what?' interrupted Rouse.

'A debate?'

'What's that?'

'Shut up and we'll find out,' Adams suggested.

'I know, Sir,' called Dudmish. 'It's when you have a sort of argument about something and some people agree with it and some people don't. They have them in parliament. You start with... um... a motion, I think it's called. Then when people have argued about it everybody decides who they agree with.'

''E's good, ain't 'e, Sir,' said Fred admiringly. ''E explains things so you understand 'em, don't 'e.'

'Well done, Jamie,' I said. 'We won't make it that complicated though. Lets have a short debate about punishment in school. Then if our visitor comes in you can jot down a few notes while I...'

'I thort we'd 'ave to write somethin'', said Rouse. 'I thort we'd get round to that bit. Why don't you just pick me? I'll come out and talk to the class.'

'We couldn't stand it. You'd bore us all stiff,' said Dudmish.

'You could get 'im to sing, though,' suggested Adams. ''E ain't got a bad voice really. 'Ow about gettin' 'im to sing?'

'Gawd!' exclaimed Susan Davis. 'Do we 'ave to?'

Fortunately there was no time to pursue this idea as there was a sudden tap at the door and Miss Bottle came into the room. The children's heads turned in unison to look at her. Their visitor was here at last.

'I do apologise, dear,' Miss Bottle said earnestly. 'It's been such a confusing morning. And then I managed to re-arrange my timetable and my car wouldn't start. Dr Williams kindly lent me his. I felt as if I was driving a bus. Anyway, enough of my troubles. How are you getting on?'

'Well Sir,' said Rouse triumphantly, 'She's 'ere'. Yer visitor's 'ere.'

I smiled weakly and shook her immaculately white gloved hand.

'Come in Miss,' shouted Adams enthusiastically. 'We was expectin' you earlier.'

'Not too badly,' I said in answer to her question. 'Things seem to be going fairly well. We've only just started the lesson, actually. John, can you fetch a chair for Miss Bottle from the library, please?' There was a murmur of good humoured laughter as the children repeated her name.

'Okay Sir,' said Rouse. 'We thort you was comin' this morning, Miss Bottle. We was all on our best behaviour this mornin', wasn't we, Sir?'

'Get the chair, please John,' I said firmly.

'It's quite all right, young man,' said Miss Bottle. 'I'm not going to sit down. I'm not that old yet! I'm going to come round and see what you've all been doing.' She beamed at Rouse and he retreated in awed silence.

'Now then children,' Miss Bottle began, 'I just want to have a little chat with Mr Kent, and then I shall talk to you. I wonder if you could just get on quietly for a few minutes?'

The children slowly took out their books and made a pretence of reading them, sitting silently so that anything my visitor said could be clearly overheard. Badger sat eyeing Miss Bottle thoughtfully, as if she wasn't quite what he'd been led to expect. Miss Bottle turned to me.

'Now then, dear, how old are these children?'

'They're eight to nine. Second year Juniors.'

'I see. And how are you finding them?'

'They're fine now. They weren't very attentive at first. They tended to be quite difficult.'

'Children can be, dear,' she said. 'You have to show them you're up to the job. Even students can be quite difficult at times, believe it or not. And what sort of things do they do?'

'Well, lots of things really. They..'

'Yes, I know dear. What I meant was, what have you personally been doing with them? This lovely wall display of the River Thames, is that yours?'

'No, we all done that, Miss,' called Adams, not wanting his efforts to go unrecognised.

'We've been doin' about the River Thames, Miss,' interrupted Susan Davis brightly. 'Sir's been tellin' us all sorts of things about it. We've done about the ships what bring in all the food, an' the cranes, an' about the famous places you can see from the river, and all the bridges.'

'And how rivers start. And where they go,' added Susan Brennan.

'We've done the docks and the wharves,' said Badger. 'We've done all sorts of stuff.'

Miss Bottle smiled and walked to the other side of the classroom.

'You certainly have, young man,' she said warmly. 'You seem to be a very hard working class indeed. And who made this lovely model of Tower Bridge?'

'I did that, Miss,' said Rouse proudly.

'Well I 'elped yer,' added Badger.

'Yeah, but I done nearly all of it.'

'Yeah, but I 'elped yer.'

'You 'elped a bit. I'm not denyin' that. But it was me what done most of it.'

'Well, I think you're both extremely clever,' Miss Bottle said. 'And all these other models are beautiful, too.'

'Would you like to see the things I dug up on the river bank, Miss Bottle?' asked Dudmish. 'It's all on the table over here. My dad took me at the weekend.'

He took her hand and led her over to a table displaying an array of artefacts he had salvaged with the help of his father. In the centre of the table there was a collection of bottles, which he had washed and arranged with great care.

'Now these are lovely,' she said, picking up a bottle from the centre of the collection, and immediately commanding the attention of the class. 'This is a very interesting one, children. This bottle used to contain poison. You can tell by the shape, and the special ridges on it, look. Even somebody who was blind could tell it contained poison, just by feeling these ridges. And this one is an old ink bottle, and look at the lovely shape of this one over here. You've got a very interesting collection, young man.'

'Thank you, Miss.' Dudmish replied. 'My dad was surprised we found so many bottles. We found all these in about an hour.'

'I expect you did, dear. That's because years ago most liquids were kept in glass or stone bottles. There were hundreds of different kinds. Nowadays, of course, things are kept in paper or plastic containers. Lots of things were buried on the river bank, too. That's why it's such an interesting place to explore. Oh, I see you've learned about cleaning up the Thames, as well.'

'Yes, Miss,' said Susan Davis. 'Sir done some Science experiments with us. He showed us how to get clean water out of muddy water by flatterin' it...'

'Filtering it,' Dudmish corrected her.

'Oh, that's it, filterin' it. An' he showed us 'ow they get germs out of it an' so on.'

'And how the goldfish are coming back to the river,' said Julie, anxious to make a contribution.

'Not goldfish. Salmon and stuff like that,' Adams corrected her.

'Well, we done somethin' about a goldfish, anyway,' Julie said conclusively.

Miss Bottle looked down at the children and beamed. 'So you've even managed to get some science into your topic,' she said admiringly. 'How delightful. I shall tell Dr Frost. You really are very clever children.'

I was delighted with Miss Bottle's enthusiasm for what we'd done, and her genuine interest in the children. Somebody, I thought, must be smiling down on me at last.

'Can I read you me water poems, please Miss? asked Susan Davis.

'Can I show you me poster about the dangers of swimmin' in the Thames, Miss?' Badger called. 'It shows someone drownin', and I...'

'I'd love to see it all, dear,' said Miss Bottle approvingly, 'but I just don't think I'll have enough time. What's all this lovely work over here?' She pointed to a wall on the other side of the classroom and moved nearer to see the pictures clearly.

'That's all about the Battle of 'asting's,' said Rouse. 'That's work we done with Miss last term.'

Hema pointed to the section showing the Norman soldiers arriving in their boats, and gathering on the beach. 'We painted a background first,' she said. 'We painted the sea and the seashore. Then we made lots of soldiers. We used felt and silver paper and things.'

'My mum sent Miss a big bag full of bits of material,' added Julie. 'She works down the clothing factory.'

'That was very kind of her,' said Miss Bottle. 'I'm sure Mrs Bridgewood found them most useful.'

Rouse thought for a moment. Since the class appeared to have won Miss Bottle's full approval, he'd obviously decided the time might be right for a little probing of his own.

'Please Miss,' he said cautiously, 'Can I ask you a question?'

'Of course, dear. What is it?'

'Oo are yer?'

Slightly taken aback, Miss Bottle raised her eyebrows and leaned forward to him. 'What do you mean, dear, who am I?'

'I think they've been wondering why you are here,' I explained hastily. 'This morning I told them they'd be having an important visitor today, but I didn't say who. Or why.'

Miss Bottle chuckled happily. 'Oh, I see. Well, I don't think I could really be called important…'

'Please Miss Bottle,' called Dudmish, having puzzled over the visit for a few minutes and arrived at his own conclusion, 'have you come to check up on Mr Kent?'

'Oh yeah, of course, 'e's a stoodent,' agreed Adams, turning and nodding at Dudmish. "E ain't a real teacher yet.'

'Course e's a real teacher,' retorted Susan Davis quickly. "E's taught us, ain't 'e?'

"E ain't a real teacher till 'e's passed 'is exams,' Adams persisted. 'This lady 'as come to check up on 'im to 'elp 'im pass 'is exams.'

'Oh, I don't think I'll be able to help him do that,' Miss Bottle smiled. 'But I shall certainly be going back to college and saying what a delightful classroom this is.'

'Well, 'e seems jus' like a real teacher to me,' said Susan Davis.

'Yeah, I reckon 'e's the best stoodent we've ever 'ad,' Rouse agreed, rather over generously. 'Shame 'e can't stay 'ere with Miss Bridgewood if you ask me.'

My eyebrows raised in surprise at the effect I'd apparently had on Rouse, especially as much of my time seemed to have been spent in telling him off.

'When Sir said we was 'avin' a visitor, we thought it might be the Queen,' Fred offered. Miss Bottle walked over to him, looked at him kindly, and patted him on the head.

'Did you dear? Well, I'm sure if the Queen had visited your classroom she would have been just as impressed as I am.'

'Cor, ain't you nice, Miss,' said Susan Davis pleasantly.

'Thank you, young lady. Now, I think I was asking you all about your lovely picture of the Battle of Hastings on the wall…'

'Yes Miss,' agreed Fred. 'You was.'

'You were,' she corrected him.

'No I weren't,' said Fred, a puzzled frown appearing on his face. 'You was.' Miss Bottle opened her mouth to say something, but decided it was probably not a point worth pursuing.

'Very well then,' she continued. 'Who can tell me when the Battle of Hastings was?'

'Don't yer know that Miss?' shouted Rouse incredulously. 'Cor!' He stared round at his friends in disbelief and Miss Bottle wagged a stern finger at him.

'Of course I know when it was, young man,' she said sharply. 'I want to see if you know. And please don't call out like that. If you want to say something, say it quietly and sensibly, preferably after putting your hand up first. It isn't at all nice to shout out like that, is it, Mr Kent?'

'It certainly isn't,' I agreed.

'It was 1066,' said Badger cautiously, impressed by Miss Bottle's ability to silence Rouse so effectively.

'Everyone knows that one,' agreed Julie. 'It's easy.'

'We done all about the Middle Ages, Miss, before Mr Kent came 'ere,' said Badger. 'We done about the places monks lived in, and 'ow they wrote their books an' that. Then we done about the things they used to do when people didn't be'ave...'

'Like if a woman scolded 'er 'usband, they put a special iron thing on 'er 'ead,' added Adams.

'Good thing too, in my opinion,' Badger continued. 'The punishments was tough in them days, Miss. They used to make you 'old these bits o' red 'ot iron, an' if you 'ad blisters three days later you was guilty. My Uncle Bill knows a man what's in prison, Miss, an' 'e was sayin'...'

'Thank you dear,' said Miss Bottle, interrupting him with finely judged precision. 'That's very interesting indeed. Now I just want to talk to Mr Kent again for a moment, and then I think I shall have to go. What were you all doing when I came in?'

'We were going to have a debate,' I said, thinking it best to own up about the events at lunchtime. 'It was a bit of a makeshift lesson. I wasn't actually expecting to take the class this afternoon. I thought I'd bring tomorrow's lesson forward and use some worksheets I'd prepared, so I went back to college at lunchtime...'

'What, all the way back to the college? That was extremely industrious of you, dear.'

'It was a waste of time. I couldn't find the worksheets. I think I must have thrown them all away by accident. The master sheets I made are here in my bag, but the copier is being mended.'

'But Mr Reed has a copier in his room. I saw it. It's an older one, but perfectly serviceable, I should imagine.'

'I didn't know that. But he's always very busy and he doesn't like being disturbed unless it's really essential.'

Miss Bottle looked puzzled and drew herself up to her full height.

'But this *is* essential, dear. What on earth is a headmaster for, if he can't help his staff when they need it? Frankly, I'd say he ought to be extremely grateful for all the lovely work you've done with the children. Give me your master sheets, and wait here.'

Fascinated, I handed them to her and watched as she strode to the door and down the corridor in search of Mr Reed.

''As she gone now, Sir?' asked Fred.

'Is she a teacher too?' asked Badger. 'She looked a bit old for it to me.'

'She used to be,' I replied. 'Now she's a different kind of teacher called a lecturer. Part of her job is to help people who want to become teachers.'

'Well she ain't the Queen, that's for sure,' Rouse commented briefly.

'I thought she was nice,' said Julie.

'So did I,' agreed Susan Davis. 'I liked 'er. Didn't we, Sue?'

'I wonder what school was like in them days,' mused Badger. 'I bet they got caned all the time. My dad says when 'e was at school they locked 'im in the...'

'Shame somebody don't lock you in one, mate,' Susan Davis commented drily.

'You dunno what I was goin' ter say.'

'I can imagine, mate.'

'Let's get on with the debate,' said Dudmish, obviously feeling that valuable time was being wasted. 'Good idea, Jamie,' I agreed. 'We were going to have a debate about school punishments, so we need a few people to argue in favour of them. Hands up those who want to do that.'

With the exception of Dudmish and Susan Brennan, all the children raised their hands.

'I'll need more people than Susan and Jamie to argue against,' I said, 'or we won't have a very good debate.'

'My dad says they ought to bring back 'angin' and floggin',' said Badger. 'Specially with some of the people what are wanderin' about these days. I went to the pictures last week and this bloke...'

'Thank you Alan,' I said gratefully. 'Perhaps you could tell us about that some other time?

'Okay Sir,' he agreed amicably.

'Now, the children who are going to be main speakers need to write a very short speech. The rest of you can finish off this morning's work. It looks as if we'll have to do the actual debate after playtime. John, you can be chairman.'

'What's 'e do?' asked Rouse.

'He sits out here in the middle and introduces the speakers. It's an easy job. When the speakers have finished you can call someone from the house to put their point of view.'

'What 'ouse is that?'

'Someone from the remainder of the class. Someone who isn't a main speaker. You call the classroom, or wherever you are having the debate, the house.'

'Oh.'

'Do you think you can do it?'

'Do what?'

'Be the chairman?'

'I 'spect so. Seems funny though. It ain't as if you're actually livin' in the 'ouse, is it?

'No. It comes from the Houses of Parliament. Anyway, it doesn't matter, does it?'

'It jus' seems funny, that's all. I think...'

'If you and I sit here debating the issue amongst ourselves,' I said wearily, 'we shall get nothing done at all. I don't think...'

'Sir', Hema interrupted, 'Mrs Bridgewood is at the door.'

Dorothy hurried across the classroom, a look of disbelief on her face. 'It's astonishing!' she said. 'We spend half our time trying to wheedle as much as a piece of paper out of Mr Reed and your Miss Bottle manages it first time. She's got him in his office with his sleeves rolled up, turning out all your worksheets. Brian says he wishes he had a camera handy. Here, I've brought you a mug of tea. It's the very least you deserve. Oh, and she thought the classroom was wonderful, You must have made quite an impression.'

'That's great,' I said. 'The children were good, too.'

'Did she say she liked us then, Miss?' asked Susan Davis, overhearing the conversation as usual.

'All except you,' Dorothy said seriously. 'She thought you were the worst of the lot.'

'Aw Miss,' Susan grinned happily.

After a riotous debate in which the children thoroughly enjoyed expressing their views about school punishment, and law and order in general, coupled unavoidably with Badger's gruesome anecdotes, I arrived back at college to find Milly dragging a bucket and mop from Gerry's room.

''Allo, me old cock,' she said, putting her bucket down with a clatter. ''Ad an 'ard day, 'ave yer?'

'Not too bad, considering,' I replied.

'Not an easy job, is it, love? I wouldn't like to do it. 'Ere, Your friend is a messy bugger. Can you tell 'im to keep 'is room a bit tidier? Don't 'e ever make 'is bed? Pipe tobaccer, bread crumbs, bacon rind, and Gawd knows what else. I didn't dare look...'

She sniffed and took her cigarette rolling machine from her grimy overalls. 'Mind you, you're gettin' as bad yourself. I cleared everythin' off the desk this mornin' so I could give it a good goin' over. I moved a lot of paper and books and stuff...'

My mouth dropped open. 'What, sheets with history pictures on?'

'I dunno what they was, love. I didn't look at 'em. But the wind was blowin' 'em all over the place so I put 'em all in the bottom of your cupboard. I didn't like to open yer desk. I 'ope that was alright?'

(ii)

It was the day of the children's visit to the Tower of London, and they were very excited.

'Ow we gettin' there, Miss?' asked Rouse. 'Are we goin' on the train?'

'We are indeed, John,' Dorothy replied. 'Now sit down while I do the register.'

'My uncle works on the tube,' said Adams, dragging a comb through his hair and then inspecting it closely. "E's up at the Elephant and Castle. Are we goin' there, Miss?'

'No, just to the nearest station. It should only take us about forty minutes. If we don't lose Rousey on the way, of course.'

'Cor, that ain't a bad idea,' said Badger. Rouse turned to take a swipe at him with the large carrier bag containing his packed lunch. The bag split open and showered everyone near him with unshelled peanuts.

'Oh for heaven's sake, John,' Dorothy sighed. 'Pick them all up. What on earth have you brought all those peanuts for?'

"Cos I like peanuts, Miss,' he said simply.

The children had been told they could bring a packed lunch and some spending money and most of them seemed to have arrived with a plentiful supply of both. They gathered in groups in the classroom, lunch bags over their shoulders and eager to depart.

'What've you brought to eat, Sir?' asked Susan Brennan.

'I'll probably buy something when we're there, but it looks as if there's enough for all of us in your bag. What on earth have you got in it?'

She grinned. 'Nothing much really. Some 'am, a packet of jam tarts, some crisps, a couple of chocolate biscuits, three apples, a can of orange, some sweets for all the kids. Oh, and some tomato sandwiches.' She thrust her bag forward so that I could inspect the contents.

'Now listen carefully everyone,' called Dorothy, clapping her hands to stop the excited chatter. 'Before we go, there are one or two things I want to say, so pay attention. Now firstly, when we get into the street we want people to think we are an exceptionally well behaved class, don't we?'

'Yes, Miss,' the children answered dutifully.

'Well then, remember to behave really well, just as you do for me in class. Next thing, and this is important. I did say bring a packed lunch, but half of you have brought enough to feed an army. You'll need to carry your bags around with you, so I don't want to see anybody starting their food until we all sit down and eat together. That won't be for a long time yet. Do you understand that, John?'

'Yes, Miss,' Rouse replied meekly, peering into the food bags of everybody round him. 'Cor, look, Miss, Alan's got some bread puddin'. I never thort o' that! Can I 'ave a bit o' your bread puddin' at dinner time, Al?'

'What you got to swap for it, then?' asked Badger.

'You two, do you mind?' called Dorothy. 'You seem to forget we're going on an educational outing. You're not storing food so that we can last out the Winter. Your notebooks are more important than your stomachs.'

'Which notebooks do you think we should take, Miss?' asked Dudmish, sorting through his tray.

'Just the one you make rough notes in. You can write about anything that interests you and then we'll do some work and a display for the wall later on.'

'There is not very much room on the wall,' said Hema. 'We've made so many pictures.'

'Our classroom looks lovely, don't it, Miss?' said Susan Davis, looking round her. 'I think it's the best classroom in the school, don't we, Sue?'

'Well, I suppose you can work quite hard when you try,' Dorothy agreed. 'Anyway, come over here by the door. We ought to get a move on now.'

She handed me some writing pencils, paper, and several packs of coloured felt tipped pens. 'They'll want to sketch some of the things we see,' she said. 'We've missed the rush hour, so at least it'll be an easy journey. You go at the front of the line and I'll look after the back. Otherwise we'll get a few stragglers.'

She lined the children up in the corridor, and I led them downstairs. Each child talked loudly to their partner about the things they expected to see. All of them, it seemed, had made a special effort to scrub themselves clean and dress smartly. Outings were events to be savoured to the full.

The main road was quieter than usual. Several women wandered through the market, and a shopkeeper swept the remains of a broken milk bottle into the gutter, pausing to lean on his broom and smile at the column of children as it filed by. Pieces of torn newspaper, vinegar stained, flicked out of a lamp post waste bin and across the pavement, stirred by the morning breeze. A woman in the queue outside the post office waved to one of the children and a hand waved back. Susan Davis slid her hand into mine.

'My bag ain't 'alf 'eavy already,' she grumbled. 'I 'ope we 'ave our dinner a bit early. Can I eat a bit of it on the train, Sir?'

'That wouldn't be fair to everybody else, would it Susan? Come here, I'll help you with it.'

'Cor, taa, Sir. Susan's is a bit 'eavy, too, ain't it, Sue? D'yer think you could manage 'ers as well?'

'You two really shouldn't have brought so much.'

I took the bags and waited at the crossing for a break in the traffic, glancing back to make sure that everybody was there. Rouse, Adams, and some of their friends were deep in conversation with Dorothy, and a handful of girls were still comparing their lunches. A bus stopped and the driver beckoned the class across.

"Ang on, Miss,' called Rouse urgently, trying to keep up with his friends, 'me shoe lace 'as come undone.'

He bent down and tripped on the kerb, thrusting his carrier bag in front of him to break his fall. Peanut shells rolled all over the crossing, and Dorothy hurried forward to push him across. Rouse seemed reluctant to leave the majority of his peanuts to be shelled by the oncoming traffic and he tried to retrieve as many as possible. Two pensioners, amused by the situation, hurried forward to help him, and he offered them several peanuts each in gratitude.

'Trust 'im, Sir, eh?' Susan Davis remarked as the children grouped outside the station. 'Still, at least 'e's lost 'alf of 'em and 'e won't go droppin' 'em all over the train.'

I shuddered at the thought and waited while Dorothy paid the fare and put the pass ticket into her bag. Then we moved the group forward into the lift. A round faced attendant with an enormous stomach looked up from rolling a cigarette.

'Stand quietly, you lot!' he ordered. 'If you jump about you'll snap the cable and then we'll all fall down the bloody shaft!'

'Oi, watch your language,' Rouse shouted.

The lift attendant turned to me and grimaced. 'I don't fancy your job, mate. Where are you goin'? The zoo? Takin' a few back are yer?'

'Nah,' said Adams, shaking his head. 'We're goin' to the Tower of London.'

'Are you now. Well, you watch it, son, or you could get beheaded.'

'Get off! They don't do that now.'

'You be careful. I 'eard they'd brought it back.'

"Ow deep's the lift shaft, mister?' asked Badger, peering through the cracks in the floor. 'I bet you'd go down with a wallop if you fell down there. I bet…'

'Oh don't keep goin' on,' said Susan Davis nervously. 'Why can't you be 'appy for a change?'

'I am 'appy. I was just sayin' you'd go down with a wallop if you fell down there.'

There was a slight bump as we arrived at the bottom of the shaft and Dorothy crowded all the children into the end compartment of the waiting train, opening as many windows as she could. The only three passengers looked up nervously, and one left the carriage as discreetly as possible. Rouse and Badger sat down opposite a tiny elderly lady reading a book of short stories. She tucked herself into the corner of the seat, smiled tentatively at the boys, and then retreated behind the pages of her book.

'Well?' Dorothy asked me. 'Do you feel worn out yet?'

'I think I can stand a few more hours of it.'

'You ought to try School Journey,' she smiled. 'We usually take about thirty five away each year. Mostly fourth and third years, but some of these have been too. We usually go to a countryside centre. They stayed on a farm once. The farmer had them up at five o'clock in the morning milking cows.'

'I shouldn't think getting up that early bothered them,' I said. 'They always seem to have so much energy.'

'Oh, it was marvellous,' Dorothy went on. 'When they found out milk came from cows, half of them said they'd never touch it again. They all thought it came out of bottles and cartons. We've been to the Isle of Wight, Devon, all sorts of places. They're going on an adventure holiday this year. They learn an awful lot. I don't think Mr Reed appreciates all the work Brian and Deidre put into it.'

'He doesn't go with them does he?'

She laughed abruptly. 'No, thank God! Only for the weekend. And I think that's only to get away from his wife. It's quite sad, really. He never speaks to the children while he's there, so I don't know why he bothers to come.'

'Why is he so disinterested in his school, then? In the children, I mean?'

'I think there are probably a lot of reasons. From what we can gather, he's in a miserable marriage, and he got his headship quite a long time ago. There's always a shortage of people who want to be headteachers, but I suppose he must have impressed somebody along the line. He might have been better when he started, but ideas change rapidly, and in teaching you've got to adapt if something new and better comes along. It's so frustrating when you have a good staff like ours and somebody leading them who hasn't a clue. It's more common than you'd think.'

'He doesn't seem to worry them much, though. I mean, the children seem very happy.'

'Mmm, that's true. But it's little things. Just think what a difference a really good assembly could make to the start of the day. On Fridays, the whole school comes in, and the children talk about the work they've done in the week. You know, show models, read stories, things like that. It's totally about the children. Deidre takes Friday assembly and it's lovely.'

The train drew into a station and she looked out at the name on the platform. 'The next stop is ours. We'd better warn the children now, or they'll all flood off in a panic if they don't know exactly when they're getting off.'

As soon as she stood up, many of the children stood up too, worried in case they might be left on the train. Dorothy immediately settled them again, and they sat quietly until the train drew in to Tower Hill station. As we reached the escalator, I noticed that Rouse had now abandoned his rapidly disintegrating carrier bag and had borrowed a smaller one from Dudmish, trying to transfer everything from one to the other as he walked. I had a fleeting vision of peanut shells jamming the escalator and Rouse trying to explain the situation to a station attendant. As we came out into warm sunshine Dorothy lined the children up again, counted them, and then made sure each child had a partner.

'Vital procedure number one,' she explained. 'Always count. Don't ever assume they're all there. A student lost a couple in Janice's class, once. They were going round and round the circle line.'

'I know,' I nodded. 'Mr Reed told me all about it.'

'I'm sure he did. It's not something he's ever forgotten.'

She led the children to the lower entrance and paused to hand in the pass. A sentry paced up and down below the railings where a moat had once encircled the monument, and the class stopped to admire his splendid costume.

'Cor!' exclaimed Rouse. 'I wouldn't mind bein' 'im, marchin' up and down all day. 'Ow d'yer become one of them, Sir?'

'I wouldn't like it,' said Dudmish. 'It would get boring after a bit. I can't understand people wanting to do that.'

'Yes, but they don't do it all day,' I said.

'I know, but I still wouldn't want to do it. Are we going inside soon, Sir?'

As we moved away, some of the children spotted a stand where they could buy postcards. There was a general rush towards it, and Susan Brennan dropped her pocket money all over the pavement. Dorothy waited while she and her friends picked it up.

'Can I go and buy some postcards, Miss?' she asked. 'I won't be a minute.'

'Wait until later,' Dorothy said, 'Just buy a guidebook now if you want to, but don't spend all your money. We've only just got here.' After a few minutes and another count the children walked towards Traitor's Gate and the tower which had held Raleigh prisoner. Rouse crammed his money back into his pocket and hurried to catch up with the others.

'I was gonna get a postcard and send it to me Nan,' he said. 'I don't 'spect she'd get it before I got back 'ome, though.'

'Course she wouldn't,' laughed Dudmish.

'I wasn't askin' you,' Rouse retorted. 'When I need your 'elp, I'll ask for it.'

'Can we see the Crown Jewels, Sir?' asked Julie, pulling at my sleeve.

'Cor, yeah!' agreed Rouse enthusiastically. 'I ain't never seen them before!'

'After lunch, probably,' I replied. 'We'll certainly see them before we go. I think we're going to have a look at the White Tower and St John's Chapel first.'

'Let's 'ave dinner now, then,' suggested Badger.

'Yeah,' Adams agreed, taking his satchel from his shoulder. 'Save luggin' this lot about any longer.'

'We're not eating yet. We'll all eat together later on.'

'But Rousey ate two oranges and an apple pie on the train,' Adams protested. I pretended not to hear this and pushed him forward to join the others, who were sketching Traitor's Gate in their books.

'Wasn't St John's Chapel built by the Normans, Sir?' asked Dudmish. 'We ought to go and look at that first because we did all about the Middle Ages.'

'I wouldn't 'ave minded bein' a Norman if I could live 'ere,' said Badger, hanging over the wall and staring at Traitor's Gate. 'Fancy bein' able to live 'ere. The Normans built that White Tower, too, Sir. It says so in that book what Darren brought.'

Some yards away from them, another school party, dressed smartly in neat grey uniforms, were listening to an elderly Beefeater in full costume who had climbed on a box to make sure his voice could be heard clearly. Feeling that her children should take advantage of his knowledge, Dorothy moved the class closer to the other party, motioning them to stand quietly and listen to what was being said. The Beefeater's deep, strong voice, honed to perfection over years of explaining the rich history of the Tower to a million tourists, rang out strongly over the children's heads.

'Up there you can see the White Tower,' he shouted. 'That was built after the invasion of King William's men. I hope I don't have to tell you when that was...'

Rouse and Adams assured him he didn't by shouting the answer out together.

'Well done, those lads,' said the Beefeater. 'Good to see you know your history.'

'That was an easy question!' Badger shouted back. Several children from the other school party turned to see who had joined them, but the Beefeater obviously enjoyed a bit of banter with his customers.

'Of course it was an easy question!' he called. 'I don't start with the hard ones. They come later. Now then, the Tower is London's most historic building. Lots of kings have added bits to it through the centuries, depending on what they wanted to use it for. Up until the time of Charles the Second, it was a royal palace.'

'We 'aven't done about 'im,' shouted Rouse. 'We're doin' the Middle Ages.'

'That doesn't matter, sonny,' said the Beefeater. 'You'll be doing about Charles the Second one day, so I'm telling you a bit about him now, ready for when you do learn about him.'

Rouse, considering this was fair enough, nodded gravely and wrote something in his notebook. The Beefeater cleared his throat, and turned to his young audience again. 'Now then, while you're here, you'll see all sorts of things, like the arms collection inside the White Tower.'

"Oo's arms are they?' shouted Badger, puzzled.

'Arms that have been used by soldiers and all sorts of people,' the Beefeater answered.

'You mean arms what've bin cut off in battle?'

Several children from the other school giggled, and the Beefeater blew into an enormous handkerchief before replying.

'No sonny, I don't mean those sorts of arms,' he said. 'I mean armour. Swords, guns, daggers, pistols, you'll see all those sorts of things inside the White Tower. And the torture instruments of course. You make sure you behave yourself in there, or we'll rent a few out to your teachers.'

The children turned to Dorothy, who smiled at the remark.

'Now then,' the Beefeater went on, 'there's a moat... Oi, are you listening to me, sonny?'

Badger had started to nibble the edge of a sandwich after offering one to a girl from the other party, and he froze on the spot.

'Leave your sandwiches alone and pay attention!' roared the Beefeater good-humouredly. 'If you don't, you won't learn anything. Now then, there's a moat running round the Tower, but there's no water in it now, of course. Who knows what a moat is?' A score of hands shot into the air immediately, and he chose a child near to him.

'Well done, lass,' he said when she'd finished answering. 'What a clever lot of children we've got this morning. Now, I'll tell you a few things about the Tower of London that you might not know. First of all, the Tower was never actually needed to defend the city of London. Surprising, that, isn't it? No, instead it's been put to lots of other uses. The Royal Mint was here at one time...'

'What's the Royal Mint?' Adams shouted.

'It's where they make the money, sonny. It's made near here now, but at one time the coins of the realm were actually minted here.'

'I wouldn't mind 'avin' a look at that,' Badger said, with interest.

'Here's another thing you probably don't know,' said the Beefeater. Eight hundred years ago, King Henry the Second kept his pet elephant here. I expect some of you know about Henry the Second. Who knows someone famous who died because of a serious disagreement with King Henry?'

'Ann Boleyn,' shouted Adams.

'No sonny, try again. That was Henry the Eighth.'

'No it wasn't. It says 'ere in this book.. Oh no, you're right, mister.'

'Well I'm relieved to hear that. Anybody else know?'

'Thomas Becket,' called a child from the other school.

'That's right, my dear, Thomas Becket. Anyway, King Henry kept his elephant here. I bet some of you little 'uns didn't know that!'

There was a pause while this piece of information was hastily committed to paper and then the Beefeater pointed over to his right. 'Over there is the Bloody Tower. And don't you look round at your teacher because you think I'm swearing. I'm not. It's called the Bloody Tower because Edward the Fifth and his brother were murdered, and their bones lay here under a stairway for two hundred years. They lay in the White Tower, that is, but they were murdered here. Anyone know where they are buried now?'

'Is it Westminster Abbey?' shouted Dudmish.

'That's it. There's a clever lad at the back there! The boys' bones have been laid to rest in Westminster Abbey. Now then, I expect the one thing you're all waiting to see today is the Crown Jewels. Well, they used to be in the Wakefield Tower at one time, but it was such a squash trying to get everybody in there we've moved 'em to a special vault underground. Only one person has ever tried to steal the Crown Jewels. His name was Captain Blood, and they executed him for trying. I don't want any of you nippers trying to steal 'em either, or I'll have your heads on Traitor's Gate.'

Fred gulped nervously, and moved a little closer to me. 'Do you mind if I 'old yer 'and, Sir?' he asked softly. 'Last time I came 'ere I got lost, and me dad gave me up for dead.'

'Right, everybody follow me!' bellowed the Beefeater. 'And don't dawdle on the way, or the sentry'll shoot you!'

He climbed down from his box, tucked it under his arm, and walked slowly up the hill leading to Tower Green and the execution square. Both school parties followed him at a slight distance.

'Sir,' said Badger, 'My dad said that if the ravens ever...'

'What's a raven?' Fred interrupted.

'Like you,' said Susan Davis. 'A raven lunatic!'

'Do you mind, Davis, I'm talkin',' said Badger angrily. "E said that if the ravens ever leave the Tower of London it'll fall down. But that's daft, ain't it? 'Ow could it all fall down, just 'cos a few birds have flown away?'

'It's a superstition,' said Julie. 'It wouldn't really fall down. Anyway, the birds can't fly away, 'cos they've all had their wings clipped.'

The children crowded round the execution site and the Beefeater climbed back on his box.

'Now then children,' he called, 'you'll like this bit. A lot of people had their heads cut off up here. You can see their names written on this plaque over here. Ann Boleyn, Catherine Howard, Lady Jane Grey, all of them were beheaded here. Ann Boleyn was the only one who didn't have her head cut off with an axe. She was beheaded with a sword.'

Rouse sniffed. 'Don't suppose it made a lot of difference to 'er,' he said.

Every child gazed at the site in morbid fascination, and Dudmish quickly made a list of the people who had lost their heads.

'Ain't it 'orrible!' Susan Davis exclaimed. 'It's 'ard to believe really, ain't it Sir? They was really cruel in them days.'

'They ought to do it these days,' Badger suggested grimly. 'I wouldn't mind comin' up 'ere on Saturday mornin's to watch a few.'

'You would,' said Susan Brennan in disgust. 'You're just bloodthirsty, that's all. You'd watch anything, you would.'

'Well I still reckon it's a good idea,' Badger declared, determined to have the last word.

The Beefeater led the way into the chapel and showed the children into the pews. Then he walked to the front, waited until everybody had completely settled, and spoke again in a much quieter voice. 'Lots of bodies were discovered in here, under the stones, he said in a hushed voice. 'Not many of them could be identified, but Ann Boleyn's could, and I'll tell you why. Hold up one of your hands.' The children, fascinated, did as they were told.

'Now count your fingers. Not your thumb, mind. Just your fingers. Whisper to me how many you've got.'

'Four,' both parties said softly.

'Absolutely right. We've got some good counters here this morning, haven't we teachers? Well now, Ann Boleyn didn't have four fingers, she had five. Five on one of her hands. So of course, when they found a skeleton with five fingers in here, they knew it was her. Fancy that.'

As he spoke, many of the children glanced at their own hands, as if half expecting an extra finger to be there. Although the Beefeater had given this talk many hundreds of times, I was fascinated by the way he held the children's attention, knowing just how long to pause so that a note or two could be jotted down to jog the memory later. I wondered if I would still be able to perform like that in the classroom in twenty years time. After giving a little more information about the chapel, the Beefeater stepped down from the front pew.

'Now this is as far as I take you,' he said, 'and I think you children have listened very well. It would take hours if I came all the way round with you and talked about it all, but I hope you'll find the other parts of the Tower just as interesting as I do. Don't forget what I've told you, now. If you have any questions as you go round, the other Beefeaters will help you with the answers if your teachers can't. Has anyone got a question they want to ask me now?'

Rouse raised his hand.

'Oh God. Keep your fingers crossed,' Dorothy murmured.

'Well, young man?'

'Please, 'ow d'yer become a Beefeater?'

'You want to become one, do you?'

'I dunno yet. It depends on what you 'ave to do.'

'Well, it's not as easy as you might think. First, you have to be very good at knowing your history. Are you good at history, sonny?'

'Not very,' Rouse admitted. 'I'm int'rested in it, though.'

'Well that's a start. Now I bet you didn't know our proper names are Yeomen Wardens of the Tower...'

He patiently explained to Rouse how to become a Yeoman, and most of the boys jotted details of the procedure down in their books. When he'd finished, he led both parties back out into the bright Spring sunshine.

'So, what did you think of it?' Dorothy asked me as soon as we were outside.

'Very good indeed. I think they'll probably remember quite a lot, don't you?'

'I hope so. They'll certainly remember the gorier bits, anyway!'

'Miss, d'you think me Mum'd miss me if I left 'ome to train as one of them Beefeaters?' asked Badger.

'I think she'd probably be relieved, dear,' Dorothy replied.

'Fancy 'avin another finger on your 'and,' said Susan Davis, with a shiver. 'I liked it when 'e told us about that. Nobody would want to marry you if you 'ad six fingers, would they?'

'Nobody 'ud marry you anyway,' Rouse said cheerfully.

'Huh! Well, if it was someone like you, I wouldn't be too worried, mate. I'd rather stay single, wouldn't we, Sue?'

The attendant at the door of the White Tower looked a little apprehensive for a moment. His sad grey eyes suggested a history of school children wandering uncontrolled through the premises he looked after. 'You will keep 'em under control, Madam?' he said nervously to Dorothy as she gathered the children in a group around her. 'Do tell 'em not to touch anything, won't you?'

Dorothy gave him a reassuring smile, and then carefully defined the limits of exploration to the children. They moved quickly round the room, peering for a few seconds into each display case and then moving on, determined to see everything first and then return afterwards to the things which had interested them most.

'Come and look at this armour, Sir,' urged Dudmish, tugging at my sleeve. I followed him to the glass case and the boy looked down in wonder at the intricate decoration on the swords and knives.

'The armour must have been very heavy, mustn't it,' he said, moving to another case at the side of the room. 'If they wore all that and carried swords as well, it must have been really heavy. They must have got really tired in battle. Look, there's a suit of armour for a boy! I wouldn't mind trying that on!'

He made a sketch of the armour and called to some of his friends to have a look. Badger and Rouse joined him, and spoke excitedly.

'It's great, ain't it, Sir! I reckon it's really int'restin'. I wish we was livin' in the Middle Ages, don't you, Miss? We could wear all this stuff, then.'

'I think you'd soon find a lot of things you didn't like about the Middle Ages,' said Dorothy. 'You wouldn't have a television, for a start.'

'Yeah, but you could 'ave a lot o' fun wearing this stuff. I suppose the bloke wouldn't let us...'

'Definitely not, John!' she interrupted firmly. 'And don't you dare ask!'

'Miss, Miss, look. I've made some notes,' cried Fred proudly, tugging at Dorothy's sleeve. 'Read 'em, Miss.'

Dorothy looked at his page and smiled. 'You'll need a few more than that, Fred. You've only written *PLEASE DO NOT TOUCH*.'

'I know Miss. It's a start though, ain't it? And it keeps me mind off goin' to the toilet.'

For the next fifteen minutes, the class stood or sat contentedly writing and drawing. The attendant hovered uncertainly, but he seemed relieved to be in the company of a class that actually took some notice of its teachers. He paused beside Rouse, who was on his knees making a drawing with his book laid flat on the floor.

'I should move your book if I were you, lad,' he warned, 'you're a bit in the way there.'

'Sorry Mister,' Rouse apologised, moving his book to the glass showcase near him.

'That won't do either, son,' said the attendant. He pointed to the notice saying that the glass must not be leant upon.

'Blimey, in school they spend all their time gettin' me to do some work, and now when I want to do some they won't let me,' he muttered darkly, moving his book to the seat of a nearby chair. Though the chair was an antique, the attendant decided to risk Rouse leaning on it. When the information gathering showed signs of losing momentum, Dorothy sent two children to collect the others together, and then everybody climbed the steep stone stairs to the second arms room.

'Be very careful not to trip,' she warned them. 'One of the stairs is wider than the others. It was very useful for making an enemy trip over when a guard was defending the Tower, but I don't really want any broken legs today, thank you.'

'Why do the stairs always go round to the right, Miss?' asked a child behind her, examining them in semi-darkness.

‘Because the sword would always be held in the right hand, and it made going up the steps much easier if you were fighting on them,’ Dorothy explained.

Rouse and Badger immediately tested this theory, pretending to duel with each other and parrying savage thrusts. I expected to hear the attendant’s voice at any moment.

‘Cor, you’re right, Miss,’ said Rouse, as Badger missed his step on the wide stair, fell backwards onto his carrier bag, and gave a cry of dismay.

‘What’s the matter?’ called Dorothy urgently. ‘Have you hurt yourself?’

“E’s all right, Miss,’ called Adams reassuringly. “E’s fallen on ‘is bread puddin’ and squashed it, that’s all.’

‘Lucky ‘e fell back like that,’ Badger observed. ‘I reckon ‘e could ‘ave gone right to the bottom. Saved by a bread puddin.’

‘I wouldn’t mind ‘avin’ a go with real swords,’ said Badger, scooping up his flattened pudding. He picked the larger pieces of dirt off it and packed it carefully back into its foil wrapping. ‘I don’t s’pose they’d let you borrow ‘em, though.’

Disappointed at the thought, but content at salvaging his mother’s culinary speciality, he settled for a long gaze at the axe used on Tower Hill. Then he shifted his attention to the torture instruments. ‘What’s that one, that thumb screw thing,’ he asked whoever happened to be nearest.

‘It’s what it says,’ Dudmish told him. ‘The prisoner’s hand was put into it and that screw was tightened until he talked.’

Adams considered this piece of information carefully. ‘I reckon that’s a bit of a waste of time,’ he said. ‘I’d get the prisoners on the rack straight away. Save muckin’ about with one o’ them things.’

I was prevented from discussing the finer points of medieval torture by the attendant, who tapped me on the shoulder and pointed out that one of my children was walking round the room with a dripping bag. It belonged to Fred, who’d bought a frozen drink before coming into the room and stuffed it into his bag. The warmth of the room had rapidly melted the drink, leaving a trail of orange juice all over the floor, unnoticed by Fred. Dorothy apologised to the attendant and turned to me. 'We'll give them another five minutes,' she said, wiping up the trail of juice with paper handkerchiefs. 'Then we'll go down and have lunch on the embankment, in the fresh air.'

'Did you say we were goin' to have our food, Miss?' asked Julie, taking her pack from her shoulder and putting it on the floor. 'Look, I've written lots of things and it must be dinner time by now.'

'In another five minutes,' said Dorothy. 'Tell the others we're going as soon as they've finished what they're doing.'

Julie ran off to round up the children, and they rapidly gathered by the door, eager to eat their packed lunches. 'Cor, my tummy's rumblin',' said Rouse, rubbing his chest and grinning. 'If we don't eat soon we might as well wait until we get 'ome for our tea.'

'Let's go and have lunch down by the cannons,' Dorothy suggested. 'They won't bother anybody there, and we should be able to get a cup of tea at the kiosk.'

The grounds were rapidly filling up with visitors and several parties of tourists, and Dorothy kept the children in lines so that they could move quickly down to the river.

'If we're lucky, we might see Tower Bridge open,' she said, picking up a dropped sandwich wrapper and throwing it in the nearest waste basket. 'It cost more than a million pounds to build, and they ring a bell when they're going to open it. Keep your eyes open. And don't drop pieces of paper all over the place.'

'Can I go to the toilet now please Miss?' called Fred, looking extremely uncomfortable.

'Good Lord,' she exclaimed, 'I'd forgotten about you. Do you know where it is?'

'Yes Miss, but I don't really like to go on me own 'cos the last time...'

'You got lost. I know. Well, I'm sure Mr Kent will go with you. If anyone else wants to go, you'd better go now, before you have your lunch.'

'I'll get some coffees on the way back.'

'Great idea. I'll sit here and watch this lot pig it!'

'It's really nice 'ere, ain't it, Sir?' said Fred, hurrying to keep up with me. 'I like goin' out. Me mum doesn't take me out much.'

'I like it too,' I agreed. 'It's actually a long time since I've been to the Tower of London.'

While Fred and the boys disappeared into the toilet, I bought two very full plastic cups of coffee and two ham rolls and walked back to where the class was sitting. Congratulating myself on keeping most of the steaming liquid inside the cups, I passed one to Dorothy and squeezed onto the seat.

'You didn't really need to buy those rolls, you know,' she said. 'Half the children's food will be left over when their tummies are full and they'll be offering it to us. How much do I owe you?'

'Don't worry, I'll charge it up to Mr Reed.'

'My, you are getting bold!'

Susan Davis, her mouth bulging with cheese and cucumber roll, came and perched on the edge of the seat beside Dorothy, holding out a pile of sandwiches wrapped neatly in greaseproof paper.

''Ave one of these, Miss,' she offered. 'They're pickle. I forgot I 'ad 'em. And you, Sir.'

'I've got a ham roll, my love,' Dorothy replied. 'Perhaps I'll have one of yours in a minute.'

'Okay, Miss, I'll save a couple for you. I'll save this couple. The others 'ave got a bit squashed. They must've bin at the bottom of me bag.'

After ten minutes, a growing stream of children began to offer us the remainder of their lunches. Fred held out some chocolate Swiss rolls, Adams some luncheon meat sandwiches, Julie six bags of assorted flavour crisps and a currant bun. Badger offered an orange he'd found in his bag, its skin savaged from his efforts to carve it into two parts with a rusty hack-saw blade Adams had found under a cannon. Two of the girls had eaten one sandwich each, filled up on toffees and a large bottle of fizzy lemonade, and then reluctantly agreed that their respective mothers had provided far too much food for them. Fred had wandered off and was sitting happily astride a cannon, eating a raspberry jelly from a battered paper plate.

'Told you there was no need to buy the rolls,' Dorothy smiled, as another deputation arrived with offerings of biscuits and sandwiches. 'They bring a tremendous amount of stuff and don't eat it. They offer it to us, then they ask their friends. They can't eat it either so they give it to the pigeons. I wonder the pigeons round here can get off the ground.'

I accepted a large currant bun from Rouse, who held it out on the palm of his hand as if it was a precious stone.

'That's very civil of you, John,' I thanked him, 'are you sure you don't want it?'

'Nah,' he replied. 'You can 'ave it Sir. I jus' dropped it.'

'Oh. Right. Thanks very much,' I said meekly.

There was a sudden loud shout from one of the girls that Tower Bridge was opening, startling Fred so much that he and his jelly slid sideways off the cannon. The children ran to the wall and leaned over in excited anticipation until the bridge was eventually raised and a ship eased its way through. Dudmish dashed along the embankment and found a good position to take a photograph, while three of the girls cheered and waved at the ship.

As the bridge lowered again, renewed interest was shown in what remained of the packed lunches and the children settled back down on their seats. The two Susans were sent to fetch two more cups of coffee, while Dorothy and I sat watching the children amuse themselves by running along the towpath, examining the cannons, or asking the Beefeater on the nearest gate some questions they hadn't thought of earlier. I had taken a few sips of my coffee when Badger suddenly appeared at my elbow, puffing with the exertion of running. He jerked my sleeve, slopping the coffee out of the cup and down my trouser leg. Susan Davis looked at my leg with interest and awaited further developments.

'Sir,' gasped Badger, 'there's a bloke over there…'

'For heaven's sake stand still for a moment and calm down,' said Dorothy.

'But Miss,' he urged, 'there's this bloke, Miss. 'E's got Rousey with 'im and they've gone off down the path…'

He pointed earnestly among the lunchtime crowds moving along the towpath and as I realised what Badger could be implying, I felt an icy finger of fear tense my stomach. Dorothy stood up swiftly and looked in the direction Badger was pointing.

'It's alright,' I said, more calmly than I felt, 'I'll go with him and find Rouse. You stay with the rest. I'll be back in a moment.' She nodded with concern and I followed Badger, half walking, half running ahead of me.

'Where exactly did he go?' I shouted.

'Along 'ere, Sir. I dunno where 'e is now, though. I 'ope we find 'im, Sir.'

'Of course we'll find him. Was he on his own?'

''E was at first. 'E was lookin' for things on the path. Then I saw 'im talkin' to this fat bloke, and then this bloke walked off with 'im an' some of the boys followed. Tommy, David, Paul, they was all with 'im, Sir. P'raps they've bin kidnapped.'

'What did the man look like?'

'I just told yer. A fat bloke.'

I found that I was now being accompanied by six of the boys, who didn't want to miss out on any drama that was unfolding. I felt a little like the Pied Piper, and distinctly uncomfortable as my clammy trouser leg flapped coldly around my calf.

'Sorry about spillin' yer drink, Sir,' Badger said brightly. 'I didn't see you 'ad yer tea in yer 'and, and… look, Sir, look! There 'e is.'

Near the side entrance of the Tower I saw Rouse and the other missing boys standing with a middle aged, expensively dressed couple who were arranging the boys in a group with a Beefeater beside the gate. With an intense feeling of relief, immediately followed by anger at being so panicked by Badger's story, I realised the boys were simply having their photographs taken by a tourist. Rouse confirmed this happily as he spotted me.

"Ello, Sir,' he called, waving his hand. 'This bloke comes from Texas, Sir. We're 'avin' our photos took. 'E'd do yours if you want. Come and stand over 'ere with us.' The man took his camera from his eye, and walked over to me.

'E's our teacher,' Rouse explained proudly. 'Cor, Sir, yer leg's all wet!'

The visitor shook my hand in a vice-like grip and explained that he'd asked Rouse to take a picture of his wife and himself. Then he'd offered to take one of Rouse and his friends, and Rouse had demanded that a Beefeater should be in the photo.

'I hope you didn't mind? They said it would be okay. I guess I never thought you might be worried. They're such friendly kids, though.'

'It's all right,' I said lamely, still annoyed with Rouse but relieved that all was well. 'If you just send them back when you've finished. We're sitting over there…'

'Sure, sure. Thank you.'

'And John,' I added, 'if you ever wander off like that again I'll eat all the sweets in your packed lunch. Is that clear?'

'Yes, Sir. I 'adn't gone far, though. I was just…'

'You were just nothing. You should have told us. And next time,' I warned Badger, 'Kindly tell me without making me spill my coffee. And make sure somebody really is missing first.'

Badger looked decidedly hurt.

'I only thought I 'ort to let you know,' he said in an injured voice. 'Only this kid I know, 'e was playin' in the road and this bloke come along in a car and…'

'Have you had enough to eat?' Dorothy interrupted quickly.

'Yes thank you, Miss. Anyway, this bloke says to this kid I know, if you come for a ride with me...'

'Well, it's turned out to be a lovely sunny day after all,' I said brightly. 'Fancy that. Who would have thought...'

'Aw, sshh, Sir,' Susan Davis interrupted, "E was tellin' us about this kid 'e knows.'

'I don't really think we want to know,' said Dorothy. 'I think we can do without his happy little story, thank you.'

'It ain't an 'appy story, Miss,' Badger objected indignantly.

'Nevertheless, I would suggest you go and play on the cannons for a while with Jamie.'

Turning my face into the sun, I gazed out across the river. 'Do you think you'll stick with the young ones when you start teaching?' asked Dorothy. 'Or do you think teenagers might be easier after this little lot?'

'It seems everybody asks me that,' I smiled. 'I shall definitely stay with the smaller variety.'

'That's good. There are too few men teaching Juniors and Infants. Infants especially. You've got to give a lot, especially to these children. You've really got to enjoy it, otherwise it could get you down very quickly. You'd be surprised at how many don't.'

'What, teachers, you mean?'

'Mmm. A lot turn out the same old stuff every year and actually get to dislike children. I reckon you can spend three minutes in a strange classroom and know by then whether the teacher's any good or not. The children take in everything you say, especially at this age. If they trust you, your word counts above anybody else's. Even their parents, sometimes. You don't realise how much you influence them. They reflect your manner, your attitude, even your sense of humour.'

'They seem lucky with the staff at Briar Road, though.'

'Yes, they are. We do an awful lot at the school. It compensates for some of the affection they miss out on at home. Look at little Julie.

She's really got a lot of ability with writing. Her stories are lovely, full of expression and style. Unfortunately her mum's on the game and she doesn't give Julie any time at all. I don't moralise about what people do, but the effect on their children is much greater than you'd think.'

'They seem so lively and friendly though.'

'Yes, they are. Sometimes these children fight the real world by using their humour. Rousey, for instance. He can really be very amusing at times. And they're very generous. Adams' mother keeps chickens in her little garden and often sends half a dozen wonderfully fresh eggs. And then I think of these children growing up. Some of them really haven't got much of a chance. Look at Fred, there. Not a clever boy, and that's an understatement, but marvellous with animals. Someone suggested he ought to be a vet. Honestly, what chance has he got of ever being a vet?'

'You never know. From what I've seen, you achieve far more with them than I'd have thought possible.'

'Maybe. But it's not much really. And whatever you do, it's never quite enough.' She sighed and was quiet for a moment. 'Anyway, we won't set the education system to rights in our lunch hour so we'd better get them together and move on. I see good old Fred has started to make paper aeroplanes out of his sandwich wrapper.'

She called the children into lines and checked the numbers once more. When everybody was ready, the class moved off towards the vault containing the Crown Jewels. The sun was very hot now, and coats were slung over tired arms as they walked.

'I'm really enjoyin' this, Sir,' said Adams happily, walking quickly to keep up with me. 'We had a great time on them cannons. Can we go on another visit soon?'

'Yes Sir,' agreed Dudmish, 'You and Miss could take us out again in a couple of weeks time.'

'I won't be able to do that Jamie,' I replied. 'I'm afraid I'm leaving Briar Road on Friday.'

Susan Davis turned to me in disbelief.

‘Friday? But you’ve only bin ‘ere for a few weeks, Sir. What are you goin’ for?’

‘Don’t you like us?’ asked Badger.

‘Not when you spill a cup of coffee down my leg!’

‘That was an accident, Sir. I didn’t mean to spill it. You ain’t leavin’ ‘cos of that, are yer?’

‘No, of course not. But I only came for a short while. Of course I like you. I like you all very much, and I wish I could stay.’

‘Aw Sir,’ said Susan Davis, ‘why don’t you stay, then? I’ll look after you, won’t we Sue?’

Heads nodded earnestly, and the children’s faces showed their disappointment.

‘If you can’t stay, you will come back and see us won’t you?’ asked Susan Brennan anxiously.

‘You can come any time,’ Rouse offered generously, like a wealthy hotelier offering free accommodation. ‘We’ll always be pleased to see yer. Oh look, here’s the jewel place.’

Now that I had only a handful of days left with the class, I felt saddened at the thought of leaving the children I had come to know so well and who had come to accept me as part of their daily lives. It was touching to know that they’d actually miss me after such a short period of time with them.

Dorothy stopped the children outside the Jewel House, reminded them once more about behaving properly once they were inside, and then lined them up along the entrance lanes. Eventually, an attendant started to move the group inside.

‘Keep ‘em under strict supervision, please gov’nor’, he said to me, patting Rouse on the head and pointing the way down to the Jewels.

The children perspired in the heat of the room, but any discomfort they felt was put aside as they gazed in wonder at the beauty of the crowns. The attendant asked the other visitors if they would mind moving back a little so that the children could stand next to the glass and have a better view.

'Are they real, Sir,' asked Rouse in a soft, awed voice.

'Of course they are,' said the attendant.

'Cor, they're lovely, ain't they?' He pressed his face to the glass, steaming it up slightly.

'See if you can identify the crowns from the postcard you bought,' Dorothy suggested.

'Come and have a look round here, Miss', called Dudmish, lowering his voice as he caught the attendant's eyes. 'Look at some of these golden plates.'

'You know, Sir,' said Badger, poking his head up under my elbow, 'you'd only 'ave to cut through a couple of layers of glass to get at the crown jewels. Don't seem much protection, does it?'

'Well, if you're going to try, I should keep your voice down so that the attendant doesn't hear you.'

'No, don't be daft, Sir. I wasn't goin' to try. But I reckon you could get at 'em quite easily really. 'Cept for those things,' He gazed at the enormous steel doors that guarded the entrance to the Jewel House. "Ow much are they worth?' he asked suddenly.

'They're priceless.'

'Yeah, but 'ow much are they worth?'

'You can't put a price on them like that.'

'Well they must be worth somethin' . I mean, are they worth 'undreds, or millions, or what?'

'I saw this film once,' said Adams in a loud voice. 'What they did was, this bloke in a gang knocked out this Beefeater what looked just like 'im, and then 'e took 'is place. The gang got the other bloke to nick the jewels and put these others that wasn't real in the case instead. Then this bloke flings the real jewels over the wall at the dead of night and...'

'Yeah,' said Fred, enthusiastically, 'I saw that on the telly.'

'No you never,' Adams retorted. 'It ain't bin on the telly.'

'Well I saw it anyway,' Fred said, not to be outdone.

'I think they've all seen 'em now, guv'nor,' said the attendant firmly, ignoring Badger who was feeling the steel doors. 'I should move 'em upstairs again now.'

'Thanks very much, Mister,' said Rouse gratefully.

'That's all right, son. Enjoyed it, have you?'

'Yeah, smashin'.'

The children were very tired, but reluctant to leave the Tower altogether. Once they were outside in the fresh air, Dorothy suggested it might be best to go now to avoid the crowds on the train.

'But we ain't seen the Bloody Tower yet,' Fred protested.

'Yes, Miss,' Susan Brennan agreed. 'Let's go and see the Bloody Tower.'

'What time will we be getting home, Miss?' asked Julie anxiously. 'I've got to bring fish and chips in with me on the way 'ome, that's all. Me mum'll kill me if I forget.'

'Don't worry. You'll be home in time to do that.'

'Yeah, I'm gettin' quite 'ungry again,' agreed Rouse. 'Can I finish off me sandwiches, Miss?'

'Not if you want to see the Bloody Tower, you can't.'

Because the Bloody Tower was small, the children were forced to huddle together inside. Their interest in this part of the building was not as easily sustained, and Badger stated that he couldn't really see what everybody found so fascinating about 'a couple of old chairs an' a bed.'

'Besides,' he added, 'Me mum's ain't that much different. They could stick 'ers in 'ere; and it 'ud be just as int'restin'.'

'Come on then,' said Dorothy. 'Let's go outside and I'll buy you all an ice cream.'

After making sure every child had one, we led the class slowly back to the station. The children were tired but contented, clutching crumpled notebooks, the remains of tattered carrier bags, and souvenirs of the visit hastily stuffed into coat pockets.

The train was hot and stuffy, and the class had to split between two compartments. They flopped wearily onto the seats, proudly waving their postcards for the benefit of passengers and leaving nobody in doubt about where they'd spent the day. I sat down beside Susan Davis and gazed round the carriage in contentment, until I noticed Badger offering some bread pudding to a priest sitting opposite. I turned to study the blackness of the train tunnel until the moment had passed.

'Well, have you enjoyed the visit?' I asked Susan, who sat strangely still on her seat, not speaking to anybody.

'Yes, Sir,' she said limply. 'Sir…'

'Yes Susan?'

'I feel sick, Sir.'

My mind froze. The train was crowded, and my first reaction was to thrust her towards Dorothy. She'd know how to cope with this sort of situation. After all, I was only a student on teaching practice. Then I realised that Dorothy was in the next carriage.

'Can you wait?' I gulped.

'No Sir,' she groaned.

'I see.' I surprised myself at how calm I sounded.

The train lurched into the station and Susan's face turned the colour of chalk. Clearly, a decision had to be made in seconds.

'Tell Mrs Bridgewood I'll explain when we get back,' I shouted at Fred.

'Eh?' Fred replied, gazing at me as if I had gone completely insane. I partly shoved, partly carried Susan through the doors and rushed her to the nearest firebucket. By the time she had recovered enough to speak, the train had sped off into the tunnel and we sat down on a wooden bench to wait for the next one.

'You're a fine one,' I said sympathetically. 'I told you not to bring so much food, didn't I? What have you eaten?'

For one dreadful moment, I thought she was going to check with the firebucket, but she leaned back on the seat and grinned weakly while the colour gradually drained back into her face. 'Nothin' much really, Sir. I only 'ad two bottles of lemonade, a bar of chocolate, me pickle sandwiches, a roll, some 'am, the ice cream wot Miss brought us and a cream slice and…'

She paused and thought carefully for a moment.

'You know what, though,' she said, like a judge summing up the evidence. 'I reckon it must've bin the two pork pies what done it.'

(iii)

It was my last day at Briar Road Primary.

The teaching practice had passed quickly and enjoyably and I was becoming very used to the routine of a school week. Since the class had visited the Tower of London, we'd filled a wall with writing, art work and models about it. Each day, the children had taken pieces of work home to finish and their extraordinary enthusiasm had impressed me enormously.

After showing their parents the postcards and booklets they had bought, the children had surrendered the pictures of the Crown Jewels, so that they could be incorporated into the display. Rouse and his friends had been to the local supermarket early in the morning, salvaging some large cardboard boxes to build a model of the White Tower. Susan Brennan and Susan Davis had painted a huge Beefeater each, one to put each side of the display, and Fred had made three crowns from pieces of cardboard and scraps of felt taken from the bag Julie's mother had sent in. Adams and Badger had spent a day making a Tudor newspaper, filled with dark deeds and doubtful goings on that merited suitable punishments, which they described in authentic detail.

Mr Reed had hardly bothered me at all, although he'd found an excuse to come into the classroom after finding Rouse sneaking out of a stock cupboard carrying two large jars of paste. Although Rouse had explained that he'd done a great deal of work which would therefore need a great deal of paste, Mr Reed had informed him testily that two jars constituted an entire year's paste allowance for one class.

'Well, it all looks pretty impressive,' said Dorothy, climbing down from a pair of steps and standing back to admire the work as the children filed out for lunch. 'They've really enjoyed doing this. Do you want to take any of this back to college?'

'I don't think so,' I replied. 'It's for the children's benefit after all. I think I'd rather leave it all here.'

'I agree. I know some colleges like their students to bring work back, though. I suppose it gives the lecturers something to talk about in education lectures. Mind you, Miss Bottle will probably find plenty to talk about anyway. Can't you persuade her to pop back and see this display?'

'She'd probably like to, but she's one of the few who's usually genuinely busy,'

'Well, it's nice that she was so satisfied, anyway. And Mr Reed certainly is. I think you've changed his opinion about students from St James's not being much good. It'll seem funny when I have the class to myself again on Monday. I've got quite used to putting my feet up in the staffroom. What do you want to do this afternoon?'

'I hadn't really thought about it, but I'd like to have them as it's my last afternoon. It'll probably be a bit quiet now all this is finished.'

After lunch, I went back to the classroom to mark some work and collect all the things I'd borrowed from various departments at the college. The classroom floor was littered with scraps of paper, cloth and discarded odds and ends from the morning's activities, and I quietly swept it all into a corner, absorbing the atmosphere of the classroom and wishing I could stay longer. I was still tidying up when the bell rang and the children came in, looking hot and tired.

'Cor, you've swept up in 'ere, Sir,' said Rouse gratefully. 'Miss usually gets us to do all the tidyin' up.'

'Well, I thought I'd do that for you because you've worked so hard for me this morning,' I replied.

'Cor, ain't you nice, Sir,' said Susan Brennan.

'What are we goin' to do?' asked Rouse, sprawling over his desk top.

'Why don't you stay, Sir?' said Dudmish softly. 'You could help Miss. She could have us in the mornings and you could teach us in the afternoons.'

'Yeah,' agreed Adams. 'It'd take a lot off 'er plate.'

'Sir, could we do some drama?' asked Julie. 'I like writin' plays.'

'Nah!' Rouse objected. 'I don't like doin' plays. Your plays are always rotten anyway.'

'No they ain't.'

'They jus' go on and on. I don't feel like doin' plays, anyway.'

'What do you want to do then?'

'I dunno. So long as it ain't plays. Let Sir choose somethin'.'

'Yeah,' Adams agreed, sucking the end of his pencil and then seeing how far he could push it into Badger's ribs. 'You choose, Sir. If we do plays she'd be the princess and one of us 'ud 'ave ter be the 'andsome prince and it'ud be the same old stuff as usual.'

'You ain't no 'andsome prince, mate,' Susan Davis remarked.

'I never said I was. Come to that, if I was an 'andsome prince I wouldn't marry you.'

'I wouldn't ask yer, mate, don't you worry.

Badger waved his hand in the air.

'I know, Sir,' he said, taking a thick comic out of his desk and running a grubby thumb through its pages. 'There's a quiz in this comic. Tells you 'ow to become a secret agent. There's a load of questions. Why don't yer read 'em out to us, Sir?'

'It's hardly what I'm supposed to be doing. 'I was going to...'

'It don't matter. We've worked really 'ard this week and it's your last day, ain't it? Read it out to us.'

Heads nodded in agreement and I took the book. The quiz involved choosing answers to questions describing deadly situations a secret agent might be faced with. It sounded fun, and I found it very tempting.

'All right, then. Take your rough work books out and we'll see who is likely to be the best spy in the class. I'll read out each question, and you write down what you think is the best answer.'

''Ow d'yer mean?' asked Fred.

'Trust you not to understand it,' said Adams. 'We ain't even started yet, and already you don't know what we're supposed to be doin.'

Badger turned round in his seat, leant his arm across Fred's chair, and spoke to him in the gentle manner of a psychiatrist pacifying a client.

'Look,' he said patiently, 'Sir reads out a question. Then there's three answers to each question. What you 'ave to do is put down wot you think is the best answer. Right?'

'Yeah, but 'e didn't say that, did 'e? 'E said write down the answers. 'E didn't say there was three answers, did 'e?'

'Well, you never give 'im much of a chance, did yer?'

'How many questions will you be giving us to this quiz?' asked Hema politely.

'It looks as if there are ten,' I replied. 'Yes, ten.'

'Cor. I don't think I'll 'ave enough room for ten,' said Rouse. 'Ave you got a spare bit o' paper, Sir? Me book's full.' Fred climbed out of his seat to go in search of a pencil, and Rouse neatly removed a page from the back of Fred's book while he wasn't looking.

'It's alright, Sir,' called Rouse, 'Fred's lent me a piece.'

I read out the first question.

'Right, imagine you are a secret agent and your enemy was on the top of a tall building...'

'Cor!' Rouse exclaimed.

'Your enemy falls from the top after attempting to shoot you. Would you try to catch him, shoot him as he falls, or just let him drop?' They took this very seriously for a few moments and scribbled down an answer on their pieces of paper. Rouse sat chewing the end of his pencil in deliberation, and then wrote something down.

'Right, I've done that one,' he announced. 'What's number two?'

'If 'e's an enemy spy 'e's prob'ly got the plans in 'is pocket,' said Adams eagerly. 'You'd 'ave to catch 'im to get the plans.'

'You could get 'em off 'im when 'e' 'its the ground,' retorted Rouse.

'Alright,' Adams argued, determined not to be outdone, 'suppose 'e's only got the plans in 'is 'ead, then. 'E couldn't tell yer much if 'e was lyin' on the ground with 'is 'ed smashed in, could 'e? You'd 'ave to keep 'im alive then, wouldn't yer!"

This seemed to make good sense to Rouse, and he considered it silently for a moment.

'Well,' I resumed, 'If you wrote the first answer you get no marks. If you put the second answer you get two, and if you put the last one, you get three.'

'Aw,' Susan Davis complained, 'I don't think that's fair. 'Ow come...'

'Oh don't keep arguing about it,' said Dudmish. 'It's not supposed to be serious.'

'Ow do you know?"

'Oh don't be daft. How could you possibly catch him, anyway?"

'I ain't written any of 'em,' said Fred brightly. 'Ow many points do I get, Sir?'

'None, I'm afraid. Let's try the next one. Right, number two. If you were about to be discovered by the enemy, would you take a suicide pill, try and capture one of them, or try to camouflage yourself so that you wouldn't be seen...'

'What's camraflage?' asked Fred.

'It's camouflage,' said Julie. 'Like when an animal hides in its surroundings.'

'Oh. What's suicide?'

'When you decide to kill yourself,' Adams explained. 'Why don't you have a go?"

'People do it when they can't take no more,' announced Badger, with obvious relish. 'My Nan said she knew this bloke once 'oo...'

'Ow d'yer spell suicide?' asked Fred.

'Sir told you. Spelling doesn't matter,' Susan Brennan replied.

'I wouldn't want to kill meself,' said Rouse thoughtfully. 'I wouldn't fancy doin' that at all.'

'I reckon the best way is to stick yer 'ead in the gas oven,' said Adams confidently. 'I reckon if I was goin' to do it, that's what I'd do. I reckon...'

'Most of 'em chuck 'emselves off bridges and such, don't they Sir?' Badger interrupted, setting himself up as an authority on the subject.

'Are we going to finish this quiz or not?' I asked.

'Okay Sir,' said Badger, 'I was jus' wonderin', that's all. My Nan said she knew this bloke once wot wanted to do 'imself in, and 'e...'

'I know. You've mentioned that already. Tell me at playtime.'

'Okay, Sir.'

'Question three. You are a famous spy, and you've been caught by an enemy agent. She is a very attractive lady and she says she will give you a big kiss if you hand over the secret plans. Would you hand them over straight away, point your gun at her, or try to run for it.'

'Blimey, I'd run for it,' said Adams. 'Before she gets a chance to kiss me.'

'That's charmin', ain't it?' said Susan Davis.

'I reckon in that situation, I'd point the gun at meself,' Badger decided. 'I reckon I...'

His voice trailed away as the door opened and Mr Reed strode into the classroom. He stood very still for a moment, as if trying to work out where he was, and then he pointed at the class register.

'Ah, Mr Kent,' he said, 'I'd like to borrow the register for a short while. I must say this classroom looks most attractive, Mr Kent. Most attractive. I hope they've learned something from all this?'

'Yes, Sir,' said Susan Davis politely.

'We've learned a lot,' added Susan Brennan. 'Would you like to ask us some questions about it?'

'No thank you. I don't have time. And what are you doing now?'

'Sir's givin' us a quiz,' Badger said. 'And I was tellin' 'im about a man my Nan knows."

'And that was to do with the quiz, was it?'

'No Sir."

'What was it to do with, then?'

'He killed 'imself Sir.'

'Really.'

'Yes, Sir.'

'I see. I shouldn't have thought Mr Kent was particularly interested in that.' Mr Reed turned to me and raised his eyebrows in question.

'It's just a quiz that was in one of their... um... books,' I said, feeling a clenching in my stomach.

'Rather a strange sort of quiz if it deals with suicides, isn't it Mr Kent?

'Sir's tellin' us how to become a secret agent,' said Adams, hoping an explanation might help me. Mr Reed stared at me in disbelief.

'A secret agent? Didn't we have all this kind of nonsense the day you arrived, Mr Kent? I seem to recall something about you being a secret agent on that occasion? I assume you *are* a teaching student from St James's, and not a reject from MI5?'

'It's a good quiz, Sir,' offered Rouse, rather lamely.

'Yes, I'm sure it is.'

He turned to me and lowered his voice so that the class wouldn't hear what he was saying, but this merely caused Rouse and Badger to move their chairs a few feet closer to us.

'It seems to me, Mr Kent, that you might find something rather more suitable to be doing with these children. I realise it is somewhat old fashioned to refer to a timetable, but if I am not mistaken, I think you should be doing PE at this particular time. On a sunny afternoon like this, I think the class might be better employed doing games in the playground than wasting time on an infantile quiz.'

Mr Reed took a step towards the door and then laid the register down on a desk for a moment, walking with measured steps to the back of the classroom.

'I hope you all behaved yourselves properly at the Tower of London?' he said.

'Miss said we was very good,' said Badger cautiously.

'Mrs Bridgewood said you *were* very good,' Mr Reed replied.

'Did she tell you as well then, Sir?' asked Badger, puzzled.

The children were uneasy. They wanted to please, but they felt the almost tangible coldness emanating from Mr Reed. Though he'd only been in the room for a few minutes, the atmosphere had lost its warmth.

'Get the children changed and take them outside, Mr Kent. It will do them good. And I'd like to see you for a few minutes before you leave today.'

He walked slowly to the door, inspected a cracked pane of glass, and rubbed the dust from his fingers. The door closed and I turned, embarrassed, to the children.

'I thought you was going to get the cane there for a moment, Sir,' smiled Rouse wryly.

'I don't like 'im much, said Julie, pulling her cardigan over her head. I pretended not to hear her.

'Look at these muscles, Sir,' called Rouse, pulling off his shirt, thrusting out his chest and pumping his arm up and down. 'Good, ain't they. I'm tough, Sir!'

'You ain't tough mate, you just smell strong,' Susan Davis retorted scornfully. Rouse took a very deep breath and proudly ran his fingers round his rib cage. Susan Davis looked at him in disgust.

'You need a few 'ot dinners Rousey,' she said. 'You look as if you'd fall to bits if someone blew on yer. If I was your mother I'd be dead worried about you.'

'Good job you ain't me mother, then,' Rouse replied cheerfully,

When the class was finally ready, I asked Badger to fetch a bat, some pieces of chalk and a rounders stump, and then I led the children down the narrow stairs in a line, taking care not to make any noise as we passed Mr Reed's office.

'What're we playin'?' asked Fred.

'It's a new game. You probably don't know it. I think you'll like it.'

'You ever bin in the army, Sir?' asked Rouse suddenly.

'No,' I replied cautiously. 'Why?'

'I dunno. You jus' look like you've bin in the army. I might go in the army when I'm eighteen.'

'I'm fond of fishin', meself,' said Adams, eager to join in the conversation and deciding this would make a good opener. 'I go on Sundays with me dad and 'is mate. I've got a garden, Sir. Only a little one. We keep chickens in our garden. Do you keep chickens, Sir?'

I smiled at the thought of telling Milly not to clean the bath out because the hens were laying eggs in there.

'It's cruel ain't it, Sir, keepin' chickens in them batt'ries. My mum says our eggs taste much better any day. I'll bring you a few on Monday, shall I?'

'I'd have liked that very much,' I said. 'but I won't be here on Monday, will I?'

His face clouded over. 'Oh no, I forgot you was leavin'. Give Miss your address and I'll send along a few for yer mum to cook. You 'ave got a mum, ain't yer Sir?'

I assured him that I had.

'You ain't married, are yer?' he asked, in horrified concern.

'Not yet,' I laughed. 'Why?'

'Seems a waste of time ter me, that's all. Having babies an' all that. That's why me dad likes 'is drop of fishin'. Anyway, 'e never invites me mum along.'

'That's a shame. She'd probably enjoy it.'

'Well someone has to cook the dinner, don't they.'

'Your dad could do that. Your mum could go fishing for a change.'

'Nah. That wouldn't be right.'

As they reached the playground, Dudmish turned and called out from the front of the line.

'We can't use this one, Sir. Mr Glover's using it. We'll have to use the infant playground.'

This was disappointing. The infant playground was on the other side of the building. It was also smaller and less suitable for games, and a ball would often be accidentally knocked over the wall and into the gardens of the neighbouring old people's flats. The infant children finished school earlier than the juniors, and a group of mothers often gathered near the gate for a chat before collecting their offspring. It seemed rounders balls had a habit of straying a bit too near them, although Brian had never been able to prove they were actually being aimed.

'You'll just have to be very careful not to hit the ball too hard,' I warned. 'The game we're going to play isn't difficult, and it's very much like ordinary rounders, but we use four chairs for the bases, and four people from the fielding team sit on them. We put the wicket in the middle... just here.'

I walked to the middle of the playground and chalked a large cross. 'When the ball has been hit, it must be thrown by a fielder to someone sitting on a chair. He or she throws it at the wicket, and if it hits, the batsman is out.'

'I don't get that,' said Fred immediately.

'It's a bit complicated, isn't it?' agreed Susan Davis.

'Not really. You'll soon see. We'll get started and have a trial run first, until you get the idea. Now stand by the wall for a minute while I sort you all out.'

I divided the children into two teams, and flipped a coin to see which would bat first.

'It's us!' called Rouse in excitement.

'I dunno what you're jumpin' all over the place for,' Susan Davis said severely. 'You ain't got no chance of winnin', anyway.'

'Ain't we? You jus' wait then. Just 'cos you won last time don't mean to say you're gonna win today.'

'Last time we beat you by thirteen rounders, mate.'

'So? I wasn't on form, was I? I 'ad an 'eadache.'

'You are an 'eadache, mate!' she said decisively, turning round to her friends, who nodded in agreement.

'Look, stop goin' on at each other an' let's get crackin'', Badger shouted. 'We ain't gonna 'ave any time left at this rate.'

The others nodded earnestly, and I sent Adams and Badger to the bottom hall to fetch four small chairs. The game started, sluggishly at first, but it wasn't long before the children began to understand the rules and the game became progressively more exciting. Rouse and Susan Davis were on opposing sides and delighted in goading each other frequently and Rouse, annoyed by an easy chance which Fred had missed, threatened to throw the ball at his head very hard indeed if his aim didn't improve rapidly.

After thirty minutes of enthusiastic play, dark clouds began to gather above the playground and fat drops of rain threatened to stop the match, although neither team showed the slightest inclination to stop playing. Badger assured me it would just be a light shower, and pointed out that everyone could have a good rub down with his PE towel when they went back upstairs. I'd almost made up my mind to stop the game for a while when there was a shout from Rouse, who had bent down to catch the ball and was now waving frantically at the bowler.

''Old it, 'old it,' he called, ''Oo's this?'

He straightened up and I saw that he was holding the arm of a very young, chubby faced girl with a mass of blonde curly hair. The game stopped and every face turned to look at her, though she seemed perfectly content to hang onto Rouse's arm and gaze at him happily. Rouse was far less content, and stared at her as if she were something objectionable that had just risen from the asphalt. I tucked up the collar of my coat, and felt the rain drip down my neck.

'Who is she?' I said.

'I dunno, do I,' Rouse replied mildly, looking down at the child in bewilderment. 'I was fieldin' 'ere and she just appeared and grabbed me arm.'

'She's 'is girl friend,' jeered Adams, 'Only 'e don't like ter say so!'

Rouse rounded on him angrily. 'No she ain't! I told yer, I dunno 'oo she is. 'Ow should I know 'oo she is?'

'She's 'is girl friend all right,' Adams concluded confidently.

'Yeah, she's about 'is size,' Susan Davis added dryly.

Rouse suddenly became very angry, and he threw the ball down hard on the ground.

'You shut up!' he yelled. 'I told yer, I dunno 'oo she is. I ain't never seen 'er before. Get on with the game.'

He resumed his position as backstop, waved for the game to begin again, and tried to pretend the child wasn't there. The little girl immediately grabbed his arm and smiled at him sweetly. Rouse stood up, put his hands on his hips wearily, and looked at her in exasperation.

'Why don't you take 'er to the pictures?' Badger suggested.

'Look, you've really 'ad it in a minute!' Rouse shouted. "Ow'd you like it if she kept 'angin' onto you?'

'Well, she ain't my girlfriend, is she.'

'She ain't mine either!'

'Yeah, I bet!'

Rouse picked up the rounders bat and moved towards Badger, intent on changing his opinion. Badger stepped back in alarm and I swiftly moved between them. Susan Brennan took the little girl by the hand and knelt down.

'Where's your mum?' she asked softly.

The child pointed in the direction of the gate, smiled, and then ran back to Rouse. She pulled the bat from him and stood ready to join the game.

'What're we goin' to do?' Fred gestured hopelessly.

The children were quickly becoming restless at the rain and the interruption of their game, but it seemed pointless to carry on until the problem of the child had been solved. It was obvious she wasn't going to be content with watching the game and I couldn't leave her simply standing there.

'Take over the game, Jamie.' I said to Dudmish. And if the rain gets any worse, go under the shed.' I took the child's hand, firmly led her away from the class, and called to Rouse.

'John, take this child to the gate and see if you can find her mother. I'll have a look at the other entrance. Everybody carry on playing until I get back. Susan, see that nobody argues, will you?'

'What are you goin' to do if you can't find 'er mum?' asked Badger with interest. 'I could take 'er to the police station for yer.'

I shuddered at the thought. 'I don't think that will be necessary, Alan. It would be helpful if you just got on with the game.'

Rouse took the child's hand, and she walked beside him obediently and happily. I hurried across the playground to the entrance where most of the mothers normally waited for their children, but the street was deserted. Very aware that I couldn't leave the class unsupervised for long, I ran to the small supermarket on the corner, hoping to spot a mother in search of her child, but all seemed perfectly calm. I decided it would probably be best to stay with the game for the last few minutes of the lesson in case the mother spotted her child from the gate. If not, I'd have to take the child into the infants department at playtime to see if anybody knew her. Happier now that I had a plan of action, albeit a weak one, I hurried back across the playground to my class.

It was obvious, even from a distance, that a new development had taken place. The game had been stopped, and the children had gathered round an enormous woman in an old brown coat that had stretched with time in an attempt to accommodate her very ample form. Her cheeks, full and round like weathered pouches, were an angry red, and she poked Badger continually in the ribs with a battered umbrella as he tried to reason with her. Eventually he gave up, shook his head in resignation and walked away, muttering loudly and indignantly to Adams. The woman turned quickly on me as I approached.

'You this lot's teacher?' she said sharply, shaking the point of her umbrella at me as the rain streaked into my face.

I opened my mouth to reply, but the umbrella approached my nose dangerously, and I felt it might be best simply to nod in agreement. The children, now oblivious to the rain, watched with interest to see how the situation might develop.

'Shall we go under the covered area and discuss this quietly?' I suggested cautiously. 'There doesn't seem a lot of point in us standing here and getting soaked.'

'You just tell me what you've done with my Tracey,' she shouted menacingly. 'I just brought 'er out of school to take 'er to the 'ealth Centre and she's bleedin' disappeared.'

I put my hand on the woman's arm in an attempt to communicate a sense of calm. She snatched her arm away immediately, as if I had been attempting to pass on a disease.

I tried again. 'Just wait a moment,' I said, 'let's think about this calmly for a moment Mrs...'

'Mrs Garrett,' said Adams. 'She lives in my flats. She don't pay her rent.'

'That's got absolutely nothing to do with it, and absolutely nothing to do with you,' I snapped.

'Okay, Sir. I was only sayin'...'

'Well don't.'

'Okay, I was just...'

'We ain't got Tracey, Mrs,' Badger interrupted, a pained expression in his voice.

'What do you mean? You said she was standin' 'ere with you, didn't you?'

'Yeah, she was. I bin tryin' to explain,' Badger persisted, shaking his rain soaked curls. 'I told yer, she's gone with Rousey. 'E'll be back in a few minutes.'

'She came up to us in the playground,' I tried to explain. 'One of the boys went with her to the gate to see if he could find you.'

'Which gate?'

'The main entrance.'

'Well what the 'ell did 'e go down there for? I stop to speak to Mrs Stoddart for two minutes about the lumps on 'er legs and then I find Tracey's bin wanderin' about in 'ere.'

'There's really nothing to worry about,' I said, far more calmly than I felt. 'He's only gone outside the gate. Do you mind if we stand out of the rain?'

'Never mind the bloody rain! We're late as it is.'

She raised her umbrella forcibly, and strode ahead of me. Suddenly aware that the entire class was likely to turn and follow me, I ordered the children under the bicycle shed and told them not to move until I came back. As I hurried after Mrs Garrett, I was fascinated to find that she looked exactly the same from the back as she did from the front.

'It's not bloody good enough,' she grumbled, adjusting the position of the umbrella with a large meaty hand. 'You ought to know better. These kids are supposed to be in your charge. One of 'em could be run over.'

Though I knew that the woman was reacting from concern about her daughter, I found myself becoming increasingly tense, though more from the woman's attitude than the disappearance of her child.

'Aren't you overreacting a little?' I said impatiently. 'We know where she is. I just...'

'Over bloody reacting? My child disappears and you call it over bloody reacting? You young teachers. Think you know everything. I can't see why you've got 'em all out 'ere anyway. It's pouring with bloody rain?'

'They wanted to stay down here. Anyway, it's not raining that hard now.'

'That's the bloody trouble with you teachers today. The kids do what they bloody well like. Well, where is she?'

We'd reached the gate and Mrs Garrett looked up and down the street several times. To my horror, neither Rouse nor the little girl were in sight. Worrying visions flitted through my mind. Perhaps Rouse had tried to take her home. Perhaps he'd taken her for a nice ride on a bus. Perhaps he had been kidnapped...

'Stay there, just in case they suddenly appear,' I said, trying to give myself a moment to think. 'I'll be back in a minute.'

I ran across the playground and under the shed, to find that a violent argument had broken out about who was supposed to be batting next.

'The game's over!' I shouted, surprising myself at the ferocity of my voice. 'You'll have to help me look for this child.'

'I thought Rousey was with her?' said Susan Brennan, disappointed.

'He was. I can't find him, either.'

'Aw Sir,' muttered Susan Davis. 'It's messin' up our game.'

'I can't help that. You've only got a few minutes left anyway. It's messing up my last afternoon with you, too. Spread out and look for them. They can't be very far. But don't go near the main road, and I want you back here in ten minutes.'

'Sir, Sir,' called Badger, 'p'raps 'e's taken 'er to the police station...'

'I doubt it,' said Adams seriously. 'They know 'im down there. They'd prob'ly keep 'im in there.'

I sighed impatiently. 'Look, just find Rouse. There's five hundred pounds for the first one to find him.'

There was a whoop of excitement and the children hurried across the playground. For a moment, I wondered whether I'd done the right thing. How would Dorothy have coped with this little problem, I wondered? Perhaps I should have gone upstairs and fetched her. I looked up and saw Mrs Garrett hurrying back towards me, head down underneath the umbrella as if she was going to charge me first and then beat me over the head with it.

'Well, Tracey ain't there, is she!' she shouted.

'No,' I snapped back. 'And I've got the entire class looking for her. Wait a minute.'

'I've waited long enough. She's probably wandered off into the main road. Gawd, I'll bloody 'ave you if she 'as.'

My patience and worry was stretched to breaking point and it suddenly snapped. Inexperience took over and I lost control of my temper.

'Look!' I roared, 'She'll turn up in a moment. I can't look after everybody else's kids as well as my own class, can I? I've got thirty children to teach, not just one to wander down to the Health Centre with. If you'd done something simple like holding your child's hand she wouldn't be missing, would she? Now it looks as if I've lost your child and half the class I'm supposed to be looking after. Keep quiet for a minute and we'll find her.'

Mrs Garrett's mouth opened and closed like a goldfish seeking extra oxygen.

'Right! Right! I'll see what the 'eadmaster 'as to say about this. I'm not 'avin' you talkin' to me like that. Bloody cheek! You shouldn't be in charge of kids at your age!'

Susan Brennan suddenly appeared at the bottom of the steps, waving her arms, and shouting at me.

'It's alright, Sir,' she called, 'We've found them. They're upstairs in class.'

Susan hurried back up the steps and the playtime bell rang as other classes began to come into the playground. Mrs Garrett charged up behind me, ploughing through the children coming downstairs and pushing them to each side of her like Tarzan hacking through dense undergrowth. The exertion quickly tired her, and by the time I reached the classroom she was still two staircases behind, panting with exhaustion and struggling to catch her breath.

Inside the room, Tracey was sitting propped up on a table, a cushion from the book corner thrust behind her back and a large bar of chocolate in her right hand. She looked blissfully happy. Rouse, standing beside her, looked up and grinned sheepishly as he saw me.

'I brort 'er up 'ere, Sir. I couldn't see 'er mum, an' then she said she 'ad a sister in the Infants so I was goin' to take 'er down there, an' then she kept cryin' so we went to the shop and I got 'er a bar o' chocolate and then I thort it 'ud be best to bring 'er up 'ere where there was a bit o' peace and quiet. She stopped cryin', then.'

His voice dropped and he looked deeply apologetic.

'Don't you realise how worried we've been?' I interrupted him angrily. 'And what on earth did you take her off to the shop for? Anything could have happened. You might at least have come and told me you'd found her.'

'I was goin' to, Sir, but what with the rain an' all that I jus' thort it'ud be a good idea to bring 'er up 'ere. I mean, she's only a little 'un,' he added limply.

Susan Brennan looked at the little girl and then at Rouse. After a moment she nodded seriously, impressed with the effort Rouse had made. Susan Davis took out a grubby handkerchief and began to wipe chocolate from the child's face. When she was satisfied that most of it had been removed and Tracey looked presentable again, she stuffed the handkerchief back in her pocket and sniffed.

'Wouldn't surprise me if she was sick after that lot,' she muttered, staring pointedly at Rouse. He thrust his hands into his pockets and stared at Susan.

'Blimey, I miss me game lookin' after this little kid, an' all I get is a load of naggin' women,' he objected.

'But you don't seem to realise how worried we were,' I said, not sure whether I was included in Rouse's sweeping generalisation. 'As it is, I've got half the class all over the place still looking for you.'

'They won't look for long,' he said miserably. 'They don't like me much anyway.'

'Of course they like you, you silly boy. I like you too. It's just that sometimes you don't think very carefully.'

'He did try his best though, Sir,' said Susan Brennan. 'I mean, if you think about it, he did look after her.'

'Yes, I know he did. But Tracey's mother was very worried. And so was I. I'll admit it was a kind thought, though. The chocolate, I mean.'

Several other children from the class came hurrying into the room, followed by Mrs Garrett, who clung desperately to the door frame and panted loudly, unable to say anything at all. Tracey climbed down from the table and ran to her mother, who gave her a hefty cuff round the ear that spun the child around and sent her into a flood of tears.

'Bleedin' nuisance, you are,' she gasped at Rouse. 'If you'd 'ave left 'er where she was we could 'ave bin at the 'Ealth Centre and gone back 'ome by now.'

Rouse looked decidedly hurt. 'Gawd!' he exclaimed, 'if I'd known you was goin' to make this much fuss I'd 'ave left 'er in the road.'

Tracey, who had obviously taken a great liking to Rouse and was upset at the verbal abuse he was receiving, retaliated by kicking her mother in the ankle. She received a second, much harder, clout on the ear and then Mrs Garrett wagged a finger at Rouse.

'I'm seein' the 'eadmaster about you,' she shouted, now fully recovered from the climb. 'And 'im,' she added menacingly, looking in my direction.

'Whaffor?' Rouse objected, immediately springing to my defence. "E never 'ad nothin' to do with it.'

'Don't you give me any more of your bleedin' cheek!' she snapped, waving a finger in front of his nose. 'Some of you kids need teachin' a bloody good lesson. Come on Tracey.'

She grabbed the child's arm and gave it a savage jerk, like somebody trying to launch a kite on a calm day. Tracey was extremely reluctant to go, and shouted defiantly at her mother as they left the room. There was an awed silence for several minutes, broken eventually by Rouse.

'Well, all I can say is, it's lucky you ain't stayin' 'ere, Sir. After all, in a couple o' years time you might 'ave 'ad to teach 'er daughter.'

Just for once, I found myself completely in sympathy with Rouse's point of view.

(iv)

The time taken up with the incident had reduced my break to a mere three minutes. There was nobody in the staffroom and I poured myself a cup of tepid tea. I was surprised to find that my hand was shaking. The door suddenly banged open and Brian hurried into the room, dumping the bats, balls and hoops he was carrying onto the large table in the corner. He took a deep breath and sighed.

'Honestly, you say to 'em, make sure you don't leave anything in the playground. You might as well talk to yourself. In fact, some of the time I think I am talking to myself. Are you really sure you want to be a teacher, Mike? Why don't you do something a lot easier? Like being a nuclear physicist?'

'I might just do that. I've just had my first run-in with a parent. A Mrs Garrett.'

Brian looked up and grinned. 'Oh, dear old Doris? Lost her kids again has she?'

'That's right. How many has she got, then?'

'Six at the last count. Four boys and two girls. She always wanted a girl, so she kept on and on until she got one. Except that she got twins by mistake. She can't really look after one properly, let alone six. And she's always losing them. They just tend to wander off while she's having a gossip. Look, are you okay? You look a bit pale.'

'I guess so. It was just a bit unnerving, that's all.'

'Of course it is. And we've all been through it. But you'll soon become hardened to the odd difficult encounter. You just have to remember that parents who come on the attack have probably got rotten things going on in their lives, and teachers are easy targets. From what Dorothy says, you've got the makings of being a smashing teacher, and that's what schools like this need. People who care. Anyway, I've got to dash after school, so if I don't see you, all the best for the future. And don't worry about Mrs Garrett.'

He smiled, shook my hand firmly and hurried out of the room.

I followed him, and after a few minutes Dorothy appeared at the end of the corridor with the class. They filed noisily into the classroom.

'Well, I'm having a great afternoon,' I sighed.

'I know. I've just been on playground duty and they told me all about it. Do you want me to take them for the last half hour?'

'No. Just put a notice on the door saying 'No parents past this point.'

'Don't worry,' she laughed. 'It's all good experience. Naturally I wouldn't let any harm come to you. We do try to look after our promising students. After all, they might decide to try for a job here. I'll come back just before hometime.'

'Well, it's my last half hour with you,' I said to the class. 'What would you like to do?'

'We've worked so 'ard these last few days', said Rouse, 'I reckon all I want ter do is sit.'

'That's all you ever want to do, mate,' called Susan Davis.

'No I don't. I do me fair share. Don't I Sir?'

'Well, I must admit I have known you to put a pencil to paper on the odd occasion.'

'Read us a story, Sir,' called Julie. 'I like listenin' to stories.'

'Yeah, a thrillin' one,' said Badger eagerly.

'Come on then,' I said, 'everybody sit quietly in the book corner and I'll read you one of my favourite stories. I loved it when I was your age. It's all about a witch with iron teeth who likes eating children...'

'Blimey!' Adams exclaimed. 'Sounds just like my Auntie Jean!'

The children laughed and hurried into the book corner. There were the usual minor scuffles over who should have the cushions and then they settled down contentedly to listen. I read the story well, watching the delight on their faces as I imitated the crackled rasp of the witch's voice, and feeling the intense concentration of their enjoyment.

'Cor, I really liked that one, didn't we Sue?' said Susan Davis, stretching her legs as the story ended. 'You don't 'alf read stories well, Sir.'

'Yeah,' Fred agreed. 'It really frightened me. That bit where the witch was chasing the little girl in that magic dish was really scary.'

'Miss is here,' said Susan Brennan, glancing at the door. 'Quick, everybody get back in their seats. It's time for... well, you know.'

'Sssh!' urged Susan Davis. 'You'll spoil it.'

Dorothy walked into the room, smiled at the class, and looked across at me. 'Sorry to interrupt, Mr Kent,' she said secretively, 'but it's nearly hometime and I think the children have something to say to you.'

Their faces glowed, as though each had a hidden secret and Rouse, obviously the elected spokesman, stood up. For the first time since I had been at the school, he looked a little shy.

'Well Sir,' he faltered, 'me and the class 'ud jus' like ter say 'ow much we've enjoyed you bein' 'ere and... er... we wish you was stayin', Sir.'

He sat down and fumbled in his desk.

'Go on,' Susan Davis shouted. 'That ain't all.'

'I know, I know,' he said irritably, piling books out of his tray and onto the floor. 'I'm jus' lookin' for it, that's all.'

'Trust you, mate. You've probably lost it.'

Rouse gave a sudden sigh of relief as he uncovered a package wrapped in bright red paper. Holding it carefully, he walked out to me.

'This is for you, Sir,' he said. 'We... er... 'ad a little collection, an' we didn't know what to buy, so we asked Miss, 'an' she said you'd like it, an' I reckon...'

'Blimey, Rousey, don't go on all night, for Gawd's sake,' Susan Davis interrupted. 'Give 'im a chance to open it.'

'I am,' Rouse objected. 'I'm jus' sayin' a few words, that's all. On these occasions someone always says a few words.'

I smiled and carefully unwrapped the package as the children watched eagerly. Inside was a beautiful edition of collected poetry for children, and every child in the class had signed the first page. I was completely taken by surprise, and touched by their warm generosity.

'It's lovely,' I said softly. 'It's really lovely. Thank you all very, very much. I'll treasure this book, and I'll read the poems to the classes I teach in the future. I'll also treasure the happy times I've had with you over the last few weeks. You've really been a great class to teach.'

'Ah, ain't you nice, Sir,' sighed Susan Davis.

The bell rang for hometime and the children went out slowly and quietly, intent on saying their separate goodbyes. Rouse smiled sadly at me and shook my hand.

'I'll miss yer,' he said gruffly.

'I'll miss you too. And don't go wandering off with Mrs Garrett's children.'

'No fear. I'm keepin' well away from 'em in future.'

When the last child had left the room, I put the story book, and my new book of poetry, into my briefcase. The classroom seemed strangely silent and peaceful.

'They're a nice lot, aren't they?' said Dorothy quietly.

'Yes, they are. I really will miss them very much indeed.'

'You'll remember them, too. Even after you've taught for ten years, you'll still remember your first class.'

'Well, I've certainly moaned at them enough. You'd think they'd hate my guts by now.'

'It doesn't work like that. Children are canny little creatures and they know when you really enjoy being with them. They don't mind being grumbled at when they know that. It's always the same routine when you have a new class in a new school. You battle through your first lesson and they try you out. You retaliate, and they usually try you out harder. So you try harder too. Then in the end they realise you might actually be worth listening to. By the end of the year, they're like your family.'

'It doesn't seem right, though, does it? I mean, you should be able just to get on with the job of teaching. You shouldn't have to battle to get their attention first.'

'If you think about it, there's no reason why you shouldn't have to prove yourself a little. I think there's a bit of the entertainer in every good teacher. You've got to have a sense of timing and be interesting. Adults don't like being with someone who bores the pants off them, so why should children be any different?'

She picked up a pile of new story books from her desk and began to stack them on the library racks in the book corner.

'Anyway,' she said, 'It's been great fun having you here and I'm sure you'll do well. I'll get all of them to write to you soon. They'd like that. You've obviously scored quite a hit with them.'

'It's really convinced me that I do want to teach,' I said. 'Even if I have to put up with angry mothers and kids being sick on school visits.'

Dorothy smiled. 'Ah, well, that's all part of the fun. The pay's rotten, sometimes you don't get a break all day, you spend most of your weekends marking and planning. But if you really like the job, there's nothing to compare with it. I really think...'

She broke off as she realised that Mr Reed was standing in the doorway. He looked cautiously in her direction, and then saw me.

'Ah, Mr Kent. Glad I caught you before I went home. You'll be pleased to know I've given you a reasonable report.'

'Thank you,' I said flatly. 'It's very kind of you.'

'There were one or two difficulties, of course. You seem to have upset Mrs Garrett quite considerably. Couldn't really understand what the woman was going on about, but she mentioned your name unfavourably a number of times.'

'It doesn't surprise me. I got a little cross with her,' I admitted, not wishing to argue the point.

'I see. Well, if you'll take a little advice, never lose your temper in this job, Mr Kent. Lose your temper and you'll end up having a slanging match. Nobody will enjoy that apart from the children. It's quite pointless. Still, in this game you learn by your mistakes. You're thrown in at the deep end and you either sink or swim. Considering this is your first teaching practice, you seem to have made a creditable attempt to swim.'

'He certainly did,' said Dorothy. 'The children liked him very much, and that's important.'

'Mmm. Well, we could debate that at some length, Dorothy. I think the fact that Mr Kent was actually able to teach them something is probably more important.'

He hesitated, decided there wasn't anything else he wanted to say, and held out his hand. 'Goodbye, Mr Kent. I wish you luck with the remainder of your course.'

Dorothy breathed a sigh of relief as he closed the door.

'Wonderful. He's such a pompous old sod. Let's go and have a cup of tea in the staffroom.'

An hour later, as I left the building and walked towards the train station, I was stopped by a child shouting behind me. I turned to see Adams running down the road towards me with a box under his arm.

'Sir, Sir!' he panted, straining to recover his breath. 'I saw yer from me window. Wait a minute, I've got somethin' for yer…'

He held up the box eagerly, and placed it gingerly in my hands. "Ere you are, Sir,' he said with a broad smile, 'they're for you.'

'Gosh, not another present? Anyone would think it was my birthday. What on earth is this?'

'Heggs.'

'Pardon?'

'Heggs. You know, Sir. I told you. Me mum keeps chickens and they lays heggs for us. She says you've got to try 'em, Sir. This lot are really fresh. Straight from the chicken's bum. I've got to go now. Come back and see us soon!'

I stood for a moment and watched as the boy ran back to the entrance of his tower block. Then, in great contentment, I hurried into the rush hour crowds to catch my train.

MARCH

A FILM SOCIETY, GLENN MILLER, AND THE BOYS FROM ST BERNARD'S

It wasn't until March in our second year that Duggan, Gerry and I got around to starting a film society. Gerry's passion for the moving image had often led us to discuss the idea, but any spare time seemed to be taken up with belonging to existing societies. Clubs and societies were a thriving and staple component of college life. Everybody joined at least one. When the students of St. James's weren't studying, writing essays, wandering around London or spending time with their partners, they were expected to be working for a society. Students could play chess, tread the boards, sing in a choir, collect butterflies or debate in a religious or political group. They could also exercise, meditate, Morris dance, roller skate, or tiddly-wink their way through numerous evenings and those who needed particular relief from the stress of the daily lectures could weave baskets, or even make kites. Starting a new society simply depended on the organiser's enthusiasm for his hobby, and students scanned the noticeboards weekly to see which societies were new, and which had collapsed due to a declining membership.

Although there was a television in each of the common rooms, it was a rare sight to find a student in front of one for very long. Indeed, you were considered a very dull person if you couldn't find at least one society that interested you, and many students joined four or five. Amongst other things, Duggan had improved his chess and I was learning to play the guitar, a skill I thought would definitely be useful when I started teaching in earnest.

Due to the heavy schedules of our social lives, the amount of work we were doing had decreased considerably, although a balance had to be maintained to give the lecturers an impression of intense study. Some tutors were more astute than others; Duggan had managed to hand in the same essay, slightly re-arranged, three times to one of his education lecturers, but tutors like Dr Frost could spot a modicum of waffle at five hundred paces and it simply wasn't worth trying to hoodwink them for a moment.

There were, of course, the end of term examinations, a minor irritant that briefly interrupted the joys of student life. Exams had to be passed, but so far they'd proved no great obstacle since invigilating lecturers often read their newspapers, marked work, filled in crosswords, or merely fell asleep, leaving the students to pass their papers amongst each other at will. After the examinations, which it seemed hardly anybody ever failed unless they'd given up after writing their names, everybody was free to return to a minimum of study and far more pleasurable pursuits, such as the corridor darts tournament Duggan had organised after we'd been given an old darts board by the landlord of the local pub for outstanding patronage.

The success of this had inspired Duggan to organise an indoor sports week for corridor three involving darts, skittles, ludo, cards, and shove-halfpenny with a board he'd found tucked away in a cupboard on teaching practice and which the teacher had gladly given him to get it out of the way. Duggan had charged a substantial entry fee, and was pleasantly surprised when the entire corridor had offered to join in, lured by the promise of half the collection going to a charity and the other half to whoever ended up as champion of the week.

'You certainly managed that extremely well,' said Gerry admiringly, as we sat in Duggan's room the following Monday morning drinking steaming mugs of coffee before the first lecture. 'Who'd have thought it would be as popular as that?'

'It's your talent for organising,' I said. 'It's obviously been great practice for running a school sports day.'

'We've been meaning to start a new society for a long time,' said Gerry. 'So I think it's time we actually did it.'

'We've got to start something that'll be really popular,' said Duggan, making a fresh mug of coffee and opening a new packet of milk. 'Apart from the drama club, practically everything here is a fairly specialist affair.'

'Then let's go for a film society,' I said. 'We've talked about it often enough. Gerry's got the specialist knowledge, Duggan's got the organising capacity. Samantha will come up here and flog ice creams and hot dogs in a short skirt and I'll work the projectors.'

'Sounds fine to me,' Gerry agreed. 'Where's the teaspoon?'

Duggan scratched around on the floor underneath his desk. 'Down here. Milly dropped it this morning when she was wiping the desk. We'll have to invest in another one soon. I think she uses this one to clean her nails.'

'I'm surprised there isn't a film society here already,' I said. 'Most colleges seem to have one.'

'There was,' Gerry replied. 'About two years ago, but when the students who were running it left, nobody started it again. Got any biscuits?'

Duggan hunted in the drawer of his desk. 'No. You should have had some breakfast. There's three slices of bread in here. They're a bit old.'

'How old.'

'Well quite old, actually.'

'What, more than a couple of days?'

'A bit more than that, I think. I could cut the mouldy corners off.'

'No thanks, I'll starve. Anyway, since there was a film society here before, all the equipment must be still be available somewhere. And the lecture hall would make an ideal cinema. There's a good sized screen in there.'

Duggan thought carefully for a minute.

'Our outlay needn't be very large. We'll have to pay for the hire of the 16mm films, of course. If we lose on that, I suppose we'd have to fork out of our own pockets.'

'I don't think so. The students' union will give us something to get going,' I said. 'After all, lots of societies have started and failed. The butterfly club, and the skiffle revival society to name but two.'

'I rather fancied the skiffle revival society,' Duggan smiled. 'I suppose nobody had a washboard.'

'Anyway, a film society is hardly a crazy idea,' said Gerry. 'It could even be a great success. If we borrow a couple of sixteen millimetre projectors from the lovely Miss Pratt's audio-visual department and have a meeting fairly soon we could probably start next month.'

'What sort of a meeting?'

'We'd have to form a committee. And it would give us some idea of how many people were interested.'

'And they'd be bound to bring their women,' Duggan added enthusiastically. 'There's a balcony at the back of the lecture theatre and they'd be queuing to sit up there. Right, one more coffee, then we'd better go. It's physical education and Mr Trainer will miss me if I'm not there. I'd hate to disappoint him.'

We scribbled a hasty list of all the things that needed to be done. Gerry would write off for catalogues from the film hire companies to give us a rough idea of how much the programmes would cost to put on, Duggan would think of ways to publicise the shows so that we reached the biggest audience, and I would look into the cost of refreshments, ticket printing and equipment organising.

The following morning, Duggan pinned a notice on the board in the main corridor, announcing the birth of a new film society provided there was enough support, and stating that the smaller common room had been booked for a short meeting the following evening. Underneath, he pinned a separate piece of paper for people to write their names on if they were interested. By the next afternoon, Duggan's piece of paper had been filled with names. William Friese-Greene, Julius Caesar, Florence Nightingale, Burt Lancaster and

Attila the Hun had all expressed a strong interest in joining, but there were at least thirty genuine names on the sheet and it was certainly a promising start.

About fifteen students were already in the common room when we arrived and they watched politely while Duggan and I placed a table and three chairs in one corner of the room, and then re-arranged the remaining easy chairs in front of the table.

'Excuse me,' asked one of the students, 'is this the Beethoven appreciation meeting?'

'No mate,' Duggan replied cheerfully. 'We're the film society. Or at least, this is the meeting for it. Fancy joining?'

'What are you showing?'

'Nothing yet. This is the first meeting. We haven't even got a committee yet.'

'I see.'

He hesitated for a moment, and then decided he'd prefer to search for the Beethoven appreciation society. As he left the room, more students wandered in, and within half an hour we had a good crowd. Dai Thomas sat in the front row, studying a battered score of Handel's Messiah. Dudley sat behind him, smiling enthusiastically and poking tobacco into a curved pipe with a massive bowl. Sitting near him, I noticed with interest, was Simon Daines. David Barton had come along, still bald because he'd become used to his appearance and now actually preferred it, and Rashid was there with his girlfriend, a beautiful Indian girl with shining almond eyes. Ben Fellows, a keen photographic student, sat at the back of the group. Together with five other students, also at the meeting, he'd started a photographic society. Surprisingly, this hadn't maintained enough support, and I assumed he felt that a film society might be the next best thing.

Three other students wandered in and asked why the television wasn't on. When they were told a meeting was about to start, two of them decided to stay and be entertained by that instead. Gerry looked at the clock on the wall, opened his notebook, thrust his long legs comfortably under the table, and carefully packed his pipe with tobacco. Alan Dawdle, a student with a hearing problem, moved to a chair immediately in front of Gerry and fiddled with his hearing aid.

'Shall we begin?' Gerry whispered.

'Pardon?' called Dawdle.

'It's all right,' Gerry replied. 'I was talking to my friend here. I was just suggesting that we should begin.'

'Oh, right. I thought you were talking to me. Sorry.'

'Definitely,' said Duggan. 'There's a good crowd here. Don't forget the main intention is to elect ourselves as the committee.'

'That might not be easy,' I said, looking round at the faces in the audience.

'It'll be okay,' said Duggan. 'Leave that bit to me.'

'You're going to do the talking then, are you?'

'No, Gerry is. He's the bloke with the knowledge.'

Gerry turned to him and choked on a smoke ring. 'You didn't tell me I was doing the talking. I'd have prepared a lot more notes than I've got here. I'm not sure...'

'Look,' Duggan urged, 'I like going to the pictures. Samantha likes going to the pictures. And Mike likes going to the pictures, especially with Samantha. But you're the one who's had a crack at making your own home movies and you also know about the arty stuff.'

'Well, maybe a bit, but...'

'Who directed 'Shane'?'

'George Stevens. What's that got to do with it?'

'Name another film he directed.'

'Giant. A Place In The Sun. Swing Time. But I don't...'

'You see? Chuck a film question at you and you know all about it. We'll back you up if you get into difficulty, won't we Mike?'

I nodded cautiously.

'Now let's get cracking,' Duggan urged. 'Before they all decide to push off down the pub.'

Gerry hesitated, tapped his pipe out nervously into the huge glass ashtray on the table, and stood up to start the meeting. The audience sensed that something was happening and the murmuring quickly stopped.

'Thank you all for... um... coming tonight,' Gerry faltered. 'Now, the idea of this film society is to show...er... films.'

'Bravo!' shouted a hearty voice from the back. Gerry thanked the student politely and continued.

'That is, films which are either acknowledged classics in their own right, or have... um... exceptional entertainment value.' Somebody on the third row coughed and looked at his watch. Dudley raised the hand containing his pipe and waved it to attract Gerry's attention.

'Sorry to stop you so early old boy, but how do you define a classic? I mean, give me an example.'

'Citizen Kane,' called a voice from the row behind him, before Gerry had a chance to reply. Dudley turned swiftly in his seat. 'Ah!' he cried. 'You see. That proves my point. My colleague here obviously thinks Citizen Kane is a masterpiece. Frankly I think it's an overrated bore. Your view of what constitutes a classic might very well be different from mine.'

Duggan's mouth dropped open. 'God, this could turn out to be livelier than I thought,' he muttered.

'There's another point, of course,' said the student sitting next to Dudley. 'You said you were intending to show films which were either classics or great entertainment value. Surely a classic should be great entertainment value anyway?'

Gerry opened his mouth to reply, but Dudley had already started speaking again.

'Not at all,' he said. 'I wouldn't call 'Intolerance' great entertainment value. Or some of Eisenstein's work. Powerful, emotive images, yes, but not great entertainment value. I think we should...'

'For Christ's sake,' called Barton. 'The bloke at the table has only said two words so far. Shut up and let him talk. I can't sit here all night listening to you. I've got to go and get my hair cut.' There was a ripple of laughter, and all eyes turned back to Gerry.

'Thank you,' Gerry said gratefully. 'Now, we... er... intend to have the shows in the lecture hall. Once a month if we get enough support. It won't be possible to please all tastes, of course, but at the moment we're thinking of making one of the monthly films a popular one... something that will be particularly well attended... and the next month's a lesser known foreign film. Some of the best foreign pictures are likely to be quite expensive to hire, so we'll have to rely on making up the charge from our popular night. Unless, of course, the foreign films we show are popular too.'

Ben Fellows waved his hand in the air, and Gerry stopped for a moment. 'What film gauge are you thinking of using?' he asked.

'Surely that's immaterial?' Dudley interrupted. 'This is supposed to be a society concerned with celluloid images, not mechanics.'

'Not at all,' Fellows argued. 'I assume that sixteen millimetre is going to be used? I mean, if I'm paying good money out of my grant to support this society, I think it's important to have crisp images on the screen. I want to see the films as the film makers intended them to be seen. Crisp and sharp and properly projected.'

'I hope you're selling nuts and ice cream as well?' said Alan Dawdle, fiddling with his hearing aid. The talking stopped and Gerry stared, nonplussed, at Dawdle.

'As well as what?' asked Duggan.

'As well as crisps. You were talking about crisps.'

'I don't think I mentioned selling crisps...'

'Ben mentioned crisp images,' I whispered. 'I think he misheard.'

'Oh, right. Yes, we'll be selling all those things. Drinks, hot dogs, popcorn. You name it, we'll be selling it,' Duggan called reassuringly, like a politician agreeing to everything potential voters were asking for. Dawdle nodded contentedly and thanked him.

'You haven't answered my question,' Ben Fellows called.

'There's a perfectly good reason for that,' Duggan replied.

'What's that?'

'We've forgotten what it was.'

'I was asking which gauge you're going to use. I mean, I'm assuming it will be sixteen millimetre?'

'Probably,' said Gerry, feeling it was his responsibility to answer questions directed at the technical aspects of the society. 'Eight millimetre would be cheaper, but we'll have to see what sort of support the society gets when it starts.'

'So what sort of things are you going to show?' asked Dudley. 'After all, if we're supporting you, it's down to you to take note of the sort of things we want to see. Otherwise we'll end up with Citizen bloody Kane every other month.'

'We could do far worse,' called the voice behind Dudley.

'We could do far better, as well,' Dudley retorted. 'In my view it was a self indulgent, pretentious piece of tedium.'

'You don't know what you're talking about,' replied the student angrily, leaping to his feet and glaring at Dudley. 'There are camera techniques in that film that had never been used before, and the editing...'

'It's two hours of unrelieved boredom. And even that's being polite about it,' said Dudley mildly.

'We haven't actually got around to making the programmes up yet,' Gerry interrupted quickly. 'We can't do that until we've got some sort of idea of the costs involved.'

Dudley scratched among the dead matches in his box until he found a live one to light his pipe. Three people immediately moved their chairs sideways to avoid being enveloped by the acrid yellow smoke that seeped from the bowl.

'I appreciate that point,' he declared at length, 'but I was just wondering if you could give us an idea what you had in mind, that's all.'

A number of people around him nodded. It was obviously a popular point and Gerry considered it for a moment.

'It might be an idea to ask you that,' he replied brightly. 'After all, the success of the society will depend on giving people what they want.'

'What about 'Nudes Around The World', or 'Diary of a French Chambermaid?' a student in the front row suggested. 'They would be popular. They'd be popular with me, anyway.'

There was a chorus of amused agreement from the group around him. Daines sighed and picked up a newspaper, and somebody sitting near the door got up and walked out.

'Funny you should say that,' Duggan interrupted quickly. 'We tried to book 'Nudes Around The World' for our first programme, but we got a letter back saying it had been shown so often in slow motion the print had gone all brown.'

'So what sort of foreign films would you show?' asked Rashid. 'What about something like Satajit Ray's Apu trilogy. People would love that.'

'For Christ's sake, who's he?' asked Barton.

'Yes, who's he?' whispered Duggan to Gerry.

'A brilliant Indian director.'

'Oh. Right.'

'Does that mean sub-titles?' asked Dawdle. 'I can't stand films with sub-titles.'

Duggan looked up at him. 'I thought it was a hearing problem you had?'

'Eh?'

'I said I thought you had a hearing problem? I didn't know you had a visual impediment as well.'

'Oh, I can see all right. I just don't like sub-titles.'

'Why's that?'

'Eh?'

Gerry turned to Rashid and stroked his chin thoughtfully, deciding to return to the original question. 'We'd probably only get a small audience for the Apu films. And we'd be hard pressed to choose between, say, the Apu trilogy and Andrzej Wadja's trilogy.'

'Bloody hell, this is getting a bit high-brow,' said Barton. 'Look, why don't you run two shows a month?'

'We can't,' I interrupted. 'We can only have the lecture hall for one Tuesday a month.'

'Alright then, run two shows on the same evening. The early show can be for the nuts who queue up at the National Film Theatre and talk rubbish in loud voices, and the other show can be for normal people like me.'

'I thoroughly object to that,' said Dudley, disdainfully.

'Why doesn't that surprise me?' Barton replied.

'What about the classic musicals, boyo?' asked Dai Thomas. 'You could show somethin' like 'Singin' In The Rain' or 'South Pacific' and have 'em cryin' in their seats. Now then, who'd like a renderin' of 'There is nothin' like a dame...?'

He turned to the meeting and without waiting for an invitation he burst heartily into the song, joined by several others for the final chorus. There was a burst of appreciative applause as he finished and took a bow.

'There you are, boys,' he said. 'Bloody magic.'

'I like that one with Julie Andrews singing about the fish,' called Barton. 'You know, the eels are alive with the sound of music...'

'Look, if we're back to talking about classics, we shouldn't be talking about nuns leaping all over a hillside yodelling about mountain climbing,' Dudley objected. 'We should be talking about Fred Astaire and Ginger Rogers...'

'Or Busby Berkeley's films,' added Fellows. 'They're full of camera sequences worth studying.'

'Look, we study here all day mate,' Barton sighed. 'We want a bit of entertainment in the evening. If you're going to have a musical, what about Elvis?'

There was a groan of disapproval. Aware that they were unlikely to get unanimous approval for whatever they discussed, Gerry stood up and waved his pipe in the air.

'We've only got this room for another fifteen minutes and we still haven't got anything sorted out. Why don't you leave the committee to work out the programmes?'

'Because they won't choose stuff I like,' Barton said. 'I don't like singing nuns, for a start.'

'Really?' grinned a student behind him. 'I thought you liked the kinky stuff?'

Daines stood up and gestured impatiently to the meeting. 'Look,' he said, 'Why not leave it to the committee to put a list of possible films on the noticeboard? Ones which might appeal to a fairly wide audience. Then we put ticks against the films we want to see. And we add any others to the bottom of the list. The committee hires the films with the most ticks.'

'It wouldn't work,' Barton objected. 'People could add as many ticks as they want. Frankly, it seems…'

'It seems you have a basic mistrust in your fellow students,' said Dudley. 'It seems perfectly feasible to me.'

There was a general murmur of approval and Gerry interrupted swiftly while the going was good.

'I think it's worth trying. At least to start with. Anyway, we'll still need to get a good crowd on our first show to recover our outlay.'

'You'll probably make a vast profit,' said the student sitting next to Ben Fellows. 'Can I be on the committee? Or have you already decided who's going to be on that?'

'We're going to do the voting in a minute,' Gerry replied.

'You want to charge a fair bit for the balcony, you know,' Barton advised. 'People can sit up there and hold hands. It'll be just like sitting in the back row of the Regal. I love holding hands in there.'

'I wondered who was holding my hand the other night,' said the student sitting next to him. 'It must have been you.'

'Probably was. I hold hands with absolutely anybody.'

'Is this relevant?' asked Dudley.

'Of course it is,' Barton replied. 'We're talking money here. If the committee sells the seats in the balcony at vastly inflated prices, they will make a lot of money. This, in turn, will allow them to spend more on films. Or even better, lower the ticket prices. You never know, they might even make enough to hire some of the crap you want to see.'

'We're not all like you, Dave,' shouted one of his friends. 'You never know, the films might be worth watching.'

'What do you mean, you're not all like me? We never see any women in here apart from Wednesdays and the weekends. If you're not like me with that sort of handicap there's something wrong with you, mate.'

'I suggest Mr Barton hires the entire balcony and a harem, and we get back to electing a committee,' said Dudley. 'This is getting ridiculous.'

'Oh, I don't know. I was quite enjoying it,' Barton objected.

Dudley turned in his seat and squinted at him. Smoke from his pipe was now enveloping the first two rows and many of the students had given up listening, turning to each other for a chat instead. Dai Thomas had rolled up both trouser legs and was inspecting a cluster of red insect bites that had appeared on his ankles. Rashid had his arm round his girlfriend and was whispering in her ear, and Ben Fellows sat chatting to his friends from the defunct photographic society about the camerawork on early Bergman films. Hearing the conversation, Dudley moved nearer to the group, pushed two chairs together to make a platform for his large feet, and launched into a discussion on the cinematic merits of Resnais and Truffaut.

Gerry looked around for help, wondering if there was any point in going on. During his first teaching practice in a secondary school, he had peeped through classroom doors and silently sympathised with those teachers who struggled to hold the attention of unruly classes. He suddenly knew how they felt.

'What do I do now?' he whispered earnestly to Duggan and me.

'Get their attention. Shout at them,' urged Duggan.

'We'll... er... put a notice up about the first show, then,' Gerry said loudly.

'Hang on, you haven't elected a committee,' said Barton.

'We've been trying to,' Duggan replied. 'You haven't got a megaphone in your pocket, have you?'

'No. I think I can help you, though.'

Barton stood up, fumbled in his pocket and took out a whistle, which he blew as hard as he could. The effect was instantaneous. Alan Dawdle's hearing aid flew out of his ear and he fell off his seat in fright.

'Playtime's over,' Barton roared. 'These blokes need a committee.'

'Thank you,' said Gerry, as all eyes turned back to him. 'Would anyone care to propose a chairman?'

'I propose you,' said Duggan.

'I second that,' I said.

'Please raise your hands if you agree,' said Gerry quickly.

'Hang on, that was a bit bloody quick,' Barton interrupted.

'Do you want to object, then?' asked Duggan kindly.

'Since Mr Barton's knowledge of the celluloid medium seems to leave a great deal to be desired, I fail to see any reason why he should object,' said Dudley.

'I'm not objecting. Not particularly anyway. I just said it was a bit bloody quick, that's all.'

'If you weren't objecting, I can't see why it was necessary for you to say it was quick,' Dudley persisted.

'I'm objecting because it was quick. There may be other nominations. Other people might want to be in the chair.'

'Do you wish to be nominated?'

'No. Other people might, though.'

Dudley turned, stood up, and spoke in a voice that reminded me of Mr Reed taking an assembly.

'Does anyone at this gathering wish to nominate somebody else as the chairperson of this society?' he asked. 'Alternatively, does anyone wish to be a nominee for that position?'

Somebody yawned loudly. Nobody else moved.

'I think that's proved the point,' said Dudley, looking in Barton's direction.

'Right. Well that's that, then,' Duggan announced quickly.

'Now a treasurer, and we've got about two minutes to do it,' said Gerry.

'I propose Duggan,' I said.

'I second that,' Gerry added. 'Does everybody support that?'

There was a murmuring of agreement. Barton stroked his bald head and looked on with amusement.

'This is ridiculous,' he said.

'Nonsense,' Dudley replied. 'These three gentlemen took the trouble to organise the meeting, so I think it would be reasonable to suggest that their interest in forming a film society must be very strong. I should point out that you can always demand your money back if you don't like the films they show.'

'I will if you don't show something I want to watch,' Barton objected. 'You put on a load of this high brow stuff and plenty of us will be voting with our feet.'

'That's a typically pedestrian reaction,' retorted Dudley. 'If you took the trouble to watch Bunuel, Resnais, Eisenstein…'

'Yeah, well, I prefer Frankenstein.'

'That doesn't surprise me. You seem to have the same brain capacity as his creature. Quite frankly…'

'His creature had an exceptionally good brain, mate. It was the brain of a genius. If Frankenstein hadn't dropped it on the floor…'

'Now hang on, are you talking about the James Whale version?' interrupted Ben Fellows. 'I think you're getting confused.'

'That's because his brain's been dropped on the floor, boy,' grinned Dai Thomas.

'And finally, a secretary,' Gerry shouted above the arguing.

'Speak up, please,' Alan Dawdle shouted back, twisting his hearing aid around in his ear. 'Have we got a committee yet?'

'Yes,' said Gerry. 'We're just on the secretary now.'

'Don't tell me, what's the betting your other mate gets nominated?' Barton said.

'I nominate my other mate,' said Duggan.

There was a roar of laughter and Duggan took advantage of it before Barton could interrupt again. 'Well, gentlemen,' he said quickly, 'I think that seems to be it. We'll keep you informed about the programmes and I...'

There was a sudden loud howl of agony from somewhere in the middle of the group. Duggan stopped talking, and all eyes turned to the row where the noise had come from.

'It's Hornpipe,' grinned Barton happily. 'He's dropped that bloody pipe in his lap. Hope it burns his genitalia.'

Dudley stood up awkwardly, clutching himself and brushing frantically at his corduroys. Hot ash showered everybody near him and chairs were hastily moved to one side as students near him jumped on the sparks that had scattered on the floor. Duggan watched for a moment and then made an attempt to finish what he had been saying.

'Thank you for all your kind attention. Rest assured we shall do everything in our power to justify the confidence and faith you have placed in our humble abilities. I now declare the film society... um... formed.'

Nobody was listening. The students who hadn't got up to leave were now watching Dudley with interest and Barton found it difficult to conceal his intense enjoyment.

'Oh well, that's the tough bit over,' said Gerry, gathering his notes together. 'Now all we've got to do is have a chat with Miss Pratt about borrowing the projectors. That shouldn't be too difficult.'

'No,' agreed Duggan. 'That shouldn't be very difficult at all.'

(ii)

It was obvious right from the start that Miss Pratt had rarely been inside a cinema since the day movies started to talk.

At her swooping invitation, Gerry and I moved uneasily into the small tutorial room and sat gingerly on the edge of the hard, upright chairs she brought forward for us. She placed the chairs precisely, almost as if we were about to be rigorously interviewed for a lecturing position in her department. Miss Pratt was in her early fifties and, it was strongly rumoured, had found life rather disappointing so far. Coming from a strict Catholic background, she had been brought up to fear God, pray regularly, and attend confession once every month, though since she was never guilty of anything untoward there was always precious little for her to confess.

Apparently she had never been a clever child, though she'd always shown an aptitude for study and a natural interest in geography and nature study. Like many of her peers, she had gone into teaching because it was a respectable thing to do, but after ten years of dedicated service in a small church school on the outskirts of South London she had yearned for a change and applied to lecture in the geography department at St. James's. Not only had she been successful, but she'd also received instant promotion when the incumbent head of the department had died very suddenly from a heart attack.

To her consternation, she'd learned that the post also involved responsibility for the audio-visual aids room, with its impressive collection of mechanical and electronic lecturing and teaching aids. Though she'd tried to keep abreast of developments in this field, she was much happier studying the flora and fauna of the countryside and the thought of handling a piece of technical apparatus even as basic as a tape recorder caused her to recoil in horror. She had never forgotten the day she attempted to play a tape to one of her tutorial groups and on being unable to make the tape move at all, refused student help and summoned the college maintenance engineer, who suggested it might be helpful to plug the apparatus into the mains supply first.

Nevertheless, Miss Pratt took pride in her position, had never had a day off since she'd started at the college, and cycled to work practically every morning. Most of her life, in fact, had been given over to academic pursuit of one kind or another, and she took a dim view of any student whose interest level in geography happened to be shallower than her own. To her immense credit, no student in her charge had ever failed the subject, and no other department could boast such a record, although as time had gone on she had become increasingly eccentric and absent-minded. Looking carefully at Gerry and me, Miss Pratt removed her spectacles with a theatrical flourish, scratched her nose, and drew up a third chair. Then she leaned forward and placed an elbow on her ample thigh, like a cub mistress about to have a serious heart to heart with a wilful tenderfoot.

'Now then, what's all this about?' she began earnestly. 'What's the problem?'

'We wanted to ask you about your projectors,' Gerry said brightly.

'Really? And which ones are those?'

'The ones that project sixteen millimetre film.'

'And what about them?'

'We've decided to form a film society,' I said. 'But we need your help.'

'I see,' she said at length, looking at me cautiously. 'So you're going to start a new society are you? What a good idea.' She beamed and shifted her gaze from me to Gerry, who took the initiative and beamed back.

'It is, isn't it?' he agreed brightly. 'We want to show our first programme in about three week's time and we'd like to borrow the two projectors from your department. With your permission, of course.'

Miss Pratt leaned back in her chair and eyed Gerry suspiciously, as if he'd made a mildly indecent proposal. Then she breathed on her spectacles, rubbed the lenses briskly on her skirt and pondered over the possible implications of Gerry's request.

'We've... er... already booked the films,' Gerry added quickly, hoping to sway her decision.

Miss Pratt's voice shifted into a lower register. 'Have you? I see. That may have been a little premature, of course. Now then, have you been along to the education department? They have projectors too, you know. I feel quite sure the education department...'

'Yes we have,' Gerry interrupted, 'but their machines are away for servicing.'

I glanced at him, knowing this wasn't true, but the projectors belonging to the education department were elderly, uncared for, and liable to give trouble, even though they would probably have been relatively easy to borrow.

'And so you want to use mine? Well now, I really don't know. Have you discussed all this with Dr Bradley?'

We nodded earnestly.

'And he gave his agreement that this society should go ahead?'

We both nodded again.

'I have to check, you know. All sorts of rather strange societies have been started here at one time or another. I remember a rather earnest young man coming to see me when I first came here. Edmunds, his name was. I think he wanted to start...'

'We'd take great care of them,' Gerry interrupted.

'Take great care of what?'

'The projectors. We were talking about borrowing the projectors.'

'Yes I know. I was merely saying that Andrew Edmunds wanted to use my epidiascope, and frankly, this wasn't on. I can't just...'

'We need a fairly quick decision, I'm afraid,' Gerry urged. 'We've booked the first programme, you see.'

'Have you? Well, I don't really give quick decisions. I need a little time to think about this sort of thing, you know.'

'It's only for one evening,' I said carefully. 'And of course, we'll return them the moment we have finished with them.'

'Well I should jolly well hope so, Mr…er…'

'Kent.'

'Thank you. I should jolly well hope so, Mr Kent.' She blew her nose briskly on a small embroidered handkerchief and thrust it firmly into her sleeve, as if a little embarrassed that noses had to be blown at all.

'I really couldn't let you have it for longer than that. One of my machines was borrowed without my knowledge last year. I had a quite dreadful time trying to track it down. It could have been stolen. Admittedly it wasn't a new machine, but I really can't take the chance of running unnecessary risks. I'm sure you understand.'

'Of course,' said Gerry. 'We would be very security conscious. Mind you, anyone trying to steal one of those machines would probably give himself a double rupture just lifting it off the ground.'

He grinned weakly and Miss Pratt frowned over her spectacles. 'It's hardly a joking matter, Gerald. You must appreciate that I have been given the responsibility for looking after this equipment and I take that responsibility seriously. Very seriously indeed.' She stood up and walked to the window, hands clasped tightly behind her back.

'And when would you want to borrow the equipment?'

'Just on the day of the show,' Gerry explained. 'We'd want to give the programme a run-through in the afternoon just to check the films are in good condition. And to find out the best running order.'

'Is that really necessary?'

'Well, yes. We want our show to be as professional as possible. The students are paying for it, after all.'

'Are they? Is that strictly legal?'

Gerry raised his eyebrows at me questioningly.

'I can't see why not,' I said. ' It's only to cover the cost of hiring the films.'

'Nevertheless, I think you should check that point. Indeed, I'd say it is imperative that you do so.'

'We will. And rest assured we'll take great care of the projectors and bring them back as soon as we've finished.'

'Them?' Miss Pratt looked blank for a moment.

'Yes. We'd need both projectors.'

'Both? Whatever for? You're not showing two films at the same time, are you?'

Gerry took a deep breath and spoke slowly and carefully. 'No, of course not. The thing is, the main film is sent to us on three large reels. Each one lasts for about half an hour.'

'Ah!' said Miss Pratt, like a detective uncovering a vital clue in a baffling case. 'That makes a difference, does it?'

'Yes. You see, the first reel is showing while the second one is being set up on the other projector, ready to take over when the first has finished.'

'The idea is that the audience won't notice the change over,' I added. 'Otherwise we'd have to take a few minutes to put a new reel of film on.'

'Dear me!' Miss Pratt exclaimed, sitting down again and pushing her hair away from her forehead. 'This all sounds very complicated. I think it would be a good idea to involve one or two of the lab technicians on this, don't you?'

'Not really,' said Gerry bluntly. 'It's done in the cinema all the time. In fact a feature film often comes in anything up to ten reels.'

'Does it really?' replied Miss Pratt incredulously. 'You really do surprise me. Of course, I haven't been to the cinema since… let me see now… I think it must have been the Maddon Hall Odeon soon after it first opened. Now… what was showing? Spencer… um… and… Katharine…'

'Tracy and Hepburn,' Gerry informed her quickly. She smiled brightly at him.

'Yes, that's right. How clever. A rather enjoyable film if I remember correctly. Rather a slight story, but enjoyable. Spencer… um… Tracy was a sports coach, and Katharine Hepburn…'

'Pat and Mike,' said Gerry decisively.

'Oh, I'm not sure if Pat and Mike were in it. I think it was just Spencer and Katharine.'

'No, the film was called 'Pat and Mike.' It was directed by George Cukor and it was made in 1952. The script won an Oscar nomination.'

'Good Lord,' said Miss Pratt at length, 'you have an extraordinary memory, Gerald.'

'Not really,' said Gerry modestly. 'I just happen to be interested in films.'

'Do you really? How interesting. And all these films are shown in ten little reels, are they? I'm rather surprised I've never noticed that.'

'The audience isn't supposed to,' Gerry explained patiently. 'When the first reel finishes, a signal appears on the screen and we start the next reel. If it's done properly the change-over isn't noticed by the audience.'

'Good heavens! How clever!'

'It is, isn't it?' I agreed warmly, looking at my watch and wondering how much longer this was going to take.

'Nevertheless,' said Miss Pratt, 'all this doesn't really explain why you need to use both my projectors.'

Gerry stared at her in bewilderment. He had felt so close to success and now it seemed as if she hadn't taken in a word either of us had said. I began to feel it might be best to try the education department after all. We were acutely aware that everything depended on the success of our opening night. If the films were good and the show was efficiently run, the audience would keep coming back. If we failed on our first night, the film society would join the other societies that hadn't lasted beyond one or two meetings. Gerry tried once more, a hint of desperation in his voice.

'But the show would be ruined, Miss Pratt. Especially with next month's film. The whole point of it is that the tension builds up throughout and we'd just lose it.'

'What, the film?'

'No, the tension in the film.'

'And what film is that?'

'Rear Window.'

'I see. Well, I've never heard of that one.'

'It's an Alfred Hitchcock.'

'Is it? I see.' Miss Pratt obviously didn't see at all and her lips pursed as if she had just put a slice of lemon in her mouth. 'Frankly,' she added, 'I've always regarded Alfred Hitchcock as a rather distasteful little man. And really, you know, I would have thought the students would welcome a few short breaks in the middle. After all, it doesn't take five minutes to put more film on, does it? I've done it myself, with the kind assistance of Mr Dunn from the lab. I really do think...'

'But that's not the point!' Gerry burst out, no longer able to contain his disappointment. Miss Pratt swung round and stared at him.

'It's no use getting annoyed with me, young man,' she scolded, 'no use at all. And I don't believe I've had your work on the Cotswolds yet, have I?'

Gerry's mouth dropped open in astonishment. 'No, but I don't see what that's got... anyway, I've done it. I'll bring it up in the morning.'

Miss Pratt's eyes narrowed. 'Yes. Well, that's not really good enough. I realise you weren't looking very well at my last lecture, but you've had plenty of time since then. Everyone else in the group has not only completed the work but also, I might add, handed it in. I really cannot see how you expect me to have your work marked in time for the next lecture if it is not handed in. Can you?'

She raised her eyebrows and the tip of her nose went bright pink, a sure sign that she was annoyed and on the defensive. Gerry remained speechless at this outburst and sat looking at her with a disbelieving grin on his face.

'And another thing,' she continued, getting into her stride

and ignoring my presence altogether, 'your essay on the source of the Medway was below the standard I expect. I don't know which reference books you used, but they certainly weren't current.'

'Yes, I know,' Gerry objected, 'but all the best reference books...'

'I really haven't time to listen to excuses. To put it in a nutshell, Gerald, we are doing British and European geography, supposedly in some depth. You started this course extremely well, but I cannot say the same for your most recent work. You seem to have muddled the French coal producing areas with the mines of Alsace-Lorraine and your essay on the industrial towns was far too sketchily written. If you are going to mention the Lyons region, I cannot see why you have left out Saint-Etienne and Le Creusot.'

'But the essay was basically about the Marseilles region,' Gerry interrupted. 'I wrote about three pages on that alone.'

Miss Pratt crossed her legs and folded her arms in a stubborn and determined pose.

'In an examination, you would be required to answer the questions you were asked. If you were asked to write about the slate quarries of Wales, there would be little point in writing about the agriculture of Scotland just because you happen to know more about it.'

'I don't think that's very fair...'

'Fairness doesn't really come into it. You know as well as I do that to pass this course you have to satisfy the examiners that you have reached a certain standard.'

She looked at me suddenly and raised her eyebrows, as if wondering what on earth I was doing in the room.

'Oh, and this projector business,' she concluded, suddenly snapping into focus, 'I'm afraid I really can't place one of my machines in your care unless I have specific instructions to do so from the Principal, and I am quite sure he would agree with me that I cannot let all and sundry use just what they want unless Mr Dunn is going to preside while the equipment is being used. If anything should be broken, my classes would be greatly inconvenienced.'

She turned to her desk and took out a pile of papers for marking, obviously considering the whole distasteful matter closed.

'Thank you very much,' said Gerry sarcastically as he opened the door.

'That's quite enough, thank you,' she replied sharply. 'And please make sure you hand in your piece of work by tomorrow morning at the very latest. If you have no other lectures today I would suggest you could be gainfully employed in finishing it, rather than planning to show... er... whatever it is.'

'The Glenn Miller Story'.

'Really. Well, I don't think I've heard of that. What's that all about?'

'Glenn Miller,' said Gerry. 'It's his story.'

She ignored the irony and returned to her papers. We wandered back to our corridor, hardly believing that such a simple request could have proved so unsuccessful and disappointing.

'That's that, then,' Gerry said miserably, sitting heavily on the chair in the corner of his room. 'What are we going to do now?'

'Two things. First, go and see the Doc. Then, if that doesn't work, we'll just have to settle for the steam driven equipment in the education department.'

'I still think it's pretty hopeless.'

'Not yet,' I said. 'Look, I'm supposed to be meeting Samantha for a coffee in a minute. Go and have a talk to him.'

'That's hardly practical. If you don't catch him first thing in the morning you have to make an appointment three weeks ahead.'

'It's worth a try. Do you want this society to get off the ground or not? He's always reasonable and he might actually be in his office. Just try and persuade him to talk to Miss Pratt.'

'All right, I'll give it one try. Then I suppose I'd better get this Cotswolds thing finished. Perhaps if I do that brilliantly she'll change her mind anyway.'

He strode off down the corridor, his long legs taking determined strides and his hands thrust deep into his jacket pockets. I wandered back to my own room and half-heartedly began to tidy it. Because the room was relatively small, and because books, pieces of equipment, clothes, mugs, coffee jars, magazines and the classical guitar I'd bought for a pittance in a local junk shop were demanding a place to be kept, I abandoned my efforts very quickly. The room was beginning to resemble a council tip under pressure. I made a mental note to get it tidied that evening, put on my only remaining clean pullover, and walked down the road to the Wimpy bar near the library. It was already very crowded, and Samantha was sitting inside near the window. She looked up, smiled and moved to give me room. I ordered some coffee, two slices of strawberry gateaux and sat down.

'What's the matter with you?' she asked, seeing the frown on my face. 'You haven't been studying too hard, have you?'

I smiled at her and wondered how she always managed to look so attractive.

'I always study hard,' I said. 'I'm a naturally hard-working student.'

'Really? Well, that's a first, then. So what are you looking so miserable for?'

'I'm not really miserable. Just a bit annoyed. We've been trying to borrow projectors from the geography department.'

'Oh, for your film society?'

'Yes. We might just as well have been trying to break into Fort Knox.' I told her all about the meeting with Miss Pratt.

'That's odd,' she said. 'I know that the people who ran a film society before you managed all right. They must have been able to borrow projectors from one of the departments. And they certainly had two of them. Perhaps Miss Pratt wasn't lecturing at the college then.'

The waitress put two plates with slices of strawberry gateaux on the table, and slipped a bill underneath my cup and saucer.

'This'll make you fat, you know,' said Samantha.

'I doubt it. Look at all the exercise I get running up and down the college stairs. And chasing you. Go on, have a piece.'

'I don't know how you can afford these luxuries on a student grant. I'll just have a half a slice. You eat the rest. It'll cheer you up. And you never know, you might get back and find Dr Bradley has said you can use whatever you like.'

'I doubt it.'

'My, we are happy today!'

'I'm sorry. It's a shame, that's all.'

'It'll be alright. I bet it all turns out to be a great success.'

She blew on her coffee and took a cautious sip. Then she looked up at me quickly.

'Look, I've got a great idea. If you want the Doc to agree, then you've got to make it appear you're doing something really worthwhile.'

'Like what?'

'Wait a minute. I'm just about to explain. Why don't you write to St Bernard's and put on a special show for some of their boys?'

'St Bernard's?'

'St Bernard's Day School for boys with behavioural difficulties, emotional problems and so on. I see one of their teachers, Alan Green, quite often. He comes to the library and borrows records and things. He's a smashing bloke, and I bet he'd love to bring a group along. Especially if you're showing The Glenn Miller Story.'

I realised her idea had definite possibilities. Dr Bradley would certainly be enthusiastic, and we could even hire a few cartoons for the special show as well.

'You're a genius,' I said, and squeezed her hand. 'Can you have a word with their teacher when he comes in the library next?'

'Of course. He'll probably come in on Tuesday. I'll ask him then.'

'It really is a good idea, Sam. What a shame Gerry's already gone to see the Doc. Perhaps he won't be in. In which case, I'll go and see him first thing in the morning. Got any more good suggestions?'

She looked at her empty coffee cup.

'Mmm. You can buy me another coffee. I've just got time. And you could take me to the proper movies tonight. 'Seven Brides For Seven Brothers' is on again at the Cameo. I like Howard Keel.'

'My God, Dai Thomas will probably be in the front row, joining in with the songs. Are you sure you want that?'

'Sounds absolutely delightful. I love the film anyway. Can you afford it?'

'Just about. Provided you buy me another slice of gateaux.'

(iii)

Back at college, I hurried to Gerry's room to discuss Samantha's suggestion and to see what had happened at his meeting with Dr Bradley. I found Duggan and Gerry thumbing through film catalogues.

'Hey Mike, guess what,' Duggan grinned, 'Gerry not only consulted the good Doctor. He actually managed to persuade him. What a clever sod, eh?'

'The man's a bit of a film buff,' Gerry explained. 'The theatre is really his thing, but he knows a bit about film as well. Loves Westerns. We sat and discussed the films of John Ford, and then he said of course we could use the projectors, and he'd see Miss Pratt about it this afternoon. So that's that. He even promised to buy a ticket for the first show.'

'Doesn't want to go in the balcony, does he?' asked Duggan cautiously.

'I shouldn't think so. I think we reserve the balcony for Barton and his entourage.'

'That why I'm afraid he might want to go up there.'

'I might even have a go at selling a ticket to Miss Pratt,' said Gerry.

'Dear God, don't let's get carried away. Anyway, if we spend the next couple of days catching up on the essays we were supposed to have handed in months ago, we can get cracking on the advertising. We need a lot of people at the first show.'

Publicity was important to every thriving college society. If nobody knew what you were doing, nobody bothered to come, and even if people did know what you were doing, they still might not come if it was raining. New ways of announcing forthcoming attractions were continually being invented by tiny but determined committees. It was especially important if more than one event was going to be held on the same night and societies had to compete with one another for an audience. A fair amount of forward planning had to be done, together with a generally unspoken agreement that co-operation was necessary to achieve a result acceptable to both parties. A lively hop was never held when the drama club was presenting a show, and the operatic society never practised next to the chess club.

The best places for advertising were the large notice boards screwed to the wall in the ground floor corridor and outside the dining hall. Practically everybody attended the evening meal, and those who were at a loss for something to do that evening always read the 'What's On In College' guide. Sometimes, a bold club secretary would bang a spoon on the table and announce an evening activity while everybody was eating, but this took some nerve as he was likely to be mercilessly heckled unless the message was wittily delivered.

Two days after Doctor Bradley had agreed that the projectors could be used, our newly-formed film society began working on the publicity side of its first performance. Duggan had decided it would be best to paint as many film posters as we could manage between us, and then display them in prominent positions around the college building. Gerry spent a morning sorting through catalogues to find three suitable short films to make up the programme length, and I filled in an order form for soft drinks, wrapped biscuits, crisps and packets of nuts for Samantha to sell during the interval.

'We need to think carefully about our refreshment tactics,' Duggan said, 'We've got to make sure we go about it in the right way. If we're going to sell all this stuff we really ought to have Samantha standing out the front in a bikini. Then we show a short documentary about the Sahara desert. By the time we get to the interval they'll be absolutely dying for a drink.'

'It's not a bad idea at that,' said Gerry. 'Suppose I took a few slides of her posing with some bottles? Then we could show them on the filmstrip projector to entice the audience to buy. We could do some stills of our future programmes as well.'

'What about it Mike?' Duggan smiled. 'Do you think Samantha would agree to all that?'

'I'm sure she would. You'd have to borrow the strip projector from Miss Pratt, though.'

'Forget it,' said Gerry immediately.

'Wait, wait!' Duggan exclaimed, pacing up and down the room, 'it needs a few other brilliant publicity ideas. We need a few stunts. Like the day we're showing 'High Noon', I could ride into the dining room on a horse. They'd like that. Or even better, Samantha could ride in on a horse. Scantily dressed. They'd like that even better. Or perhaps Miss Pratt would do it. What about it?'

'Got any more ideas like that?' Gerry asked coldly.

'Stacks. Like when we show the Polish war thing, you blokes could dress up as Germans, run into the dining room and kidnap somebody.'

'Great,' I said.

'Marvellous,' said Gerry. 'I notice you don't tend to include yourself in these brilliant suggestions.'

'Of course not. Someone's got to organise it all. I'd be the man on the outside.'

'To return to the matter in hand,' said Gerry, taking a roll of paper from behind his wardrobe, 'I suggest we move into Duggan's room. Or Mike's. Milly has just tidied up in here.'

We gathered together the paper, brushes and paint that Gerry had managed to smuggle out of the art room, and carried it into Duggan's bedroom, only to find that Milly was now busy in there. Since my room was still in a very untidy state we decided to do what we could in there, and then spread out along the corridor. I shifted my books and equipment from the table and floor, Gerry rolled back the carpet and Duggan went off in search of old cups to mix powder paint in. He returned with eight plastic beakers borrowed from the kitchen and a selection of spoons for stirring the paint. The roll of cartridge paper was divided up into a dozen sheets of reasonable size and we set to work, sketching first and then painting. The small room very quickly became a publicity production factory.

After an hour of feverish activity, there were several puddles of paint on the floor because Duggan had kicked over the same beaker three times while working in a very confined space. Scribbled ideas littered the desk, used tea cups piled up on the window sills, and the air was thick with smoke from Gerry's pipe, which he always puffed copiously when his mind was switched to active mode. The smell was particularly strong because he'd burnt a hole in my bedspread after absent-mindedly putting his pipe down on it for a moment.

Even though I'd removed all my books from the shelves to protect them from the mess, the edges of several had become smeared with green and I'd packed them tightly into the top of the wardrobe out of the way. Meanwhile, Duggan had attempted to give the edges of his poster an attractive mottled effect by dipping a toothbrush in paint and then pulling a piece of card across it. Unfortunately, on a practice run, he had pulled the card the wrong way across the bristles and the brush had distributed its load across everything except the piece of paper.

Even so, by late afternoon we had produced enough posters to advertise Glenn Miller in each of the corridors, the staircase, and the main hall. Gerry applied a match to the bowl of his pipe, attempted to brush some dried powder paint from his trousers without the slightest success, and stood surveying the results of his work so far.

'They're not bad, you know,' he said. 'I didn't know I could paint. I should have taken art as a main subject.'

'Shame we're not still on teaching practice,' said Duggan, washing out some of the brushes. 'The kids could have turned out hundreds of these posters. I bet they'd have loved it, too.'

'I might pin one on Miss Pratt's bum,' said Gerry thoughtfully.

'You've got quite a thing about her,' said Duggan, picking flecks of paint from his trousers. 'I'm getting quite worried. Anyway, we need about a dozen more posters.'

'The roll of paper's finished,' said Gerry. 'I'll go up to the art room and see if I can get a bit more.'

'Okay. I'll wander down the road and get a packet of tea.'

When they had gone, I gathered some of the posters together and laid them end to end in the corridor outside my room to clear some space before we began again. I decided there wasn't much point in tidying up if we were going to carry on for a while, so I sat down on my bed, picked up my guitar, and thumbed a few chords I'd learned at guitar club the night before.

A few minutes later there was a sturdy knock at the door. Expecting to see Gerry loaded down with paper, I threw it open, to find Miss Bottle standing outside with a very tall woman in her late fifties. I had never seen her before. She was immaculately dressed in a light blue two piece suit, and she obviously took great care and pride in her appearance. Miss Bottle took a step back and looked quizzically at the splashes of purple and yellow paint on my face. Then, recovering from her initial surprise, she smiled doubtfully and peered round the door, as if a booby trap might be lying in wait for her the moment she took a step inside.

'Ah, dear, it's Mr Kent, isn't it?' she asked brightly. 'I'm so glad you're in. Nobody else seems to be in along this corridor.'

I wasn't surprised. The college was usually fairly deserted on Wednesday afternoons when there were very few set lectures.

'This is Miss Trent, dear,' Miss Bottle announced, taking a bold step inside the room and searching for a relatively uncluttered piece of floor before she edged her companion in as well. 'She's a lecturer, too.'

'I'm from Fenchurch Road Teacher Training College. For female students, of course,' Miss Trent explained briefly, recovering her composure after the initial shock, and holding out her hand. I held mine out too, and then withdrew it quickly as I noticed the purple paint on my fingers, and Miss Trent's spotlessly white gloves. I smiled happily instead, and Miss Trent looked at me carefully, as if unsure whether it really was purple paint on my face, or a recently contracted disease.

'My, you certainly seem to be busy,' Miss Bottle commented diplomatically, feeling that something ought to be said about the condition of the room before moving on to discuss higher things. 'I didn't know you were studying art, Mr Kent. I thought science was your subject?'

'It is. We've started a film appreciation society and we're painting posters to advertise the first show.'

'Is that what the pictures in the corridor were? How exciting. And what are you showing? I'm afraid I didn't read the posters.'

'The Glenn Miller Story.'

'Oh, I don't know that one. What's it about?'

'Glenn Miller. It's his story. We're not advertising very successfully then.'

'Don't worry, young man. I read them,' said Miss Trent briskly, revealing large, perfectly white teeth behind her liberally applied lipstick. 'I noticed because somebody hasn't spelt Glenn correctly. There should be two 'n's.'

I looked out of the door at the posters. Duggan's last four had indeed been spelt incorrectly. 'You're absolutely right. My friend must have been so keen to finish them he didn't notice.'

'Probably got caught up in a creative flow,' said Miss Trent enthusiastically. 'It happens with children all the time, of course. They become so involved with their writing they want to get all their ideas on paper as quickly as possible and ignore their spelling.'

'Yes, I noticed that on teaching practice,' I said. 'It's quite annoying. They forget to put in full stops, capital letters, speech marks...'

'I hope you didn't interfere and place too much emphasis on grammar and punctuation?' Miss Trent interrupted. 'That just becomes a quick way of stunting the river of creativity. We have to be jolly careful about marking children's work too. The quickest way to put children off writing is to point out their mistakes.'

'But surely,' I objected, 'children need to learn…'

Aware that a tricky dialogue might be developing, Miss Bottle quickly steered the conversation in a different direction.

'Mr Kent did jolly well on his first teaching practice,' she interrupted. 'I supervised him. He brought a lot of science into the work he did.'

'So you're studying the sciences, are you?' asked Miss Trent.

'That's right. Science and English literature were my best subjects at school.'

'Really? That's rather a strange combination, isn't it?'

'Judging from what I saw on his teaching practice, he seems to have a jolly good knowledge about all sorts of things,' said Miss Bottle. 'Don't you, dear?'

Miss Trent took a decisive step into the middle of the room and leaned against the study bench near the window. It shuddered and then moved forward as she disturbed the book that was supporting one of its legs. Her hand slid from the edge of the bench and she momentarily lost her balance.

'Dear me,' Miss Bottle gasped, leaping to the assistance of her visitor and leaving a large footprint in the middle of one of our posters. 'They really ought to fix your workdesk, Mr Kent. Has it been in that state for long?'

'Quite a while,' I said. 'I've mentioned it, but nothing has been done so far.' My face coloured slightly as I remembered Duggan accidentally banging the table against the wall when he was setting it up for table tennis during our corridor sports week. Miss Bottle put a hand gently on my shoulder.

'Don't worry, Mr Kent. I'll speak to the caretaker about it and have it repaired. You must find it most frustrating.' She jotted a few words in the tiny notebook she always carried around in her handbag, and then turned back towards her visitor.

'Miss Trent is extremely interested in our education syllabus, dear,' she continued. 'We've had a fascinating chat about it. She wanted to have a look at our study-bedrooms to compare them with the sort of facilities they have at Fenchurch Road. I'm sure you don't mind. We didn't want to go barging into somebody's room if they weren't in.'

'I don't mind at all,' I said. 'It's just that we weren't expecting anyone. Otherwise I'd have cleared up a bit.'

Miss Trent screwed her eyes up and stared at the floor, as if unable to believe that a room could be quite so untidy, even for a male college.

'It's quite all right,' she said unconvincingly. 'After all, we have called without an appointment. I quite understand you being busy. Never time to waste. My room was always like this... well, not quite like this... when I was at college. Always untidy when I was researching one thing or another.'

'It is rather a mess, dear,' Miss Bottle added. 'I always thought you were such a tidy person. Your displays of work on teaching practice were so precisely arranged.'

Miss Trent gingerly took one pace nearer the window, removed a glove, and wiped a streak of dust from one of the panes with her finger.

'What a splendid view from here,' she murmured. 'You can see Big Ben and.. oh...' She stopped in mid-sentence, realising that her left foot had trodden heavily on a chocolate eclair and the cream had shot neatly inside her shoe.

'That's not a very sensible place to leave a cake, dear,' Miss Bottle said, tutting sympathetically. She picked up a paintbrush and handed it to her companion, who scraped some of the eclair from her shoe, wrapped the remains in a paper handkerchief, and then deposited the distasteful little package in the overflowing waste bin. Unable to find anywhere to put the paintbrush, she replaced it carefully on the floor near the radiator, which was currently being used to dry four pairs of my underpants.

'Really, dear,' said Miss Bottle, 'there are plates in the college you know.'

'I would imagine they are probably used for mixing paint,' Miss Trent commented grimly. 'Just as the bookshelves seem to be used for storing it. You don't seem to have many books, Mr Kent. Where do you keep them? Under the bed?'

'I've moved them into the cupboard while we paint,' I replied quickly, beginning to feel a little irritated.

'And do you find two bookshelves enough? Our girls at Fenchurch Road have two, but we're considering making it three per room.'

'It's probably a good idea to keep your books in the cupboard anyway,' said Miss Bottle brightly, her loyalty to me undiminished. 'What with all the new buildings going up outside you must find everything gets very grubby.'

'And of course they do tend to make excellent wedges for table legs, eh, Mr Kent?' Miss Trent added. 'I am sure it was one use of her work on the psychology of teaching that Eleanor Snellings never considered.'

'Frankly, I think it's a very good use for it,' I said irritably. 'It's a thoroughly annoying book.'

Miss Trent's moved her spectacles down her nose and stared over them at me. 'Really? I'd beg to differ. It is a very highly regarded work.'

'Well, so it may be, but I don't think the author has had much experience of what teaching is really like. I mean, my classroom experience may be limited, but it seems to me you've got to teach children to read before they can do much else...'

'The book doesn't argue with that...'

'Yes it does. It's full of crackpot ideas, like letting children choose their own books to read and throwing reading schemes in the dustbin. Presumably they are supposed to learn to read by osmosis.'

'Reading schemes are very limiting, Mr Kent. You have to build on the natural sense of wonder in young people. They must acquire skills, of course, but they must acquire them naturally as part of what they are doing, and not just in isolation.'

I had a vivid mental picture of my last class, and John Rouse in particular. A sense of wonder wasn't, I thought, a phrase that one could readily apply to John Rouse.

'Excuse me, dear,' said Miss Bottle, 'I think I just ought to mention...'

'Look,' I interrupted, 'Children need a sense of stability and progression. They've got to value school, and they've got to value their classroom. And it seems to me they've got to be taught. In a lot of schools children wander round the classroom on the pretence of doing something and not really achieving anything at all. The classroom I was in on teaching practice was extremely successful because the teacher was outstanding. The children wanted to learn, and she moved them gently forward all the time...'

'I don't doubt it for a moment,' Miss Trent replied, her face becoming flushed. 'Equally, there are many teachers who are pushing small children much too hard. Do you know much about reading readiness, Mr Kent?'

'Judging from what other students have said about their teaching practice schools, there are lots of inner city children who get half way through their junior schools without being able to read at all. And some of the teachers themselves are bewildered by half-baked theories they get from books like that one.'

'I would suggest you keep an open mind, Mr Kent,' Miss Trent persisted, reddening more. 'I would have thought it essential that students at least make some attempt to embrace current thinking.'

'I do. I'm also anxious that we don't fail children. I think we should proceed cautiously, and make sure things work before we adopt a practice just because it happens to be fashionable. And that book, in my view, could do a great deal of damage.'

I felt suddenly amused by the absurdity of the situation. I was trying to reason with an irritating woman while standing in a tiny room amongst a clutter of paint-filled plates and colourful posters. My hair was sprayed yellow, there were streaks of purple on my face, and a chocolate éclair was leaking its contents across the floor. Miss Trent stood her ground, looking very annoyed but afraid to move unless she accidentally soiled some other part of her clothing. I assumed she was rarely challenged by her female students.

'I'm sorry you feel that way about the book,' she said firmly. 'Personally I feel it has some very worthwhile thinking.'

'Really? What makes you think that?'

'Probably the fact that she wrote it, dear,' Miss Bottle interrupted quickly. My mouth dropped open.

'I beg your pardon?' I gasped.

'She wrote the book, dear,' Miss Bottle repeated.

'But the author's name…'

'It's a pseudonym, dear.'

I blushed quickly. 'Oh, I'm sorry,' I said, wanting to roll myself up in one of the posters and drift gently away down the corridor. 'Obviously I wouldn't have been quite so…'

'Mr Kent is actually going to be a very good teacher,' said Miss Bottle quickly and diplomatically, feeling it essential to pour just a little oil on very troubled water. 'As I mentioned, I supervised his last practice.'

'And where was that, Mr Kent?' Miss Trent asked curtly. 'A Victorian establishment still coming to terms with the monitorial system?'

I could feel my cheeks reddening. 'Briar Road. In Islington.'

'Oh yes, I know it well. We use it ourselves. Mr Reed is the headteacher. Extremely good fellow. He's developed some very interesting classrooms there. You were very lucky.'

I frowned, annoyed to hear Mr Reed being given credit for the dedicated work of the teachers I had been involved with at the school.

'It's all down to the staff, actually,' I said. 'I can't say I was particularly impressed with Mr Reed.'

Miss Trent looked quite shocked.

'Really? Personally I have always found him most obliging. I hardly think a few weeks in a school is enough to make a measured judgement of a headteacher's qualities, Mr Kent.'

'Why not? Students are assessed after a few weeks on teaching practice.'

'The two things are totally dissimilar. A headteacher must have the skill to recognise ability in his teachers and develop them to the full. In my view, Mr Reed...'

'We did have some trouble with the photocopier, as I recall,' Miss Bottle interrupted gently, grasping at any available straw.

'Absolutely,' I agreed. 'There's a case in point. All I wanted to do...'

There was a crash outside the door, followed by an agonised yell. 'Open the bloody door, Mike!' Gerry's voice shouted. 'I've dropped the lot all over the place.' I swung round and put my head out of the door to warn him, but it was too late.

'Got stacks of the stuff,' Gerry said loudly. 'So long as no-one misses it. Look, I've got these tins of...'

His expression changed abruptly as he caught sight of Miss Bottle, who made an effort to talk in a very loud voice to Miss Trent about the lovely study-bedrooms the students had. Gerry made an ineffectual attempt to conceal the tins of powder paint and then his face went a violent red.

'And this is one of your companions, is it, Mr Kent?' asked Miss Trent.

Gerry hovered for a moment, took the pipe from between his teeth, and opened his mouth to say something. His eyes moved cautiously from one woman to the other, and then, after a brief but intense silence, he decided there wasn't really much point in saying anything at all. He replaced his pipe and grinned with embarrassment instead.

'Come in dear,' said Miss Bottle cheerfully, 'Miss Trent and I were just leaving.'

She stepped over the rubble in the corridor, helped Miss Trent to do likewise and stared straight in front of her down the corridor. 'We'll… er… leave you to it so that you can carry on with your… um… posters,' she smiled. 'Jolly good luck with your film thing. What was it you're showing?'

'Well, a mixture really,' Gerry said, obviously wanting the meeting to end as pleasantly as possible. 'We're starting with a film about Glenn Miller, then there'll be some Hitchcock, a couple of musicals.. and some foreign films by people like Ingmar Bergman.'

'Oh yes, I've seen her in several films,' said Miss Bottle enthusiastically. 'Now what was that lovely one some time back, about the life of Gladys Aylward?'

'I think you mean Ingrid Bergman,' said Gerry politely.

'That's right dear. Who did you think I meant?'

'I was talking about Ingmar Bergman. The director. The film you were talking about was 'The Inn Of The Sixth Happiness'.'

'Oh dear, was it?' she said, looking puzzled and staring closely at one of the posters on the floor. 'Anyway, jolly good luck with it.'

'Oh God!' Gerry groaned as soon as they had gone down the stairs. 'Do you think she heard what I said? Miss Bottle, I mean?'

'I shouldn't be at all surprised,' I said. 'Unless they're both extremely deaf.'

'Oh my God. Miss Bottle is bound to tell someone I've taken that stuff without asking.'

'Not necessarily. She didn't really know what was going on. Anyway, she might think you asked for it.'

'I've asked for it all right. Who was she anyway? The other one, I mean?'

'It was his mother,' said Duggan, appearing in the doorway with a freshly made pot of tea. 'Have you got any cups there without paint in?

'No,' Gerry muttered. 'Who was she?'

'I told you. It was his mother. She came up to bring him some clean underwear. Here you are, it's a bit weak, I'm afraid. They only had cheap teabags.'

I passed the cup to Gerry. He piled sugar in it and sat nestling the cup dejectedly in his hands.

'It was a lecturer from another college,' I said. 'She was wondering if you had enough bookshelves to hold all your books.'

'Was she? That was sweet of her. She didn't bring any teabags, I suppose? Hey, look what she's done to my bloody eclair!' He inspected the remains sadly and tossed them into the bucket.

'I couldn't help that,' I said. 'You left it there.'

'You might have told her we eat off the floor. Real cream, too. Almost cost my entire grant. I suppose you've eaten all yours?' he added hopefully.

I nodded.

'I thought so. A shame I wasn't here, I'd have taken her along to my room and sold her a ticket. Never mind, I suppose it's time the world knew the truth about your laundry.'

'Thank you.'

'Don't mention it. Here, drink this quickly, and then let's get on, or we'll never be ready for premiere night.'

(iv)

Amazingly, the first meeting of the newly formed St James's Film Society exceeded even the committee's expectations.

As the first night approached, events and ideas quickly gathered momentum. Friends from the art department offered to paint additional publicity material, and three days before the show it was impossible to walk more than twenty yards without coming across a visual reminder that Glenn Miller, supported by Tom and Jerry, would shortly be making a celluloid visit. An older student, who had worked for a while as an electrician before deciding to become a teacher, offered his services in rigging up a set of coloured lights around the screen that would dim effectively and help create a cinema atmosphere. Gerry bought some cassettes of movie themes to pipe through the screen loudspeakers before the show and during the interval, feeling that money spent on minor details would help counter the discomfort of the hard wooden lecture seats, especially the long benches in the balcony that had survived since the last brick of the building had been cemented into place.

Since Gerry was also determined to bring a little culture into the proceedings, he had compiled a small programme booklet, containing a few notes about the feature and the three supporting short films, followed by two paragraphs about the society and its intentions. He had also persuaded four of the local shops to pay a small sum in return for having their services advertised in the programme, and this had covered the cost of producing the booklet. On the last two pages, he had put a list of possible future films, with a request that students should put a tick against any they would like us to show in the future.

Leaving no stone unturned in our efforts to ensure a successful evening, we'd also spent a frustrating Saturday morning in the park trying to photograph Samantha holding a selection of refreshments that would be available during the interval. Unfortunately, after a handful of photographs the session had been threatened by rain and an elderly park keeper who stated that he was sick of photographers from soft porn magazines taking pictures of girls in his park. When we pointed out that we were trustworthy academic students from the local training college, he said it wouldn't have surprised him if we were the bleedin' lot who had tried to nick a goose off the pond last week, and he would appreciate it if we left, right now.

Our original intention had been to show the advertisements on one of the geography department's slide projectors. Since Gerry flatly refused to consider another encounter with Miss Pratt, Duggan had said he would go and ask her, provided Gerry agreed to copy up some science notes for him. Assuming her discussion with Dr Bradley was mainly responsible, Duggan was pleased to discover Miss Pratt's attitude towards the society had mellowed considerably. He was even more surprised when she enquired, with interest, how the film about the miller went.

'She's bringing the slide projector herself,' Duggan announced when he returned from her lecture room. 'She's going to bring some slides as well. She said something about her holiday on the Isle of Wight.'

'What?' Gerry gasped, looking up from the desk where he was making tickets with a children's John Bull printing outfit. 'What did you say?'

'She's coming to run the thing herself,' Duggan repeated. Gerry's jaw dropped, and he caught his pipe as it was about to fall into his lap.

'What? With her slides? What d'you mean, run the thing herself?'

'I couldn't really refuse, could I? She says she's taken about forty slides of birdlife in Shanklin and she thought they would probably go down quite well.'

Gerry sat transfixed, staring at him across the room. 'Duggan, you didn't actually agree to...'

'I couldn't refuse. I mean, she asked so nicely.'

'But... but...'

'He's messing about,' I said. 'She'd never come near the place.'

'Oh my God!' Gerry cried, accidentally printing a ticket on the back of his hand, 'I thought you were serious. I tell you, if you'd been serious I wouldn't have been there...'

But Miss Pratt did come. Three other lecturers came too, including Miss Bottle, who had dressed for the occasion as if she was attending a gala premiere in Leicester Square. About a hundred students and their friends crowded into the small lecture theatre just before seven thirty, and despite the already inflated price for balcony seats, there was an immediate scramble for them. Deciding on the spur of the moment that the balcony represented the ideal seller's market, Duggan doubled the price and was astonished when nobody objected. Outside the hall, Dudley Hornpipe had set up a hot dog stand to raise money for charity and he beamed at the business that flocked in his direction before the show had even started.

As the house lights were switched off and the coloured bulbs around the screen slowly dimmed into darkness, I experienced a momentary pang of anxiety. Suppose a projector failed, or a lamp blew, or somebody accidentally trod on a loudspeaker wire. Everything had been fine during the afternoon run-through, but now the moment we had planned for during the past six weeks had finally arrived and we wanted it to be right. I glanced round at Gerry, operating the second projector, and Gerry grinned back at me happily. Keeping my fingers crossed, I flicked the machine into life. The MGM Tom and Jerry logo flashed onto the screen and the familiar opening theme filled the auditorium. Not expecting a cartoon, the audience roared with delighted approval. It felt, I thought, just like the Saturday morning picture shows I'd loved as a child.

Gerry's choice of award-winning short films that filled the first half of the programme had been well chosen, and there was something for all tastes. After the second film, Dudley shrewdly moved his hot dog stand into the doorway, contravening every fire regulation but sending a tempting smell of sausage, fried onions and ketchup across the first ten rows. As students succumbed to slipping out and buying another one, Gerry realised, along with other members of the audience, that his pamphlet of programme notes was almost tailor-made to wrap around Dudley's hot dogs.

By the time the interval arrived, the popularity of the evening had been assured. Samantha battled to keep in line the queue that formed to buy drinks, crisps and nuts from her, and she was invited out to dinner nine times before she managed to appeal for some assistance from Rashid's girlfriend and Barton's muscle. In ten minutes she had sold everything on the table, and she made a mental note to order double the amount next time. Then she carried the last two cans of orange up to the back of the lecture theatre, handed one to Gerry and the other to me, and then snuggled into the cramped space beside me. Then the hall lights dimmed again in readiness for the main film of the evening.

There was a brief moment of panic in the second half of the programme. The Glenn Miller Story had obviously been hired out many times and a splice came apart in the first reel. For a moment, the screen was flooded with white light while Gerry carried out a hurried temporary repair, teeth clenched firmly on his pipe, and muttering under his breath. I flashed one of the slides he had prepared for just such an emergency onto the screen, stating that the film would continue as soon as the projectionist had returned from the lavatory. There was a sympathetic cheer from the crowded hall.

The rest of the evening passed uneventfully, and ninety minutes later, as the Glenn Miller Story moved into its final reel, I glanced around in contentment at the audience and savoured the moment.

'I think your film society is going to be very successful,' Samantha whispered. 'Especially if tonight is anything to go by.' In the warmth and closeness of the evening, I could smell her perfume and I was captivated by her beauty. I moved very close to her and kissed her hair softly.

'Do you fancy coming up in the balcony?' I said quietly. 'Duggan could take over here.'

'Now come on,' she smiled, 'Keep your eye on your projector. You don't want them all asking for their money back, do you?'

'It's your fault. You shouldn't smell so gorgeous. I could really…'

'I know you could. Watch Glenn Miller instead.'

The music swelled as the last scene of the film came to an end and the credits began to appear on the screen. The students applauded and cheered enthusiastically and when the lights were turned on they sat chatting contentedly to each other for a few minutes before gradually moving towards the door. The couples in the balcony, many of whom hadn't even noticed that the lights had come back on, seemed very disappointed that it was all over and put their coats on slowly. Barton emerged from under his enormous trench coat, and a tiny but very pretty redheaded student he had met at a rock concert the week before emerged a moment later.

'Great stuff, lads,' he said, taking a deep breath. 'Going to be weekly, is it?'

'Probably,' said Duggan. 'If the next few evenings are as successful as this, we won't go into teaching, we'll go into entertainment. Enjoy the film?'

'Certainly did. Bit frightening, though. That's why Deidre kept dragging me under the coat.'

Deidre shuffled with embarrassment and her cheeks reddened.

'You lying sod,' she said. 'You told me you were cold. I wanted to watch the film.'

'Really? I didn't get that impression.'

Deidre's cheeks became redder, Barton grinned sheepishly, and he gently steered her towards the door. When the hall had finally emptied, Gerry carefully packed the projectors into their pristine cardboard boxes, and locked them in the large cupboards behind the screen, where Miss Pratt had insisted they were to be kept overnight. Duggan took down the screen lights and dismantled the sound system, while Samantha cleared the litter that had been dropped during the course of the evening. Then, flushed with the success of the venture, the four of us walked slowly back to Duggan's room.

'Are you going to chance my coffee, Samantha?' Duggan asked.

'Coffee? I think it ought to be a gin and tonic at the very least. Especially after all the work I've done for you lot tonight.'

Duggan put his arm round her shoulders and pulled her to him. 'I know. We couldn't have done it without you. You're a treasure. Isn't she, Mike? I tell you what, I've got a teeny bottle of scotch in my drawer somewhere. I bought it after a hard day on teaching practice. You can have a drop in your coffee.'

Gerry pushed the door of Duggan's room open and heaved the bag of money onto the table.

‘We seem to have made a staggering amount by the look of things,’ he said. ‘At this rate we’ll soon be able to hire Ben Hur in 70mm and six track stereo. I’ll put the kettle on. You and Mike count the money.’

After ten minutes of concentrated counting, Duggan looked up.

‘Wow!’ he cried, ‘This is bloody amazing. And I haven’t done the drinks money yet. Or the percentage from the hot dogs.’

‘What percentage from the hot dogs?’ Gerry asked.

‘Dudley’s stall. I said we’d expect fifteen per cent of his takings for letting him flog his food to our patrons. Actually, I was joking, but he agreed straightaway. Well, we might as well have it, eh? And the drinks. We seem to have done very well on them. Or at least, Samantha did. And Gerry hasn’t paid for the three wafer biscuits he nicked at the run-through this afternoon.’

‘What wafer biscuits?’

‘The wafer biscuits I saw you eating just after the Tom and Jerry.’

‘I didn’t have any wafer biscuits.’

‘Yes you did. You took Tom and Jerry off the projector and asked me where Glenn Miller was. Only you couldn’t, because your mouth was full of wafer biscuits.’

‘I’m sure it wasn’t me. What did they look like?’

‘What?’

‘The wafer biscuits.’

‘They looked like wafer biscuits. Things in foil paper. Exactly like the two hundred we sold. Only we sold a hundred and ninety seven because you ate three.’

‘Oh, those wafer biscuits.’

‘Yep. They’re the ones.’

‘You’re not seriously thinking of charging me for those, are you?’

‘Well, I want the accounts to be straight. After all, the committee won’t be able to afford a decent holiday if members start consuming all the profits.’

‘Could I pay it in instalments?’

‘Bugger off.’

The kettle boiled and Samantha added water and milk to the coffee granules and then handed the mugs around.

'But that money's supposed to be going to charity,' she said doubtfully to Duggan.

'Yes, I know. Quite a lot of it isn't, though. About ninety per cent of it isn't. I mean, I've got to have a new suit sometime, and you have to admit I've worked very hard for it. Painting posters, cutting up tickets, switching lights on and off, masterminding tonight's very successful show...'

Samantha looked distinctly upset.

'You can't do that,' she objected. 'I thought you were just paying for the hire of the films and then sending any profit to the children's hospital?'

'Is that what you thought, Sam? You really thought we were going to send all this money to the children's hospital?'

'Of course I did. I wouldn't have...'

'But what on earth would they do with it all?'

Samantha looked at him sharply and her eyes flashed angrily. 'What do you mean, what would they do with it all? That's a really stupid question, isn't it? I would have thought...'

'He's winding you up, Sam,' I said quietly. Samantha turned to look at Duggan, and he grinned sheepishly.

'I'm winding you up,' he said.

'Then you're a rotten sod.'

'I know. I'm a rotten sod. I'll buy you a gin and tonic to make up for it. Not out of the profits, though. Honest.'

Gerry yawned and stretched his arms.

'Well,' he said, 'I'm going to bed. I'm worn out with lifting equipment, and I'll have to get that lot back to Miss Pratt tomorrow.'

'We'll have to get it all out again on Wednesday,' said Duggan. 'We're doing the free show for St Bernard's boys.'

'Oh yes. I'd forgotten about that.'

'I'll come and help,' Samantha offered. 'It's my afternoon off. I don't mind doing refreshments again if somebody keeps the children in a reasonable queue.'

'That'd be great. They're sending a few teachers, so we won't even have to look after them. It'll be a straightforward, no nonsense, entertaining film show for a group of under-privileged kids.'

'We need to get in a few more boxes of wafer biscuits,' said Duggan.

'Good,' Gerry agreed. 'I rather like those.'

'It's been noticed. The committee trusts this shrinkage problem won't escalate, don't we, Mike?'

Gerry got up and stretched his arms. 'Let's get this money locked away,' he said. 'Then we can drink to the success of the evening, and go to bed.'

Duggan raised his eyebrows. 'What, all of us together?'

'I'm not sure how to resist,' Samantha said. 'Mike, tear me away and take me home. I'll see you both on Wednesday. I'll put on my riot gear for the wafer biscuit queue.'

'Don't worry,' said Duggan happily. 'It'll be an absolute doddle.'

(v)

Since St Bernard's was a school for boys with behavioural and emotional problems, the arrangements for the show had been made with meticulous care.

Shortly after Samantha had suggested the idea, I'd sent an invitation to the school, suggesting that if things went successfully, we could possibly make it into a regular event. A pleasant letter had arrived several days later, thanking us for our kind offer and asking if they could send a group of about twenty boys, accompanied by several teachers. That seemed fine, so I'd telephoned and said that one of us would meet the party outside the college gates at two o'clock. I also mentioned that although the show wouldn't cost the school anything, the boys might want to bring a little money to buy some sweets and crisps in the interval. We'd changed the programme a little too, leaving out the short supporting films and adding another cartoon instead.

On the Wednesday afternoon, still flushed with the success of our first night, we set the equipment up again in the lecture theatre, while Samantha organised what seemed to be developing into a confectionery shop by the wall. Since the earlier show, she'd charmed an arrangement with a newsagent close to her library, who'd offered her a range of inexpensive snacks and confectionery, on sale or return, at a very reasonable price.

'This is very impressive, Sam,' I said admiringly. 'You've got a greater range than Woolworths.'

Samantha laughed. 'Not bad, is it. I'll probably sell a lot of it too. So long as the kids bring a reasonable amount of money. I've got some packets of drink here. Give me a hand to put them out. Then you'll have to go down to the gates. It's almost quarter to two.'

When everything had been prepared, Gerry and I walked to the entrance, half expecting the party to be waiting there already. At ten minutes past two, Gerry looked up and down the busy main road, and then at his watch.

'They're late,' he muttered. 'They'll have to come soon. The modern dance lot have got a slide lecture in the theatre at five.'

'Don't panic. They probably missed their bus or something.'

'I just like things to start when they're meant to, that's all. If they said they were going to be here by two, then they should be here by two. I suppose they've got the right date?'

'Of course they have. Stop worrying. Anyway, we can always drop one of the cartoons.'

'Maybe. Trouble is, the cartoons are probably what they'll enjoy most.'

After another ten minutes, I began to feel uneasy, and Gerry was pacing the pavement alarmingly.

'Look, I'll go and phone,' I suggested. 'You go back up to the theatre and let Duggan know. It's warmer up there. I'll join you in a minute.'

When I eventually managed to get through, and a message had been relayed to somebody who knew what I was talking about, I was assured the party had left in good time for the show and should have arrived about half an hour ago. I left a message with the caretaker to direct the party towards the lecture theatre, and hurried back to the others.

'It's alright,' I assured them. 'They're definitely coming.'

'The bus has probably broken down,' said Samantha.

For want of something to do, Duggan began to fiddle with one of the projectors, cleaning the film channel with a corner of his handkerchief. As he reached across the controls, he accidentally leaned on the main switch and the machine whirred into action, pulling his handkerchief with it.

'Oh bugger!' he exclaimed loudly, slamming the switch to the off position and tugging on the other end of his handkerchief. Gerry hurried over to the machine.

'That was daft,' he said angrily. 'Why didn't you leave it alone? For God's sake get it out quickly!'

'I couldn't help it! I was just cleaning the thing.'

'What for? We cleaned the bloody things before we laced the film in.'

'I know. I was just...'

'Well for God's sake get your handkerchief out.'

'All right. Calm down. Pass me the screwdriver. I'll try and move it bit by bit. Good thing it wasn't my bloody tie. I could have been chewed up inside the thing and projected alongside Glenn Miller.' Gerry grimaced angrily and passed over a pair of scissors and a tiny screwdriver.

'It's jammed under the sprocket,' he said bluntly. 'You'll have to unscrew the sprocket. Let me have a look.'

They changed places. Gerry took his jacket off and rolled his sleeves up, looking as if he was about to disembowel the machine.

After several minutes of tinkering, he turned and looked in disbelief at the part he had removed.

'Looks like we'll be running on one machine after all,' he said miserably. 'I don't see what else we can do. The sprocket doesn't look too damaged, but I wouldn't be keen to rely on it.'

'Give it a try,' urged Duggan. 'You never know.'

Gerry replaced the component, connected the mains lead, and switched on. The projector whirred into action again, but after several minutes the speed faltered intermittently. Duggan poked the screwdriver inside the casing again.

'The sprocket's holding alright,' he muttered. 'So what the hell's the matter with the thing?'

'Miss Pratt'll have us for this,' said Gerry. 'We can't possibly be lucky a second time.'

Duggan offered an uncomplimentary remark about Miss Pratt, and Samantha winced.

'It's no good saying that,' said Gerry. 'We'll probably never be able to borrow the machines again.'

'Well, it'll run for a bit,' Duggan replied. 'Let's worry about it afterwards. If we keep our fingers crossed it'll probably get us through a couple of reels. What's the time?'

'Twenty to three.'

'Then where have they got to, for heaven's sake?'

'I suppose we could leave out the middle reel,' I suggested. 'They probably wouldn't notice.'

'We'll be skipping the whole show if they get here much later,' said Duggan. 'My God, a dodgy projector, the wrath of Miss Pratt, and no audience. Samantha, come and show me some affection while we're waiting.'

'I'll show you a wafer biscuit if you like.'

'Wonderful. That'll do. Show Gerry one too, but don't let the bugger eat it.'

'I don't want one,' Gerry grunted miserably.

Duggan straightened his back, stretched his legs, yawned, and sat down heavily on a bench in the front row.

'Hello,' he said suddenly, nodding towards the door, 'who's this, then?'

A large West Indian boy, aged about twelve, was leaning against the door. He stared around the hall for a moment and then ambled over to Gerry, looking at the two projectors with obvious interest. Samantha smiled at him.

'Hello,' she said kindly. 'Are you from St. Bernards?'

The boy considered this carefully, like a candidate pondering an ambiguous question in a difficult interview. Then he nodded slowly.

'Where are the others?' Gerry asked. The boy removed the large piece of gum he was chewing, inspected it, and carefully replaced it in his mouth before replying.

'Dunno,' he grunted.

'What do you mean?'

'They was outside by the front gate.'

'You mean they're not there now?'

'Dunno.'

'Well you must know!' Gerry retorted sharply.

'I s'pose they're still there. Mr North told me to come in an' see if this was the right place.'

'Is Mr North your teacher?'

'No.'

'Well, if he isn't your teacher, who is he?'

'Shall I tell 'im to come up 'ere?'

'That would seem to be a good idea. And tell him to bring the others.'

'Okay.'

The boy turned, hurried out of the door, and several minutes later the sound of loud, excited voices drifted up the stairs. There was a sudden, bellowing command from a voice obviously belonging to somebody much older, and the noise level immediately dropped slightly. A short, slightly built man, younger than he looked, strode through the door. He wore an old sports jacket frayed at the cuffs, and he walked with a round-shouldered stoop. His ginger hair was receding badly, and though he had tried to disguise this by combing it carefully forward, the effect hadn't been very successful. He barged his way heavily through the crowd of boys standing near the door, smiled a little uncertainly, and then extended a limp right hand towards Gerry.

'So sorry we're late,' he apologised. 'I'm afraid I had a job getting them all on one bus. And then Davis managed to jam the whole… *stand still* Barry Cross, you stupid, stupid boy!' He screamed the command at the boy nearest to him, who had been hovering, like a bee near a honey pot, to see what was on offer. The pitch and volume of the man's voice made Samantha jump and a large pile of wafer biscuits fell from the corner of the table. The boys were silenced for several seconds, but then the noise level quickly crept up again. It was obviously a tactic they had all become extremely familiar with.

'We'd better get started,' said Gerry anxiously, looking at his watch. 'We've only got the lecture theatre till five.'

'Of course. I hope we haven't spoiled anything by being late. I'll get them in, shall I?'

'Are you the only teacher with them?' I asked. 'We thought a teacher called Alan Green…'

'He's got to cover another class because a lot of the staff are sick. I'm a supply teacher. I've done St Bernard's fairly regularly but I can't say it's a barrel of fun. Kids are a nightmare. Couldn't even bring one of the helpers today. Mind you, they'd probably have murdered her in the bus or something. Frankly, it's been quite an achievement to get here at all.'

'They're making an awful lot of noise in the corridor,' said Samantha. 'Do you think we ought to go and bring them in?'

'That's typical,' Mr North said bluntly. 'It's bad enough if three of them have to wait for five minutes, let alone thirty five, and I…'

'Thirty five?' Duggan interrupted.

Mr North looked surprised. 'Yes, didn't you get the phone call? They asked if we could bring a bigger group because they're so short staffed. Anyway, I'd better go and get them in before they wreck the place.'

The noise outside had reached a deafening pitch. Most of the boys were shouting at the tops of their voices and there was a sudden crash of broken glass that caused an instant and miraculous silence.

'Oh my God!' Mr North exclaimed. 'What now?' He sighed like a man sentenced to a long term in prison and hurried outside.

'Johnson knocked that vase off!' somebody shouted gleefully.

'No I never,' a loud voice objected.

'You did. I saw yer.'

'I bloody never done that! You watch it!'

'Yeah?'

'Yeah. Shut it!'

There was another high pitched scream from Mr North and the boys began to surge through the doors, pushing, nudging and shoving each other as they dived for the seats nearest the screen. Those who sat down first were thrown off the seats again by the bigger boys, who didn't bother hurrying because any seat they fancied could easily be reclaimed with a little unfriendly persuasion. There was a sudden sharp crack as the arm of a front seat snapped in two, and the three boys trying to sit on the seat fell in a jumbled heap on the floor, causing the others a great deal of amusement. Mr North dashed across to them.

'Sit *down*!' he screamed, the strength of his voice causing an echo round the lecture theatre. 'Where do you think you are? You, sit there! John Cross, sit there! Murphy, sit here! Johnson, sit on the end.'

The large West Indian boy's face creased into a moody expression.

'I don't wanna sit on the end.'

'Johnson, SIT..ON..THE..END!'

'I don't like sitting on the end...'

'Johnson...'

'I can't see properly on the end.'

'You can sit on the end or you can sit in the corridor.'

'Can I sit up there, then?'

'Up where?'

'There. On that ledge thing.'

'No.'

'Why not?'

'Because I said so.'

'That ain't much of a reason.'

'Do you want a good slap round the ear?'

'No. I'll sit on the end.'

Johnson sat down cautiously and another five minutes passed while Mr North struggled to get the rest of the boys seated. Then, breathless, he climbed the short flight of stairs to the back of the theatre where the projectors were and sat down heavily next to Gerry, wiping his forehead with a folded handkerchief.

'Are they always like this?' Gerry asked in a horrified voice.

'No, no. Sometimes they're worse. It's the excitement. They've been looking forward to this for days. It would have been a lot easier if I'd had somebody else with me. Oh, by the way... that broken vase... if you just get a bill sent to the school I'll see that it's paid.'

Aware that time was passing quickly, Gerry turned on the cassette player containing the interval music. As the boys heard the music through the loudspeakers, the noise died a little and they began to settle into their seats, aware that something was about to happen. Johnson had stopped talking and was now sitting sideways in his seat, staring moodily at a length of rope he had taken from his pocket. I shuddered to think what he might use it for.

'Come on,' Gerry urged, 'let's start while it's quiet.'

He motioned to Samantha to turn the lights out, and as a Bugs Bunny cartoon appeared on the screen the boys howled and shrieked with delight. It reminded me of the enthusiasm the opening cartoon had been greeted with a few nights previously, but instead of dying down as the cartoon began the cheering and shouting merely increased in volume.

'They'll never hear the bloody thing at this rate!' Duggan shouted above the noise, turning up the volume until distortion threatened to wreck the loudspeaker.

'They'll settle in a minute,' Mr North shouted back confidently.

'I hope so. You've got more faith than I have.'

The noise was now so intense that nobody could hear the soundtrack at all. Nevertheless, the visuals caused untold delight, and one boy, bigger than most, turned to his partner and began slapping him on the back each time he found something particularly amusing, until his partner swung round angrily and threatened to smash his head in if he didn't pack it in right away. As the film progressed the boys became interested and involved, but as soon as it finished there was an instant and excited chattering again. Duggan hurriedly flicked the repaired projector into life, and the children cheered again as the Tom and Jerry cartoon we'd shown the other night burst onto the screen. Nobody seemed to care that it was running at a third of its usual speed.

'Shame we haven't got a few more of these,' said Gerry. 'I just hope they enjoy the Glenn Miller.'

'Oh, they will,' said Mr North. 'Put 'em in front of a screen and they'll watch anything.' He took out a small tin of tobacco and a packet of papers, and began to roll a very thin cigarette. A coil of smoke rose into the projector beam, and I waved it away from me.

'Sorry,' said Mr North brightly. 'I didn't think you'd mind.'

Half way through the first reel of the Glenn Miller Story, I realised that at least a dozen boys were not watching the screen at all. Peering through the darkness I could see Johnson attempting to lash his partner's hands to the chair with his piece of rope. Another boy had crawled underneath his seat and was amusing himself by pinching the bottoms of the boys in front, finding it intensely amusing when they turned round to wallop the person responsible and found themselves staring at an empty seat. Samantha, absorbed in the film, didn't notice one of the smallest boys scuttling across the floor on his hands and knees to give the refreshments table a premature inspection. Manoeuvring himself into a shadowy corner underneath the table, he sat waiting for a distracting moment in the film that would allow him to remove some of Samantha's stock without anybody spotting him. She caught him just as his hands reached upwards, and throwing caution to the winds gave them a smack. There was a squeal of surprise, and the fingers disappeared from view. Glancing around, I noticed that four others were sitting up in the balcony, even though the staircase had been carefully screened off. I suspected it wouldn't be long before they found some items to throw over the edge.

'I think you'd better get them down from there,' said Gerry. 'They shouldn't be up there anyway.'

'Best to leave them at the moment,' said Mr North. 'They'll get involved in the film soon. The trouble is, they soon get bored with things.'

'Then at least have a word with the others. I'm a bit worried about the leads,' Gerry persisted. 'The mains wire runs right underneath the seats. 'So does the speaker wire, come to that.'

'Leave it for another ten minutes.' said Mr North. 'If they're not quiet by then, I'll speak to them.'

'Well… it's up to you. I don't want any of them electrocuted.'

Mr North grinned. 'I wouldn't mind, frankly. It would shut a few of 'em up.'

He settled back into his seat and concentrated on watching the film. For a while it did seem as if the boys were settling as they began to follow the story. As the action moved to the suspect projector Duggan watched the machinery like a hawk, his nose hovering a few inches from the troublesome sprocket.

'I think it's going to be okay,' he whispered to Gerry, closing the projector cover and settling back into his seat with relief. Nobody seemed to be concerned that James Stewart's voice had slipped an octave, but the calm was quickly shattered as soon as he played the first love scene of the film. Immediately, there were hearty jeers and crude comments as each boy tried to outdo the previous suggestion. Samantha looked at the front two rows in astonished disbelief, furrowing her eyebrows and shaking her head sadly from side to side. When the scene extended into several minutes, the boys began to boo loudly. One of the boys, more scientifically aware than the others, stood on his seat to intercept the projector beam and a silhouette duck suddenly appeared between the couple on the screen. This was considered highly amusing and the other boys shouted with delight as everybody raised their fingers to try a few variations. I began to worry that the noise might bring some of the lecturers into the theatre to see what was going on, and then a clattering from the faulty projector caused the film to slow down dramatically.

'Oh Jesus, that's it!' Duggan groaned, opening the cover of the machine and staring hopelessly as the sprocket wobbled in its mounting. 'It's never going to finish this reel now.'

'Do you mind telling them to shut up?' Gerry said bluntly to Mr North. The teacher stood up uncertainly for a moment and then sat down again.

'Don't worry,' he shouted cheerfully. 'They're bound to get sick of it in a minute.'

'That's not the point,' Duggan shouted back. 'I'm going to have to stop this machine anyway.'

As he spoke, the clattering from the projector grew louder and he flicked the off switch, forgetting in his agitation to turn the sound down first. Glenn Miller's voice faltered in mid-sentence and slurred to a halt. There was a loud cheer, and several boys turned around in fascination at this new effect, obviously hoping that Duggan would do it again.

'What the hell do we do now?' Duggan hissed at Gerry, staring first at the machine and then at the audience. 'They'll tear the place to bits if that bloke doesn't shut them up.'

'First things first,' Gerry said. 'Let's get the lights on.' He gesticulated at Samantha and waved his arms. She hurried across to the switches on the wall and the boys sat blinking in the light for a moment, unsure what was happening now. Duggan suddenly looked across at Gerry.

'I've got an idea,' he said.

'Oh God. What?'

'You might not like it.'

'Try me. I'm desperate.'

'You talk to 'em.'

Gerry's eyebrows shot several inches higher and his mouth dropped open.

'Talk to them? Me? What about? Why me?'

'Because you are going to teach in a secondary school.'

'I'm not going to be teaching kids like these.'

'But you're good at things like this. Look how you handled that meeting when we elected the committee. If you can handle that, you can handle anything. Go on. I'll get the next reel loaded and we'll skip the rest of the dodgy one. They'll never know. Hurry up, before it gets worse.'

'But I can't! What am I supposed to talk about?'

'You'll think of something.'

'This isn't fair!'

'Go on! You can do it. Samantha, let him have a wafer biscuit.'

Gerry stared round wildly for help, only too aware there wasn't any. Then he walked to the front of the theatre like a man walking to the scaffold, while Mr North tried to make himself inconspicuous, more than happy for somebody else to take on the task. Gerry climbed onto the stage area, gesticulated hopelessly and then suddenly pulled himself up to full height.

'Listen!' he bawled at the top of his voice. Only the front row heard him. The boys in the second row had turned round to annoy everybody in the third row, and the four in the balcony were aiming pellets of paper at whoever happened to be moving directly underneath them. Gerry watched in disgust while Johnson took a ball of bright orange bubble-gum from his mouth and looked around for somewhere to deposit it. His partner looked at him and pointed earnestly towards the jacket pocket of the boy on the other side of him.

'Nah!' Johnson shouted, struggling to make himself heard. 'I ain't puttin' it in there. 'E's me friend.'

'So what,' the other boy shouted back. "E's just put a bit in yours.'

Thinking an alternative tactic might be the way forward, Gerry grabbed a rounders bat that had been left in the room and whacked it down hard on the low bench near the screen. Heads turned immediately in his direction, a look of interest and mild surprise spreading over the boys' faces.

'Listen!' Gerry roared again. 'I have something to tell you.' This time there was almost silence, and the boys looked at him expectantly, wondering if what he had to say might be more interesting than The Glenn Miller Story.

'We're going to stop for a short break,' Gerry said quickly, while he had the advantage. 'We've got to stop the show for a few minutes while we put the next reel of film on the projector. Those of you who've brought some money might like to buy something from the table over here.'

He pointed towards Samantha, who trembled slightly. Gerry struggled for something else to say.

'Now look, if you want to stretch your legs for a minute or two or go to the toilet you'd better follow me.'

'That was a mistake,' Mr North murmured softly.

The audience need no second invitation. The boys clambered noisily out of their seats and divided themselves between Gerry and the refreshments table. Stepping backwards, he dived through the swing doors, followed by about twenty children. I hurried to

Samantha's side, and we were soon struggling to deal with a multitude of hands containing money thrust at us, while trying to make sure nobody was stealing the stock. Few of the boys knew what money they had, or what change they should be receiving, and some didn't bother waiting for any. Then, hands full of refreshments, they moved back to their seats to inspect what they'd bought. A few boys wandered to the back of the theatre to look at the projectors and Duggan moved towards the machines protectively.

When the queue at the refreshments table was short and Samantha looked safe, I hurried out into the corridor and ploughed my way through the rest of the boys until I found Gerry, red-faced and very angry, trying to organise a reasonable line and at the same time make sure that nobody wandered off. It seemed to be an impossible task.

'What the hell's that bloke supposed to be doing?' he snapped at me.

'I don't think he wants to know.'

'That makes two of us. I'm never doing this lark again, I can assure you of that. It's like trying to control a bunch of bloody Houdinis.'

By the time we reached the toilet I was sure half the group was missing, and several others tried to creep away even while they were being watched. We stood like sentries while the boys disappeared inside and came out again almost immediately, not wanting to be left behind if there was any likelihood of exploring the building. Gerry caught the jacket sleeve of one of them, and the boy looked at him distastefully.

'Stay here!' Gerry urged.

'What for?'

'Because you'll get lost.'

'No I won't. I wanna go with them.'

'You stay here. The ones who've gone off are going to be in a lot of trouble for this.'

''Oo said?'

'I did. Now stay here!'

'Let go of me jacket, then.'

'Well don't wander off, then.'

Gerry released the boy's sleeve. The child inspected it for damage and then stuffed his hands sulkily into his pockets, half wondering if it was worth making a run for it.

It was now so obvious why the attendants at the Tower of London, and other ancient monuments visited by large parties of school children, always wore such a dismal, pained expression. Good discipline was vital for effective control of children and Dorothy Bridgewood had been able to command respect and affection so easily from her pupils, while Mr North quite obviously couldn't. Although these children attended St Bernard's because they had emotional and behavioural difficulties, I was convinced that most of them would probably have thrived with a teacher of Dorothy's calibre. Perhaps that was it. The quality of teachers and teaching was paramount, and these boys were products of homes or teaching systems that had failed them badly.

Gerry nudged me and my mind snapped back into focus as we pushed, urged and ordered the children still with us back into the hall. Mr North had at least stood up, and he was shouting loudly at the other boys to sit down. Samantha and Duggan were patrolling the ends of the rows.

'I hate to say this,' I said, 'but I think we've got quite a few missing.'

'It's impossible to keep them in one place,' Duggan shouted in Mr North's direction. 'Why did the school send so many?'

Mr North shuffled awkwardly. 'Well, as I explained…'

'Yes, but it doesn't exactly make it very easy for us, does it? I mean, this is just ridiculous. Some of them will probably be all over the college by now.'

Gerry's face went a chalky white, and he closed his eyes.

'I expect they'll be alright,' said Mr North, but any confidence had disappeared from his voice.

'It's not them I'm worried about,' said Duggan angrily. 'God knows what they'll get up to if they get into the lecture rooms. I mean, we've had one breakage this afternoon already. At least the Principal's out today.'

'We'll have to go and search for them, that's all,' I said. 'How many have we got at the moment?'

Mr North counted the children, but even this was difficult as they wriggled about in their seats and moved between the rows.

'I make it nine missing. That's not too bad, I suppose. I lost more than that at the zoo once. I'll help you look for them but you'll have to show me the way. I don't know the place.'

'Oh God,' Gerry moaned softly.

'Gerry, stay here,' said Duggan. 'Just in case they try to take the projectors to pieces.'

'I'll stay too,' said Samantha. 'They keep offering to help me pack the stuff away. I think I'd better do it quickly before the shop gives us a huge bill for stuff we can't account for.'

We hurried grimly along the corridor and into the main building, with Mr North in hot pursuit. It would soon be time for the dance group to use the lecture theatre and it was obvious there would be no time to finish the film. Duggan began to search the area around the main hall, while Mr North and I peered through the windows of any empty lecture rooms.

'I don't know how you cope with this,' I grunted moodily. 'It's crazy.'

'I'm not exactly wild about it myself. We all start out with good intentions. You will too, but they get to you eventually. Try teaching in a third rate comprehensive for a few years.'

We followed a noise coming from inside a history tutorial room, and Mr North leapt forward in time to stop two of the smaller boys from leaning dangerously out of a window. He took hold of each boy roughly by the arms and half dragged, half marched them out into the corridor, where he shook both forcibly.

'Morris, Benwell, what are you doing in here?' he barked, tightening his grip on their arms. 'You're supposed to be in the hall watching a film show.'

'It's boring,' said Morris. 'I don't wanna watch the rest of it.'

'I couldn't care less what you want to do. You and the others who wandered off have ruined it for everybody else.'

'They never liked it much neither.'

'Where are the others?'

'Dunno.'

Mr North prodded the boys forward, while I looked briefly into each of the rooms along the corridor. All of them were empty.

'Wait a minute. Let's try to do this logically,' I suggested. 'Imagine you were them. Where would the most interesting places be? How do their minds work?'

'They don't have minds,' Mr North said simply.

I suddenly realised where we would probably find the strays, and I hurried Mr North and the captive boys down a short flight of stairs and along to the section of the building containing the craft workshops and laboratories. A lot of cheerful noise was coming from inside, and I hurriedly threw open the door of Ernest Benton's craft workshop. Inside, three boys were hovering suspiciously around one of Mr Benton's historical treasures, a washday mangle that he had bought in one of his regular junk shop forages. A smaller boy stood at a strange angle in front of it, partly hidden by the others, and for the moment I couldn't work out what they were doing.

'Harris, what on earth are you doing?' Mr North roared. Harris jumped and turned quickly.

'Nothin'.'

'Nothing? It doesn't look like nothing to me, Harris. What are you doing with that mangle?'

'Nothin'.'

'Yes you are. What are you doing?'

'Seein' if it works?'

'What do you mean, seeing if it works?'

'We're tryin' it on Charlie's tie. We're seein' if it flattens it out.'

'Really? And who told Charlie he could take his tie off?'

''E ain't taken it off. It's still around 'is neck.'

The small group stood back, and it was suddenly obvious why Charlie looked so uncomfortable. His neck was perilously close to the rollers of the mangle, and his face was turning purple.

'You stupid fool, Harris,' Mr North shouted. 'You could have throttled him!'

'Charlie don't mind,' said Harris. 'It's just a bit of fun, ain't it Chiles?'

Charlie grunted unhappily. 'They jus' grabbed me, Sir,' he croaked. 'I couldn't stop 'em.'

'Well get out of it at once!'

'I can't, Sir. I can't reach the 'andle. Me tie's stuck.'

'Harris, get him out. Now!'

Harris smiled sheepishly and turned the large handle of the mangle backwards. Charlie took a deep breath as he was released, and then fingered the muscles of his neck gingerly. Mr North ushered the boys towards the door, a look on his face suggesting he might murder the first one who dared to wander off again.

'I know where Johnson and Creamer are,' Harris offered suddenly, feeling that if he had to go back he might as well make sure the others returned as well. Mr North stared at him.

'Well? Where?'

'Down there. In that room.'

We hurried into the biology laboratory. Johnson and two of his friends had dragged a life-sized skeleton from one of the equipment cupboards and made it sit upright on a stool beside a work bench. A clay pipe had been stuck between its teeth and there was a pair of shoes on its feet. A boy with chubby pink cheeks and an angelic expression was gently stirring the water in the fish tank with a ruler and watching the effect it had on the fishes, while another child was exploring the shelves to find an interesting chemical to drop in the water. Johnson looked up and grinned at Mr North.

''Allo, Sir,' he said.

'I'll give you hello, my lad,' Mr North shouted, grabbing him by the collar and dragging him towards the others. 'Now get moving, and stay just in front of me. Creamer, Davis, Matthews, you as well. Creamer, get away from those bottles.'

'I was jus' lookin' to see if they 'ad any gunpowder,' said Creamer politely.

'That doesn't surprise me at all. If I had some, I know where I'd put it. Now get down, and get over here.'

I held the door open and the group moved sheepishly out into the corridor. Johnson slouched in front of the others, frequently glancing back and scowling at Mr North.

'He really is a right bloody headache, that one,' Mr North said irritably. 'He hasn't been at the school long. His mother hates his guts and so do I. Nobody knows who his father was, her included. She spent half her youth tearing around the countryside on the back of a motorbike. Hasn't got a clue how to look after kids of her own. His sister's already in care. You can reason with a lot of the kids, but not Johnson. He's the sort who smiles at you while he's sticking the knife in.'

I felt the wave of hatred in Mr North's voice and I was rapidly coming to strongly dislike the man and his attitudes. Johnson was a mere twelve years old, and it seemed his life had already been set on a downward spiral. Mr North was clearly fuelling the fire with his own bitterness and disillusionment and however hardened I eventually became to teaching, I vowed I would never become like that.

'The trouble is, he's not thick, either, just half crazy,' Mr North continued in a louder voice, as if he no longer really cared whether he was overheard.

'Can't you do anything?'

'Do anything? What on earth can we do? We need a dozen more teachers at the school before we can do anything.'

'That seems a bit negative.'

'You try handling kids like Johnson. The social worker said the smell from their flat was so bad it started seeping through the walls next door. His bed is continually broken. He set fire to it once, to make his mother get a new one. Then he went and phoned the fire brigade and stood on the pavement watching while they put the fire out.'

I was shocked and disturbed by what I was hearing. My own suburban childhood seemed a million miles from experiences like these. I'd known the Barton children in the next road, whose father was in prison, and I'd often wondered why their mother seemed so worn and unhappy, but I rarely played with them at school. And on the occasions I did get up to a bit of mischief outside school, I was very aware that my parents, a reliable and united constant in my life, would be extremely displeased if they found out.

The boys were walking more quietly now, and Mr North led them back into the lecture theatre while I went in the opposite direction to find the others who hadn't been caught yet. There was a sudden shout from the end of the corridor, and Duggan appeared leading two more boys by the hands.

'I cornered these two upstairs with Milly,' he said. They were offering to help her scrub the floors. How many have you got?'

'Most of them, I think. North's taken them back inside the theatre.'

'That's no indication he can keep 'em there. I hope Samantha and Gerry are managing all right. Where do you think the rest are likely to be?'

'Haven't a clue. We've looked in all the likeliest places. There's only three missing now. I'll look in the rooms at the front of the college. You take these two back. Gerry will probably need some help, anyway.'

I hurried back down the corridor, wondering how I was going to explain things to the dance group. As I turned the corner, I collided with a boy carrying a large bunch of daffodils. For a moment, we stared at each other suspiciously.

'You're from St Bernard's, aren't you?'

'Yeah,' the boy replied, trying to walk past quickly. I caught hold of his arm and swung him round.

'Where did you get those flowers?'

'Eh?'

'The flowers. Where did you get them?'

'I'm takin' 'em back for Mrs Clinton.' The boy clutched the bundle tightly to his chest in case I tried to take them from him.

'Whose are they?'

'Whose are what?'

'The flowers, of course. I want to know where they came from,'

'Oh, them. I got 'em from out there.'

He pointed out of the window, and I realised the daffodils had been pulled from the beds surrounding the front lawn. With an icy hand clutching at my stomach, I hurried outside, just in time to stop the remaining boys from ruining the flower beds completely. Hands filthy with damp earth, they were busily selecting the best blooms and groaned in disappointment when I insisted they get off the lawn immediately.

'We've only got a few,' the taller of the two objected, standing upright and wiping his hands on his shirt. 'We ain't taken many.'

'Why didn't you ask? In any case, you're not even supposed to be out here. You're lucky the caretaker didn't catch you. He locks people up who walk on his lawn.'

The boys looked distinctly uneasy.

'We was only takin' a few back for Mrs Clinton,' the smaller boy said meekly. 'We thought it 'ud be nice, that's all. She and Mr Green are our best teachers. Can't see 'ow anyone's gonna miss a few flowers. It ain't as if you ain't got many.'

'I'm afraid you'll have to give them to me immediately.'

Looking decidedly hurt, but sensing the firmness in my voice, the boy picked the bundle up and put it carefully into my arms. I held the flowers for a moment, and then suddenly handed them back to the boy.

'Here, take them,' I said quietly. 'You might as well have them. They're cut now. And I'm sure Mrs Clinton will like them.'

'Cor, thanks, Mister!' the boy exclaimed, surprised and pleased. 'Mrs Clinton really likes flowers.'

'And she 'elps us with our gardening,' said the smaller boy enthusiastically. 'We wanted to take some back for 'er when we saw these. We wouldn't 'ave taken 'em 'cept Billy said it 'ud be alright...'

'I never said that,' Billy interrupted. 'I said I don't suppose they'd miss a few.'

'You never said that. You said...'

'It doesn't matter,' I said quickly. 'Anyway, you'd better follow me now.'

They walked meekly beside me, proudly carrying a bunch of flowers each. I silently prayed we didn't meet anybody who was familiar with the college flower beds.

'Well, how lovely,' Samantha smiled as we entered the lecture theatre again. 'Mike's bought me some flowers.'

Gerry looked horrified. 'If I recognise those,' he said slowly, 'we're in for it. They haven't come from where I think they've come from, have they?'

'Possibly.'

Duggan's mouth fell open. 'You're bloody joking! Dear God, that's the last straw!'

'What could I do? I couldn't very well put them back, could I?'

'Well it would be a good idea if you did. Go and stick 'em upright in the earth. The Doc will think there's been a frost in the night. You know what he's like about that lawn and the beds.'

'Look at the size of their bunches,' groaned Gerry, hiding his head in his hands. 'Oh God, are there any left at all?'

'Of course there are. Some, anyway. They're taking them back for their favourite teacher.'

'Not Mr North, I assume?' said Samantha. 'Oh, what does it matter? They're only flowers. It's a lovely thought.'

Mr North herded the children into rough lines and looked at his watch. 'I think I'd better try to get them back to school while they're reasonably calm. We've caused you enough bother for one afternoon.'

'You can say that again,' Gerry muttered. 'We'll help you get them to the gate.'

We moved the boys towards the door. Students from the dance group were beginning to enter the lecture theatre, and I motioned to Samantha, standing in a sea of empty crisp packets, drink containers and biscuit wrappers, to explain as best she could. Carefully spacing ourselves along the column of children, we marched them at a forced pace to the main entrance, where Mr North turned and held out his hand.

'Thanks very much,' he said. 'I'm sorry they were so… don't forget to send a bill for the broken vase.'

'Don't worry,' said Gerry, 'we won't.'

'Thanks Mister,' said one of the boys carrying the largest bunch of flowers, 'it's been great.'

'That's alright,' I said. 'We'll send you a bill for the flowers. Don't forget to put them in water.'

With an ineffectual shout to the children that they must keep on the pavement and in twos, Mr North led the group around the bend in the road and out of sight.

'Next time we want to do a bit of social work, let's invite a group of pensioners,' said Duggan. 'At least they move slowly. Anyway, we'd better help Samantha clear up, and then buy a bag of bulbs for the flower beds. All things considered, I think I've had enough for today.'

Later that evening, I was stopped in the corridor by Dr Bradley.

'Ah, Mr Kent,' he called, removing his spectacles with a flourish and polishing them briskly on his gown, 'a word, if you please.'

I stepped inside the Principal's room like a condemned man. Dr Bradley smiled suddenly. 'Well, it appears you did a very good job this afternoon,' he said brightly. 'Miss Cavell has just been on the phone to me and she was most enthusiastic about it all. Says the boys arrived back safely and she sends you her thanks for entertaining so many this afternoon. They're not easy children. I gather they all behaved properly?'

'They were... um... an interesting group of boys. Yes, certainly.'

'Good. Well, it's all valuable experience, isn't it? Perhaps we ought to invite them up to watch one of our drama productions sometime. Do you think they'd like that? A bit of Brecht perhaps? A smidgeon of Webster? Some Richard the Third? What do you think?'

I gulped. 'I'm not really sure. I think they might...'

'Might what, Mr Kent?' Dr Bradley raised his bushy eyebrows and stared quizzically over his spectacles.

'Actually,' I admitted, 'they were dreadful. It was an awful afternoon. Nothing went right. And we've broken a sprocket in one of Miss Pratt's projectors. It was quite dreadful. It was one of the worst afternoons of my life.'

'I know, Mr Kent. I know.'

I stared at him, not understanding. Dr Bradley stood up, walked across to the window, and stared out at the lawn.

'You see, Mr Kent, I got off the bus as they happened to be getting on it. I say getting on it, but commandeering it might be a more accurate description. I recognised Colin North. I've seen him in action before. I also recognised some of my daffodils.'

I felt weak at the knees, and my hand gripped the back of the antique chair a foot away from me.

'You don't know Edith Clinton, of course,' Dr Bradley continued. 'She teaches at St Bernard's and she never has the slightest problem with any of the children. Strange, isn't it, that some people should be so able with practically any kind of child, and others be so ineffectual. Why do you think that should be, Mr Kent?'

'I'm not sure. At least, I wasn't sure, but I think I'm beginning to realise. I imagine Mrs Clinton is like the class teacher I worked with on teaching practice. She was very talented.'

'It's more than talent, though, isn't it? I understand from Miss Bottle that you did particularly well on your own first teaching practice?'

'I had an outstanding class teacher to work with.'

'Yes, I'm sure. But what is it that makes a class teacher outstanding? Lots of teachers are very good, Mr Kent, but some have an indefinable quality that makes children respond to them instantly. Children are funny creatures, aren't they? They understand adults more than we think. And they manipulate brilliantly. Now, where do you think I should put this daffodil? One of the boys handed it to me as he was getting on the bus.'

Dr Bradley smiled and picked up a slim white porcelain vase from the window sill. It contained a single flower, and my eyes stared intently at the floor in embarrassment.

'Don't worry, Mr Kent,' Dr Bradley said, looking at me steadily. 'You see, I can grow plenty more daffodils. A bulb will grow again and again, producing a perfect flower each year with a little love and attention. Perhaps somebody ought to explain that to Colin North, eh? Anyway, I mustn't keep you. I'm sure you have lots to do.'

He opened the heavy oak door gently, and patted me on the shoulder.

'Thank you,' I said softly.

'My pleasure. And incidentally, don't worry about Miss Pratt's projector. I'll see her myself. It will be repaired in time for your next show.'

I nodded in gratitude. Then he walked slowly and thoughtfully back into his room.

MAY

MEETING THE MAJOR AND STARVING IN DORSET

One deliciously warm morning in early May, Miss Bottle was late for her lecture.

This was a rare occurrence, for both Miss Bottle and Dr Frost were meticulously fussy about student punctuality and set an example they expected everybody else to follow. Although they often disagreed with each other about the way their particular sciences should be presented to the students, and Miss Bottle was far more aware of current trends in educational practice, their intense devotion to their subjects couldn't be faulted. Although the failure rate in physics was a continual source of disappointment to Dr Frost, the blame certainly didn't lie with his stringent attempts at instilling knowledge into lesser minds than his own. Miss Bottle had a similar outlook. During my first college year, I had learned that she had once taken it upon herself to visit a student intent on abandoning chemistry and opting for the arts instead. After a solid hour of earnest persuasion, Miss Bottle had managed to make him change his mind.

Both lecturers prepared their sessions down to the last detail and nothing ever seemed to be overlooked. Their approach could have been profitably imitated by several other departments, though since they had both been lecturing for a long time, I assumed it was a skill that became honed with enough practice.

Only illness ever prevented Miss Bottle from appearing in the laboratory a good half hour before her students, and our group had assumed she was ill this particular morning. The last time this had happened, when she had caught an unusually heavy cold and gone to bed for two days, she had scribbled detailed messages on the blackboard listing alternative arrangements in order that no time should be wasted. When she had recovered enough to get back on her feet, she had returned to lecturing too quickly and promptly lost her voice. Even that hadn't deterred her. Armed with a pad and a pencil, she had simply wandered around the laboratory issuing written instructions.

For a while, the group sat in the laboratory, looking through previous notes. After fifteen minutes had passed, David Barton suggested we might just as well return to our rooms and revise there. Then, at twenty to ten, she suddenly breezed into the room and hurried anxiously to the front bench.

'Good morning everyone,' she said brightly, looking round for a stool to sit on. 'I do apologise for being so late. I'm afraid I simply overlooked the time for once. Dear me, it's a quarter to ten.' She pushed the stool behind the bench and cleared a space in front of her.

'I've been on the phone making the final arrangements for your study week at Elderberry Hall. I think I might as well tell you something about it now, though I believe Dr Frost mentioned it briefly some time ago?'

Several heads nodded. Dr Frost had talked about the practical study course much earlier that year. Elderberry Hall had once been a minor stately home and was situated four hours away, on the border between Somerset and Dorset. It had been leased for educational purposes, and although the exterior and grounds retained their original 18th century character, the interior had been carefully converted into a specialist field study centre for biology, botany and geography. It was also quite difficult to book, since it was used throughout the year by training colleges and secondary schools from all over South England. Since practical work was an essential part of the science courses, Elderberry Hall offered a unique opportunity for supplementing theoretical work done at college.

'Well now, let's see,' Miss Bottle continued, taking a neat pile of typed papers from a drawer. 'Ah, here we are. As you probably know, you will stay at the hall for five days to study the botanical and biological life around the Dorset countryside. It's a very beautiful place, and you'll thoroughly enjoy this part of your studies. I'm afraid you'll have to cram an awful lot of work into a very short period, but I don't suppose you'll mind that. And if the weather continues like today, you should all lose that dreadful London pallor you've got in your faces.'

She smiled kindly, and then went to the window, pushing it open with great effort, as if she wanted to start introducing her students to fresh air right from that moment.

'When are we going, exactly?' Barton asked.

'Well, the only time they could take this group was in three week's time. And I did want you to have as much of Major Beddington's time as possible. He doesn't do all the groups himself now, of course, but he has such a detailed knowledge of Dorset wildlife. Some of you have probably come across one or two of his books? 'Dorset Habitats and Environments'? 'Exploring Freshwater Streams and Springs'?'

She raised her eyebrows in expectation, but nobody had.

'Well, never mind. They're in our library of course. Now then, I'm going to give each of you a new folder for your work at Elderberry Hall. You will have to submit this work at your oral examination in the finals. And as you know, they aren't that far away I'm afraid.'

She passed round loose-leafed folders and a plentiful supply of paper. 'Of course,' she went on, 'I shan't be coming with you myself, and nor will Dr Frost this time. Not that you'll need us to supervise what you all do. I know you'll co-operate with Major Beddington and his team and take full advantage of his very detailed knowledge.'

Photocopied lists of clothing and equipment that would be required for the stay were handed round. Though all college visits to Elderberry Hall were generously subsidised, students were expected to contribute towards any special equipment that couldn't be supplied from the department itself.

'This really doesn't sound at all bad,' I said, reading through the description of the facilities. 'A free week in the country soaking up the sun.'

'Don't you believe it,' said Duggan. 'I seem to remember Gerry talking about the place after one of his geography groups had been there. Wasn't it where they spent a day on the moors digging lumps of mud out of the ground in the pouring rain? Wasn't it where somebody had to be rushed to the hospital with chronic bronchitis. Didn't he die, or something?'

'Rubbish. Anyway, it sounds quite good to me. Do you think they'd let me take Samantha?'

'Of course they would. They positively encourage that sort of thing. I'm sure she'll have a great time, sitting around when it's raining reading copies of the Coppiced Woodland Gazette.'

'Well, just think of the country pubs you keep on about.'

Barton overheard and laughed humourlessly. 'You won't be allowed near those, mate. You won't even be allowed out. They've got an electrified fence and Alsatian dogs. From what I've heard, you sit around looking up beetles' backsides with a microscope when it rains, and you wander about gathering specimens of cowshit when it doesn't.'

'Sounds pretty entertaining to me,' said Duggan lightly.

'Does it? Enjoy examining cowshit, do you? I mean, when you come to apply for a teaching job at one of these tough inner city schools we keep hearing about, you'll be able to say you've had a lot of experience examining cowshit.'

'How do you know so much about it?'

'Deidre's been there.'

'Who's Deidre?'

'The little raver I usually bring to your film society things. She's a geography student. She says Major Beddington's a barrel of fun, too. Knows the name of every plant and insect in the British Isles and treats you like a five year old.'

He shuffled a dozen sheets of paper and snapped them into his file gloomily. Duggan shrugged.

'Oh well, it's only for a few days. I knew I should have just done physics. I don't know a thing about plants and insects. Not a thing.'

'I shouldn't worry,' Simon Daines said kindly. 'I'm sure you'll be able to fill in any gaps on this course.'

'They aren't gaps. They're more like wide open spaces. I wouldn't mind betting that we get an examiner in the finals who specialises in biology. And it won't be a matter of just trotting out the latin name for a daisy, either.'

He suddenly rummaged in his bag, took out a diary, and flicked through the pages.

'I thought so,' he said. 'Do you realise, we're going down on a Thursday? That means we'll probably have to work right through the weekend as well. I haven't worked on a Saturday since I did a paper round. That'll be a novel experience, anyway.'

Miss Bottle began speaking again, running her eyes over one of the sheets and ticking off some of the items her department would be able to provide.

'Not everything you'll need is listed,' she said, 'and a lot of it applies to the geography students, of course. There didn't seem much point in making separate lists. I would advise a net of some sort for butterflies, gathering stream life and so on. Mr Dunn should be able to sort out all that kind of thing for you. I'll mention it to him. And some soil testing kits are essential, of course.'

She pencilled a few notes on the sheet, and then thought intently for a moment.

'You must take a good British Flora with you. That really is a priority. There are bound to be a few in the library at Elderberry Hall, but you'll need at least one between two. You can have a look in the college library but if you do borrow books, please return them as soon as you get back. I imagine quite a few of you already have your own Floras anyway?'

She looked over her spectacles at the group, and seemed mildly disappointed when only Daines and Charlton raised their hands. Duggan fidgeted and stared out of the window.

'Look at that gorgeous sun,' he murmured. 'And we're sitting in here. What a dreadful waste.'

'I'm sorry, Mr Phillips,' Miss Bottle called, 'did you have something you wanted to add to the list?'

'Lots of sunshine,' Duggan replied.

Miss Bottle smiled. 'I'm sure dear, I'm sure. However, I understand the long range forecast is a very good one, so you could well be lucky.'

She put her sheet of notes back down on the bench and walked over to the cupboard, taking out a microscope and a set of prepared slides. 'I think that's all for the moment,' she said, putting a slide under the microscope and adjusting the focus. 'Before we carry on with this morning's work, are there any other questions?'

Simon Daines raised his hand.

'How full are our notes expected to be?'

Miss Bottle raised her eye from the microscope. 'As full as you can make them, dear, especially as your file will eventually be looked at by external examiners. I imagine you'll end up with a fairly large section on water life, a study of animals and insects, the local flora of course... I would suggest you put in as many photographs as you can, line drawings, maps and so on. Possibly a few pressed flowers with full descriptions. There should also be time for a little individual experimentation, though I believe Major Beddington runs a very busy course.'

There was a low groan from most of the group at the weight of this information.

'Of course,' she added, ignoring the noise, 'some of you are already more knowledgeable than others about certain aspects of this subject. There is a lot of expertise in this group which can be shared amongst you. For example, we know Mr Daines already has 'A' levels in botany, biology and chemistry.'

'And cowshit...' Barton muttered.

'I'm sorry? Anyway, we must get on or we'll get nothing done at all this morning. Major Beddington will give you much more detailed advice, of course, as soon as you get there. And just think. Much of what you do could be adapted into very interesting studies for children as well. Even very young ones.'

She looked at her watch, turned to the blackboard, and chalked a heading on it.

'And now we really must get on. Last week we were discussing the molecular structure of an organic compound. I want to do a little more on that before the coffee break, and then you can finish the microscope work you started.'

An hour later, during the coffee break, Gerry discussed the prospect of our course with us. He sounded a little envious.

'It'll be great if you get this weather,' he said enthusiastically, echoing Miss Bottle's words. 'And Dorset, too. It's bound to be better than that place in Wales one of our groups went to. They said it was like being in Colditz.'

'I thought Elderberry Hall was for geography students too?' Duggan said.

'It is. They had to go to Wales because they were putting central heating or something in at Elderberry Hall. Mind you, isn't Elderberry Hall the place where...'

'Where what?'

'Well, I think the meals might come as a bit of a shock.'

'Who told you that?'

'Somebody in our group was talking about it. I don't think they believe in overfeeding students. Still, that won't do you any harm, eh? It'll be a sort of health spa week, too.'

He prodded Duggan's stomach and smiled. 'Of course you'll have to watch out for Miss Fosdyke. Her reputation...'

'Who's she?'

'I'll say no more,' he said darkly, putting his mug down and gathering his notes together for the next lecture. 'Anyway, a couple of mature scientists like you two should find it all most fascinating. You'll see what I mean.'

He laughed heartily at some private joke.

Although it rained for much of the next fortnight, the brilliant sunshine had returned by the day of departure. Even Duggan looked more optimistic as he threw a bottle of suntan lotion on top of the clothes in his holdall.

'You never know, we might even get a chance to use it,' he said. 'Now then Mike, I suppose it's okay if I rely on you for soap, tooth paste, after shave, corn plasters, underwear and a goodnight kiss?'

'Of course.'

'And you're taking spare pyjamas, are you?'

'No. Why, are you?'

'I'm afraid I shan't be taking any pyjamas at all.'

'Where's yours, then?'

'Milly offered to iron them yesterday and she burnt a hole in the crutch. I had to scrape them off the ironing board. They look ridiculous.'

'You mean you've only got one pair?'

'Yes, and everybody'll be able to see 'em through the hole in my pyjamas.'

'God, you sound like David Barton. I meant one pair of pyjamas.'

'Of course. Haven't you?'

'What do you do when you're washing those then?'

'Sleep in my tie. Of course, I don't really mind doing that at Elderberry Hall, providing you don't really mind either.'

'Who said you'll be sleeping with me?'

'Well, I might not be, of course. I might be sleeping with Major Beddington. Or the mysterious Miss Fosdyke, perhaps. Now there's a thought!'

'You don't even know who she is yet.'

'True. Anyway, we'll find out this morning. Are we taking all these books? Where did you get them all? Don't tell me, Samantha...'

'Yes. We've got them for three weeks.'

'Let's hope nobody else in Westminster wants a library book on flowers. You've got the entire natural history section here. What did she do? Smuggle them out?'

'I don't know. We just have to make sure we don't lose any.'

We pushed our bags out into the corridor, where Milly was leaning on her mop and staring out of the window. She jumped as the Duggan's bag shot between her legs.

'Ad enough, 'ave yer, darlin'?' she called, recovering her composure. 'Packed yer bags, 'ave yer?'

'It's the pressure of work,' said Duggan. 'We need a break. We're shooting off to the South of France for a few days.'

Milly dumped the mop back in her bucket, and leaned against the wall, always ready to while away a little time in conversation.

'Are yer darlin? And my aunt's the Queen Mother. Where yer goin', then?'

'On a field study.'

'Yeah? What's that?'

'We're going to study things in a field.'

'Are yer now? Dirty couple of sods then, aren't yer! I ain't studied nothin' in a field since I was sixteen, but I ain't got anythin' worth studyin' these days.'

'It's part of our course. For science. We've got to look at cowshit.'

'Ave yer, darlin'? Well you shouldn't 'ave much trouble recognisin' it. Can't see what it's got to do with teachin', though. Unless you're gonna teach an 'erd of cows. Sounds a waste of public taxes to me.'

She sniffed and took out her packet of tobacco.

'I shan't enjoy it without you,' said Duggan. 'Do you want to climb in my suitcase?'

She laughed abruptly. 'Chance 'ud be a fine thing, darlin',' she said, and coughed her way back along the corridor.

A large, comfortable forty seater coach was already waiting outside the main gates and there was plenty of room to spread out inside. A few students were already sitting inside reading magazines and papers, but most were still carrying bags and cases across the quadrangle or talking to each other in small groups. The driver took the bags as they arrived and pushed them into the boot, while dodging the four different sized nets that Samuel Charlton was carrying.

'You all going fishing then?' he said to Charlton. 'I thought you lot had to do some work up here?'

'Butterflies,' Duggan explained. 'We're rather hoping to capture a cosmolyce boeticus.'

'Are you mate? Well don't set it on me. You'd better put that net on the rack with the others. If you're lucky you might get an eyeball on the end of it as well.'

'Really?' said Duggan, 'Thanks very much.'

'That's all right, mate. Just watch it isn't mine, that's all.'

Miss Bottle had come to see the group off, and she hovered between the doorway and the driver, checking names off against her list and making sure nothing had been overlooked or forgotten.

'Simon's gone a bit overboard, hasn't he?' Duggan whispered. 'All he needs is a bloody harpoon gun.' He nodded towards Daines, who was packing a wide stream net, rubber swimming flippers, a case of specimen bottles and a collapsible fishing rod onto the luggage rack.

'Maybe,' I said. 'But I bet we've got more books than he has.'

The driver pulled the door shut, Miss Bottle waved frantically, and the coach edged its way out into the morning traffic. The sunshine was already very strong, and though all the windows had been opened, the coach soon slowed to a crawl as it joined the heavy traffic through the centre of London. The Thames sparkled lazily as the coach inched its way over Westminster Bridge and around Parliament Square, and it wasn't until mid morning, when the motorway was reached, that any real progress could be made. The driver switched on his radio and a crackle of music mixed with the hum of the engine. I put down the crossword I'd been solving, settled further into my seat, and gradually drifted into sleep. I was awakened two hours later by the brakes being applied sharply. I sat up quickly, wiped the sweat from my face, and stared out of the window. The coach had obviously left the motorway some time ago.

'It's all right,' said Duggan. 'A lorry pulled up a bit dangerously in front. Do you want all your cheese sandwiches?'

'Not really. Where are we?'

'Salisbury. Not too far now.'

The coach sped through Stockbridge and turned off the main road at a signpost saying Blandford Village. By now, the heat in the coach was overwhelming and the atmosphere uncomfortably stuffy. Few students at the college ever went to bed early, and our group was no exception. Most were still asleep and I noticed that Simon Daines' wide stream net had fallen off the luggage rack and neatly across his head, like an over-sized hairnet.

The coach suddenly slowed down, negotiated a small roundabout, and then picked up speed again, running easily along a recently widened lane shadowed by oak and beech trees. I drifted back to sleep again and was abruptly woken up half an hour later by the driver turning the volume of the radio up to a deafening level. Then he switched to public address and called through the microphone.

'Okay, lads. Wakey wakey. You're here. Elderberry Hall Holiday Camp. Wake up, unless you want to travel back to town with me.'

He nudged his coach through enormous wrought iron gates and into a wide gravel drive that lay between extensive and beautifully maintained lawns. Elderberry Hall sat imposingly at the end of the drive, a large brown-stoned early eighteenth century country house in an excellent state of preservation. The main frontage had all the features a wealthy family might have demanded of a typically well designed home; large windows, gables and pinnacles of local stone mellowed to a rich golden brown, with large, formal garden areas around it. The house had been extended, but tastefully and in keeping with the grand style of the main building. At the right hand end of the Hall, a modern but carefully integrated study-laboratory had been added.

The smell of freshly cut grass mingled with the scent of honeysuckle and jasmine as we climbed down from the coach, pulled our bags onto the grass verge, and sat down on them for a while, welcoming the opportunity to sit in the fresh air and enjoy the warmth of the late afternoon sun.

'Well, this is rather fine,' said Daines, putting a pair of sunglasses on and staring contentedly into the distance. 'What it must have been like to be monied and influential two hundred years ago, eh? I think I shall rather enjoy this.'

'Think of the parties you could have in here,' said Barton. 'Perhaps we can have one on Saturday night. I'll ask the Major when I see him.'

'You can ask him now,' said Duggan, nodding towards the entrance. 'This has got to be him.'

An extremely tall man in a shapeless brown jacket and thick brown twill trousers came out of the doorway and hurried purposefully down the steps towards us. His thinning silvery hair blew gently around the sides of his freckled, sunburnt head and he moved very quickly, carrying a clipboard and pen in his right hand. Though I guessed he was probably in his middle fifties, he looked exceptionally fit and strong, and his long legs travelled over the ground in careful, measured strides.

'Right, you lads, come along, hurry up, thought you were never coming,' he called in a loud voice. 'Look, don't leave your kit there. Can't you see the grass has just been mown? Put it up by the entrance while I talk to you.'

The bags and cases were moved nearer the great oak doors, while the Major watched, hands on hips and his legs astride. When he was satisfied that the group was attentive again, he took a cherrywood pipe from his cavernous jacket pocket, pushed a handful of tobacco into the bowl, and set light to it with a match. Then he carefully pushed the spent match all the way into the earth at the edge of the lawn.

'Right then,' he said, raising a huge, very muddy wellington-booted foot and lowering it onto Duggan's suitcase. 'We're all here now, are we? Twenty eight of you, isn't it? One botany man coming tomorrow? Well, he'll just have to make up tonight's work when he gets here. Stand by your kit, will you?'

He called a register of everybody's name. Then he prodded Duggan's suitcase, as if to test its breaking strain, upended it and sat down on it. Presuming this to be a signal to follow suit, everybody else sat down too. The Major spoke again, his strong mellow voice and careful enunciation making him clearly audible across the lawn.

'It can't have escaped your notice, gentlemen, that this is an historic building in an excellent state of repair. It dates from 1756. We like to keep it in that condition and we therefore have strict rules for its use. You may use the drawing room, the library, and the front lawn. You may not use the Great Hall, the Oak Room, or the formal gardens. Meals are served in the Beech Room. You may not be in the bedrooms during the day unless it is essential, you may not smoke in the building at all, and you may not bring drink, food, portable audio equipment or members of the opposite sex into the building without my personal permission. Since this is a male student group, this eventuality will not be an issue, of course. You must be in by ten, because the doors are locked at ten by the warden. For those of you interested in history, you'll find booklets available which detail the history of the Hall. They are very reasonably priced.'

He paused to stand up and grab at a flying insect which seemed to be attempting a forced landing on his forehead. Trapping it neatly between his fingers, he held it a foot away from his face and examined it carefully, screwing up his wrinkled eyes. Then he opened his fingers gently and watched it fly away before speaking again.

'There will be evening lectures of course, and some of your time will be spent in the laboratory. You'll need to carry notebooks and a pencil with you at all times, and each day I shall lecture immediately after the evening meal.'

He picked up one of the butterfly nets from the pile beside the cases and whipped it in the air like a riding crop.

'Hmm. Well, I'm glad to see that you've come prepared. Now then, there's a map of the sleeping accommodation on the notice board in the hall, but I'll be escorting you to your rooms myself. The main meal is at six, and there will be packed lunches at mid-day to give us maximum time in the field. Kindly keep your bedrooms neat, tidy and in good order. The slightest damage will be charged to your college. No specimens from the field are to be taken into your rooms. Nor are Hall library books.'

He paused to check the notes on his clipboard.

'Right, I think that's about all for the time being. Except to say that my name is Beddington and our other resident lecturer is... ah... around here somewhere. Phyllis?'

He bellowed at the top of his voice, and looked around.

'Miss Fosdyke is a specialist on plant life, as some of you may already know. One of the best in the country. She's also damn good on ticks and mites if that's your particular field. *Phyllis!*'

The bushes parted and a slight, roughly dressed middle-aged woman clambered out of them like a naughty child caught hiding. She was as suntanned as the Major, and had a scarf tightly tied round her head to protect her hair from the twigs and leaves she obviously relished clambering through in her search for new specimens. An ancient camera was hanging round her neck on a piece of string. She hurried towards the Major.

'I'm sorry Andrew,' she apologised. 'There's an awfully interesting specimen on the beech behind the clematis. Not absolutely certain what it is yet. Have to wait for the snap to be developed. I do hope I've wound the wretched thing on properly.'

She fumbled with the camera, squinted through the viewfinder and sighed.

'It'll probably come out black again,' she said. 'Can't think why they make these things so awkward. I'll just have to get one of those modern ones. Get the snap in a couple of seconds, then. Never as reliable as the human eye, of course.'

'This is Phyllis Fosdyke,' Major Beddington said again, standing out of the sunlight and surveying her as if he was seeing her for the first time. 'She'll be giving you your first session in the field tomorrow.'

'She's a bit old for it, isn't she?' said Barton innocently.

'I rather think we'll find it's the common mealy bug,' Miss Fosdyke said. 'I really don't think it could be phlloxera quercus. Not at this time of year.'

'What?' the Major snapped.

'Mealy bugs,' Miss Fosdyke repeated. 'I can't be absolutely certain at this stage. The snap should give us a definite answer. And who are these young men, Andrew?'

'This week's college group. Students from St James's in London. They're the reason I called you from the bushes. Is there anything you want to say to them?'

Miss Fosdyke put her head to one side, rested her chin on her fingers, pursed her lips and thought for a moment. 'No, I don't think so. Plenty of time for that later on.'

She frowned and disappeared back into the bushes. In the excitement of finding a rare bug it seemed she hadn't really been aware of our arrival at all. The Major watched her departure for a moment and then waved his hand at the bags and suitcases.

'Right, get your kit inside the house,' he ordered. 'I'll speak to you again in the Oak Room. Follow me.'

Gathering our belongings, we followed the Major up the driveway and into the spacious hall. The interior of the house was immaculately preserved, with sections of ornate, decorative oak panelling and freshly painted white plastered walls. A wide curved staircase covered in plush green carpet led to the floor above, and vases of freshly picked flowers had been spaced at regular intervals, picked out by the rays of the late afternoon sun streaming brilliantly through the huge windows. An aspidistra stood at the foot of the stairs, and along the wall by the doorway stood an enormous mahogany table, its surface gleaming with polish. Three unopened letters lay on it. Major Beddington picked them up and put on a small pair of spectacles which seemed out of place on his rugged features. They slid to the end of his nose and perched there precariously.

'Cartwright, Sayers, Kent,' he announced. 'Is that any of you? Probably the lot who left this morning. I am continually forwarding mail.'

I raised my hand. 'I think that one's mine,' I said.

'Are you Cartwright, Sayers or Kent?'

'Kent.'

'Mother worried about you already, is she?'

Duggan looked at the Major and grinned. 'His mother said she'd come down for a visit, if that's alright with you?'

Major Beddington looked puzzled for a moment. Then he stared at Duggan coldly.

'You'll have no time for visits here, my lad. No time at all. You won't have much time for jokes, either. Right, leave your kit here and we'll move into the Oak Room for a moment.'

He led the group along the hall and into an attractive sunlit room, converted as a lounge and filled with deep and comfortable easy chairs. The parquet floor and furniture in the room had been lovingly polished to perfection, and on the large table in the centre of the room there were numerous magazines about country life and a huge empty glass ashtray, as polished as the table itself. The shutters on the windows had been pushed back to their fullest extent, offering an exquisite view of the ornamental gardens at the back of the Hall, contrasting sharply with the rugged fields and woodlands beyond. The Major stood in the centre of the room and ushered the group around the table.

'You'll sleep between two and four men to a room. Letters can be collected from the table outside, though if your women can't stand to be parted from you for five days without putting pen to paper it's a good job you're not staying here for a fortnight, hmm?'

He looked round at us, eyebrows raised, mildly amused by his attempt at humour.

'Do we have any free time?' asked Michael MacKenzie, a Scottish student from the main biology group whose passion was countryside rambling and wild flower gathering.

'All depends what you mean by free time,' the Major replied. 'If you mean do you get ten minutes after the evening lectures to get some fresh air into your lungs before you go to bed, then the answer is more or less yes. If you mean do you get time to wander around this lovely building aimlessly discussing the sort of philosophical claptrap students usually witter on about, the answer is no. You are here on a concentrated course, paid for by money from the public purse. I have no desire to see the money wasted.'

'Do you have a television?' asked Charlton. 'I mean, for those rare occasions when we do have a moment to relax?'

'We do not,' the Major replied emphatically. 'We have an excellent library filled with books instead. Right, follow me. And bring your kit.'

He led us out of the room and up the stairs, where he pointed out the bedrooms. As we walked along the corridor, Duggan and I stayed close to each other near the back of the group, hoping to be allocated the same room.

'You'll find your way about soon enough,' the Major said. 'The two lavatories are on the ground floor, and there are bathrooms at each end of the corridor. But don't use them unless it's essential.'

'What, the toilets?' asked Barton. 'I'll never last the whole week.'

There was a ripple of laughter. The Major's face remained stonily immobile.

'I was referring to the baths. I would prefer you not to use them.'

'Is there a reason?' asked Daines politely.

'There are several extremely good reasons. Firstly, after a day in the field students invariably leave them in a filthy state and that creates a lot of extra work for the cleaners. Secondly, central heating was installed in this building recently and at the moment the plumbing rattles like a dying tractor. Thirdly, students sometimes think they can lie in there for hours doing nothing except wasting time.'

'Thank you,' said Daines softly.

'Right. I might add that the air here is fresh enough to stop you smelling for at least a month, provided your mother has given you enough clean underwear, so you won't need a bath anyway. Now I shall leave you to unpack. Make sure you are on time for the meal. Latecomers will go without.'

The room Duggan and I were using could quite easily have slept six. There were four beds, one in each corner, and we spread our belongings out on the two beds that wouldn't be used. The room was attractively decorated in a delicate pastel blue and the late afternoon breeze moved the white lace curtains restlessly against the windows as clean air breathed softly into the room.

'God, the beds are a bit hard,' said Duggan, pushing his mattress gingerly with his fingers. 'I wonder if they got them from a prison camp.'

'I don't suppose you'll get much chance to use it.'

'No, it doesn't look like it. Who's your letter from?'

'Samantha. She misses me.'

'Rubbish. I bet the council wants the bloody books back. Now, where do you think the electric socket would be?'

'There aren't any sockets in the bedrooms. There's a notice about it in the hall.'

'You're joking! What do I do? Plug my razor into a tree?'

'The shaving sockets are in the bathrooms.'

'Sod it, then. I'll grow a beard.'

We finished unpacking and walked back downstairs to the library.

The shelves were crammed with books on every aspect of biology, botany and field science, and down the centre of the room was a long table scattered with recently dissected plant life. A new chalkboard, filled with delicate sketches of plant sections, had been screwed to the wall near the door. Through the windows, I could just see several of our group still lying on the lawn stripped to the waist soaking up the last of the sun.

A door from the back of the library led out into the new laboratory. Reference books had been stacked neatly on the tables, and above the work benches lining the walls were newly fitted adjustable lamps for microscope work and close observation of specimens. Charts of Dorset's natural history filled any available wall space, and rows of bottles lined the shelves and cupboard tops, each one carefully labelled and stored out of reach from the rays of the sun. A huge aquarium stood on the front desk, and what appeared to be the stomach of a pigeon had been stretched and pinned to a drawing board beside it. There was a strong smell of formaldehyde in the room.

'Can't stand this sort of thing,' Duggan grimaced, looking at the bird distastefully. 'Cutting up frogs and worms to look at their nervous systems and lacerating the innards of birds. It's a bit Burke and Hareish, isn't it? I never enjoyed doing it at school.'

'Let's go and sit on the lawn before dinner. It's probably the only chance we'll get.'

'Good idea. God, I'm starving!'

'That's the fresh air. Perhaps we'll have jugged hare. Or salmon. Freshly caught.'

Duggan chuckled. 'I doubt it. We'll probably have that bloody wood pigeon.'

A gong sounded from the entrance hall and the group filed into the Cedar Room, where tables to seat four had been arranged, in the manner of a small countryside hotel dining room. The country air had sharpened appetites mercilessly, especially since most of us had only eaten a meagre packed lunch on the coach. Samuel Charlton sat down opposite me and rubbed his hands vigorously in anticipation.

'I'm ready for this!' he said eagerly. 'I hope it's a roast.'

As soon as everybody was seated, two very thin waitresses swept into the room and began to serve the high table occupied by Major Beddington, Miss Fosdyke, and another woman we hadn't met earlier. Charlton peered impatiently over the top of his chair to see what was on offer.

'They don't eat much,' he said. 'Look.'

I glanced across to the Major's table and saw that the waitress had put down a plate of pilchards, four tomatoes, a bowl containing several boiled potatoes and a plate with three tiny oatmeal buns.

'I expect he's probably on a special diet,' said Duggan drily. 'He's probably got ulcers from wondering if somebody's turned the bath taps on and used a pint of illegal hot water.'

'You'd think he'd be starving after being out all day,' said Charlton, eyeing the waitress approaching their table. 'Unless he had a massive lunch or something.'

'Move your arm, please,' said the waitress very softly, as if she was serving a meal in church with the service in progress. She placed a plate of pilchards near Duggan's elbow.

'That's not too bad, then,' Duggan said, pulling the plate carefully towards his own. 'Any potatoes?'

'I'll bring them in a moment,' the waitress whispered, turning to another table. 'You can be serving the pilchards out while you're waiting.'

'Serving them out?' Duggan said, aghast. 'Serving them out to who?'

'The rest of the table, of course. They're for the four of you.'

'You mean serve them out between all four of us?'

'Of course. What did you think I meant?

'You're joking.'

‘I most certainly am not!’ she answered firmly, looking mildly hurt. On the table opposite, Barton stared at the pilchards in disbelief and prodded one with his spoon.

‘Oh come on love,’ he urged. ‘You can’t just give us this. Food is a major part of my life.’

‘And sex,’ the student beside him added.

‘And sex. But right now I’m just hungry. You can’t expect these pilchards to go round four people.’

‘Why not?’

‘My God,’ laughed Duggan hollowly, ‘and I thought this plate was just for me!’

‘Who do you think you are, dear?’ said the waitress, her temper rising visibly. ‘Royalty?’

Other students began to object in voices that rose to a steady grumble, until Major Beddington stood up and walked over to Duggan’s table.

‘Is there something wrong?’ he asked.

‘It’s this lot, Major,’ said the waitress awkwardly. ‘They don’t think they’ve got enough to eat, that’s all.’

‘Really? I fail to see anything wrong with the pilchards.’

‘There’s nothing wrong with them,’ Duggan said. ‘There just aren’t enough of them, that’s all.’

The Major leaned across the table and examined the plate. ‘I can’t see why not. There are two each. That should be ample, in my view.’

‘Must be a bad year for pilchards, then,’ Barton muttered.

‘Well, that’s all you’re going to get, young man,’ the Major said firmly, giving Duggan an icy stare. ‘They are standard rations and nobody has ever complained before. Of course, if you are used to stuffing junk food inside yourself several times a day it is possible your stomach will notice the difference. However, after your very moderate stay here I venture to suggest you might emerge as a leaner and fitter man. Angela, furnish this table with a dish of potatoes and leave them to it.’

‘Yes Sir.’ She went back into the kitchen and returned with a small bowl of steaming boiled potatoes, which she placed in the centre of the table.

‘And that’s all there is,’ she said stiffly. ‘If you don’t like it I’ll give them to a table that does.’

Duggan chewed heavily on a slice of brown bread, and poured a little water into the glasses on the table. I picked my glass up and sipped the water miserably.

‘Don’t drink too much of it, Mike,’ Duggan muttered. ‘You’ve probably got to bathe in it as well.’

‘Didn’t Gerry say something about the food?’

‘Even Oliver Twist would have said something about this stuff. Maybe we could alert the Red Cross or something. Get a few food parcels flown in. I really don’t know if I can handle a week of this.’

A moody silence hung over the dining room as each person tried to make the meal last as long as possible, while the waitresses stood by the door and watched until every morsel had disappeared. Then, silently and efficiently, they removed the empty plates and dishes from the tables. There wasn’t a scrap of food remaining on any of them.

‘I shouldn’t imagine they have to do any washing up here,’ said Charlton. ‘The plates probably get licked cleaned by ravenous visitors.’

The second and final course came almost immediately. One of the waitresses wheeled a trolley from table to table, depositing four bowls and a dish containing a brown, jelly-like substance.

‘I don’t think I can manage any more, love,’ said Duggan, smiling at the waitress and sitting back in his chair. ‘I’ll just have a tiny slice of the blackforest gateau.’

‘Just a coffee and a cigar for me, please,’ said Barton.

‘You’ll have this and like it,’ the waitress snapped, slapping four spoons on the table and staring at him angrily. ‘And there’s no more of that, either.’

The brown substance in the large bowl resembled a strain of matured junket that had gone watery round the edges. Duggan stared at it in disbelief.

'It's a local speciality, actually,' said Barton.

'Really?' Duggan replied sarcastically. 'What do they call it?'

'Cowshit.'

'Yes. I thought they might.'

A murmur of laughter rose from the next table. One of the group had removed a small purple flower from a pot on the window sill and planted it in the middle of the dessert, pointing out the advantages it had over regular fertiliser.

I felt a deep flush of sympathy for the plant.

Half an hour later, we assembled in the laboratory, hungry and restless, to listen while Major Beddington outlined the form the course was going to take.

'I advise you to make notes,' he announced briskly. 'I shall talk for an hour, and tomorrow we'll start into the field as early as we can. There is a great deal to get through. Tomorrow morning we shall examine Rosepine Valley, Barrow Hill and Fletchers Wood, providing the weather holds.'

There was a light knock at the door, and Miss Fosdyke tip-toed into the room, apologising briefly and taking a stool near the door. Major Beddington waited until she was seated comfortably, and then began speaking again.

'Right. Once we're out in the valley the first thing we'll need to do is an insect and animal count. That will probably take most of the morning. You might like to give the soil a going over with your testers while we're out there. I presume some of you have brought your own testers?'

'Did he say testes?' asked Barton. 'I've got my own set of them.' Five students raised their hands tentatively.

'I see. Hmm. I thought there would be more than that. We'll just have to make do with what we've got. Phyllis, perhaps you'd be good enough to check on the state of the testers in the lab.'

Miss Fosdyke appeared flustered. She stood up quickly and moved towards the door.

'Not right now, Phyllis,' the Major said. 'Tomorrow morning before we go will do.'

Miss Fosdyke's cheeks reddened, and she hovered for a second, aware that everybody was looking at her. Then she sat down carefully on the stool again, her hands on her lap and her knees clenched tightly together.

'Right. Now where was I? We shall be bringing back a number of specimens for identification in the lab. It will be worth your while writing half a page of notes about them. Remember, I shall want positive identification, not some half-baked theoretical claptrap. I shall also want to see your notes each evening. If you haven't brought your own specimen bottles you can take a few from this cupboard here, but mind you bring 'em back. Had a lot down here a few weeks ago who left half of 'em in the valley. The locals thought the junkies had moved in. Breakages must be paid for, of course.'

He snorted contemptuously.

'Now then, You'll need to have a rough idea of what this county's all about. I'll put a few jottings down on the board and you can copy 'em down. They'll give you some background information and help you with soil identification and so on in the morning.'

He opened a drawer and selected a stick of chalk, which snapped abruptly as he stabbed a heading on the blackboard. Tossing half of it back into the drawer, he began to scribble notes in tiny writing that was completely illegible from the back of the room. As he wrote, like a dying man anxious to scribble out a new will, he commented in short meaningless phrases about what he had written.

'Small county, Dorset. Fertile valleys of course, well wooded… chalky uplands to the South East… fringed heathland… chalk hills running down to the coast. The Isle of Portland, of course. Actually a peninsula joined to the mainland by Chesil Beach... Portland fascinating, practically treeless. Predominantly agricultural country... clay soil on the South Western side...

He stopped and looked across at Michael MacKenzie, who had put down his notebook and was sitting with his arms folded.

'What's the matter with you?' he asked. 'No pen?'

'I canna read your writing,' MacKenzie said simply.

'Why? Are you blind?'

'No. It's too small.'

'Move to the front, then,' said the Major dismissively. 'Nobody has ever complained before.'

'They probably never got from the house to the lab,' said Barton grimly. 'They probably died of hunger on the way.'

Major Beddington ignored him, and turned back to the blackboard. When he had covered it with notes and diagrams, he put down his piece of chalk and walked slowly round the room, looking over shoulders and scrutinising what was being written.

'Right, when you've copied the notes you can study the maps of the countryside. You'll find them in the drawers under the workbenches. Then I suggest you go into the library and sort out which books you need. Up here, there's a wall chart Miss Fosdyke drew some time ago which shows you the local flora. I should make a few notes on that too.'

Miss Fosdyke shuffled self-consciously in her seat, smiled at him, and took the chart down for the group to pass around and copy. For half an hour, the silence was broken only by the rustling of pens on paper, and the loud ticking of a large wallclock above the blackboard. At nine o'clock, Major Beddington stood up and coughed loudly.

'Pencils down a moment, gentlemen. I shall leave you to finish off on your own. Don't take too long though or you won't get into the library before midnight. You will be expected to be up by seven in the morning. Breakfast is at seven thirty. Kindly be on time.'

MacKenzie raised his hand, thought better of it, and quickly lowered it again.

'Do you want to ask something?' said the Major, pulling the window closed behind him.

'Aye. I was just thinking about lunch tomorrow...'

'Well?'

'I was wondering whether we come back here for it, or whether we can buy something out.'

'We'll be miles away at lunch time. We have packed lunches during the day. They are provided by my cook. I did mention this, I believe. I assume you didn't have your hearing aid plugged in.'

'What do we get for our...'

'Lunch is neither here nor there, young man. This isn't a gourmet's convention. It's a field course. Which reminds me, if you've brought any of your own puddling tools you'll need them tomorrow. Small trowels will be useful for soil sections. Or if you have to dig about in dung.'

Duggan lurched forward with laughter and then swallowed it as he caught the Major's eye.

'Something amusing you, young man?'

'No, it's just that Milly would have been amused to hear you say that.'

'Milly? Who's Milly? I don't recall saying anything amusing.'

'No, you didn't. It's just that...'

'Is this relevant?'

'Not really. I...'

'Then I suggest you return your efforts to your drawing.'

Gathering up his notes, he turned sharply and strode out of the room. Miss Fosdyke followed him at a safe distance.

(ii)

I found it very difficult to sleep. By the time I'd finished my notes, illustrated them, and organised my clothing for the morning, there seemed little else to do except read the latest edition of Country Life or go to bed. I'd also promised to ring Samantha as soon as I'd found a phone, but on enquiring I was told the only telephone was in a small side room which Major Beddington used as his office, and applying for the use of it was like asking for the keys to Fort Knox. I was also very hungry indeed, and cross with myself for not listening more carefully to students who'd been here before. At the very least I could have brought a few extra food supplies.

Because Duggan hadn't slept on the coach, he'd fallen asleep in bed very easily. For several hours I lay awake listening to Duggan's snores, punctuated at intervals by the enthusiastic hooting of an owl in a tree near his window. This was followed by the regular honking of what sounded like a pair of stray mallards talking to each other on the front lawn. It seemed I had only been asleep for a few moments when I felt a hand shaking me gently. I turned over quickly, and heard Duggan urging me not to make a sound.

'Listen!' he whispered. 'Keep still!'

There was a rattling noise at the window at the far end of the room. The moon had disappeared behind a cloud and I peered intently through the darkness. The lower part of the window was stealthily being pushed upwards. I yawned and sat up quickly.

'What is it?'

'Burglars,' Duggan whispered. 'We've got bloody burglars!'

'What are we going to do?'

'Catch the bugger! Get out of bed quietly and go on the other side of the window. At least there's two of us. We'll jump on him when he climbs through the window.'

I pushed the sheets aside, climbed cautiously out of bed, and moved to one side of the window, my senses sharpened as I caught the night breeze blowing through the opening. Duggan picked up a large bath towel and crawled on his hands and knees to the other side of the window. Then he hunched himself into a ball and screwed his eyes up in an effort to assess the size of the dark shadow moving outside. I noticed that he was naked, apart from a jockstrap embroidered with the Union Jack.

There was a sudden movement outside, and the window slid completely open. With a grunt of exertion, a figure in a black trench coat heaved himself through the opening and collapsed in a heap on the floor.

'Right Mike,' Duggan shouted triumphantly, 'jump on him!'

The intruder yelled loudly and then struggled desperately to stop himself from being suffocated by the towel that had been thrown over his head. Suddenly, the bedroom door was thrown open, the light clicked on, and the huge frame of Major Beddington in a starched nightshirt filled the doorway.

'What the devil is going on in here!' he bellowed. 'What sort of behaviour is this?'

'You've got burglars,' Duggan grunted.

'Burglars?' he roared. 'We don't have burglars here. Who is this fellow?'

He watched in disbelief as the intruder struggled round the room with the towel on his head, held tightly by the pair of us. We looked like a splinter group from a rugby scrum.

'Stand still, man!' the Major roared again. 'You two, stand back! Get the towel off that fool's head.'

Cautiously, we released the intruder. The towel dropped to the floor, revealing the bearded features of Dudley, who blinked in the light and looked severely put out.

'Look, this is a bit much, old man,' he complained, pushing his beard into shape and panting with exhaustion.

For a moment, the Major seemed lost for words. I noticed that Barton, in a red silk dressing gown, had also appeared in the doorway and was peering over the Major's shoulders to see what was going on.

'Who the hell are you?' shouted the Major at Dudley, suddenly recovering his composure.

'Dudley Hornpipe, old boy. Who are you?'

'Hornpipe? Aren't you supposed to be coming in the morning? What the devil are you doing here at this time of night?'

'I got away earlier than I thought. I've just walked five miles from the station.'

'What's the matter with the bell, man? Didn't it occur to your addled brain to ring it?'

'I tried it. It doesn't work.'

'Why didn't you knock, then?'

'I tried that, too. Nobody came.'

'Hardly surprising this time of night, is it? So you think you can shin up the walls instead, do you? Who do you think you are? Dracula?'

'It was either that or sleeping on the lawn,' said Dudley simply. 'And frankly, I didn't relish that idea.'

'Didn't you indeed. So instead, you wake up the entire hall and attack a dormitory?'

'Force of circumstance, I'm afraid. I rather think the dormitory attacked me.'

The Major's cheeks reddened and puffed out, as if a head of steam was rapidly building up inside them.

'Kindly get the light off and go to bed,' he barked. 'You've got to be up by seven.'

'Seven? Is that really essential? I think...'

'Yes, it damn well is!'

The Major swung round from the door, and almost knocked Barton over. 'Good God, another one!' he said testily. 'Who are you?'

'I heard the noise,' Barton said. 'I just thought you might be having a midnight feast.'

'Go away!' the Major shouted at the top of his voice, glowering fiercely at him. Baron retreated quickly, and the Major turned and marched angrily off down the passageway.

'Well, this really is a bit much, chaps,' Dudley said again as the door slammed shut. 'I get away from my Grandmother's funeral early, and I get a welcome like this. He should think himself fortunate that I've bothered to come at all.'

'You should have tapped on the window,' said Duggan.

'Didn't want to wake you, old chap. Just shinned up the first drainpipe I found and looked in the window. You get used to climbing up things when you're looking for bird's nests.'

'You took a risk, climbing in like that. Mike could have killed you. He's got a black belt.'

'Has he? That's very impressive. So is your patriotic jockstrap, old boy'

'I'm glad you like it. It's part of the required equipment. You have to use them as slings for killing your own lunch.'

Dudley stroked his beard thoughtfully. 'I see. That bad, is it? So what have I missed so far?'

'Food, basically,' said Duggan. 'There's a shortage of it in these parts.'

'Really? Well I rather think I've got a packet of custard creams in my rucksack. I've left it on the ground outside. Do you want me to shin down and fetch it?'

'It's alright,' I said. 'We can dream about them. It'll be something to look forward to in the morning.'

'Nonsense, old boy. It won't take me a moment.'

He pushed his legs through the window and disappeared. In just under a minute he was back inside the room, carrying a small packet. 'No custard creams, I'm afraid. I've got half a treacle tart and two packets of fish paste sandwiches. I've only brought the tart up, in a manner of speaking. The sandwiches look a bit iffy, if I'm honest. I've left them in the porchway.'

He took a penknife from his back pocket, carved the treacle tart delicately into three large portions and handed them round. 'Have we really got to be up at seven?' he said. 'I usually skip breakfast at college.'

'We'll probably be skipping it here,' said Duggan. 'There probably won't be any.'

'Oh dear. Well I hope this isn't going to be one of those formal events where we wander round in a cluster looking at clumps of fescu. I intend doing a study of owls while I'm down here. There's a family of Tawnys in the trees just outside.'

'I know,' I said. 'They kept me awake for ages.'

'I think you'll find the Major's itinerary doesn't actually allow for individual expression,' said Duggan. 'If you're lucky, you might get five minutes before bedtime.'

'Really, old boy? Well I don't think I shall be taking too much notice of that. Now, where do I sleep?'

'You've got a choice of two,' said Duggan, pointing to the beds in the corner of the room.

'Two? Jolly good. I'll take both.'

He pushed the beds together, stripped the bedclothes and remade them as one. Then he pulled off the heavy rambling boots he was wearing and tossed them onto the floor.

'Look,' he said, 'Will it disturb you chaps if I read for a little while? Unless you want to go on a badger hunt or something?'

He raised his eyebrows questioningly. We stared at him in disbelief.

'No? Well, perhaps you're right.'

'Not unless we can cook what we catch,' said Duggan. 'Turn the light off when you've finished reading.'

'Of course, old boy. Give me a nudge in the morning, will you? Or do they bring tea round?' He smiled pleasantly, tucked himself fully clothed into bed, put on his spectacles and settled down to read a book on woodland birdlife.

By eight o'clock the next morning we were sitting on the lush cool grass of Pinerose Valley in the hot morning sunlight, grouped around Major Beddington like wolf cubs at a very subdued pack meeting. The journey into the valley had hardly been a leisurely stroll, and Major Beddington had obviously not forgiven Dudley for waking him up during the night. Moreover, he seemed grumpily determined to make everybody else suffer for it too.

After walking several hundred yards into the valley, four of the students had removed their shirts in the boiling heat. They were instantly reprimanded by Miss Fosdyke, who seemed to feel that the Major's methods of dealing with these often tiresome young men should be supported without question at all times.

Breakfast had been brief and minimal; a boiled egg, two triangles of toast, a solitary sausage and a cup of weak tea. Everybody had appeared on time except Dudley, who had refused to get out of bed until the housekeeper, a vast lady with muscles like a weight lifter, had ripped the blankets away and demanded to know why he happened to be sleeping in two beds. Since nobody had woken him up in this manner since he was ten, Dudley refused to answer, or even acknowledge that the woman was in the room, and she strode off in exasperation to look for the Major. Dudley then decided that since there wasn't much chance of getting back to sleep, he might just as well go and wash instead.

Immediately after breakfast, the Major had divided the party into small groups and issued canvas bags of equipment to be carried to the site in the valley he intended the group to study. Ravenously hungry and uncomfortably hot, nobody had shown any enthusiasm for carrying anything at all, and they made themselves discretely busy whenever Miss Fosdyke or the Major approached them. Miss Fosdyke herself was entrusted with a smaller canvas bag containing the packed lunches, the Major obviously taking the view that if he'd given them to anybody else, they would almost certainly have been eaten immediately. Miss Fosdyke took up a rear position and followed the group into the valley cautiously, often looking over her shoulder as if half expecting some sort of prehistoric specimen to charge her from the bushes and steal a sandwich.

When we had reached the site for investigation, the Major stopped and looked around carefully as if checking the suitability of the area. Then he took a large rusty penknife from his pocket, cut a small piece of turf from between his feet, and rubbed a little of the soil from it between his fingers.

'Right, gentlemen,' he said, straightening up and dusting the soil from his hands, 'this should be fine. For the first three hours we shall work in groups on soil sections, specimen collection and animal counts. You'll find the equipment you need in the canvas bags. Don't break it, lose it, or mistreat it. If you need help on points of recognition, Miss Fosdyke and I will assist. I also want a bag of soil taken back to the lab. You can use the soil kits on it out here but we'll go into the composition thoroughly back at the Hall. The kits should give you a rough idea of the texturing.'

He gathered the canvas bags into a small pile, and tossed trowels, soil testers and specimen bags to each group.

'We'll make a monolith when we get back. Divide it into work sections, I think. What do you think, Phyllis?'

Miss Fosdyke hovered eagerly, like a large bird searching for a worm. 'Oh certainly, Andrew. Shouldn't have to puddle on too much with this stuff. It's quite heavy soil for anybody to carry much of it back, though. I wonder whether...'

'Nonsense Phyllis,' the Major retorted. 'Bribe 'em with a sandwich.' He barked heartily at his own joke and pulled a white peaked cap over his head to shield his eyes from the sunlight.

'Now, keep your flora specimens in the plastic bags and anything else you consider interesting. You'll find plenty of saxifrage, mouse-ear, ribwort, yarrow, keck...'

'Och, I hope I find a slice of that,' said MacKenzie.

'What?'

'A slice of keck, Major. Even a slice of Scottish oat-keck would be welcome.'

The Major screwed up his eyes and stared at him. 'Is your stomach all you think about, lad?'

'Och, no. I think about Scotland quite a lot too.'

'Do you? Well kindly think about dropwort and campion instead of haggis and porridge, will you? You've got five week's work to pack into five days. Now, where was I?'

'You were talking about slices of cake,' Barton offered. Miss Fosdyke tutted.

'You were telling them to keep their specimens in bags, Andrew,' she said.

'Thank you Phyllis. Damn good job somebody's listening. Now, you'll probably need your floras for the rarer flower varieties, but you'll recognise the common ones. I think…'

He stopped as Miss Fosdyke tapped him gently on the shoulder. 'Don't forget the orchids, Andrew.'

'What orchids?'

'You know. We usually warn them…'

'Quite right. Make sure you are careful about what you pick. All plants need to be treated with respect, but some are rarer than others. Don't tread on orchids, or pick them. Anybody not know what an orchid looks like?'

Several people raised their hands.

'It's a little early yet for them, of course,' said Miss Fosdyke. 'An erect little plant, anything up to about fifty centimetres. You might just spot an early purple. Look for the hood and spur. Occasionally mistaken for the foxglove, of course. Very distinct smell of… um… how would you describe it, Andrew?'

'Cat's piss,' the Major said. 'Now, I assume you're all familiar with the standard animal count method? Since I seem to be doing all the talking, would one of you like to stop worshipping the sun and explain the animal count?'

He looked round the tired eyes and blank expressions, and then picked up a solid wire frame from the pile of equipment in front of him. Simon Daines raised his hand.

'Well?'

'You choose a piece of ground at random, and throw the frame. Then you count all the insects you can find inside it. Then you move the frame to a different section, and so on.'

The Major nodded.

'Good. Not every brain here is an addled one, obviously. Of course, it's not a strictly scientific method, but it does give you a very rough idea of the insect life. Especially if we compare it with the banks of a stream later on. Make a complete list of everything you find, will you? Spread right out on the floor of the valley.'

'I expect you've tried this with the youngsters at school,' added Miss Fosdyke.

'There's not a lot of call for it in the city centre,' said Duggan.

'Tommyrot!' snapped the Major. 'You've got parks, haven't you? You're not all going to teach in the middle of London, are you? Where's the oat cake man?'

MacKenzie took a step forward.

'Where are you going to teach, my lad? Look at the animal counts you can do if you bung a few frames about in the Trussachs.'

'I'd never thought of it that way. Fascinating.' Miss Fosdyke agreed.

'Right then. Choose your piece of ground and throw your frames on the sward. Keep to the grassier bits. And keep well away from each other. About twenty yard intervals. Off you go.'

Each person took a frame and wandered off to find a piece of ground. Dudley grabbed my arm, and passed me a small package. 'It's a bar of Kendal mint cake, old boy,' he said. 'I found two packets of it in my coat. I'm afraid I don't know how long it's been there, but if it was good enough for Edmund Hilary it should be good enough to keep you going for half an hour.'

I thanked him gratefully and gave half the packet to Duggan, who snapped off a chunk eagerly and bit into it. Miss Fosdyke wandered over to see if we had everything we needed.

'Awfully beautiful morning,' she said enthusiastically. 'Apparently it's not going to last through the day though. Dreadful shame. First real sunshine this year, you know. You really are awfully lucky.'

'Oh? And why is that?' asked Dudley.

'Why, the weather of course. You're lucky to have such good

weather for your study period. What is that you're holding? Birdfeed?'
She looked at him strangely, as if wondering why she hadn't noticed a person with a large black beard the day before.

'Kendal mint cake. You wouldn't like a small section, would you?' Dudley asked generously. 'Might as well finish it up.' Miss Fosdyke looked surprised and peered at the packet closely.

'I really don't think you should be eating your lunch just yet, you know,' she said. 'I think Major Beddington agreed that we would all have our lunch together when we get to Barrow Hill.'

'This isn't my lunch, dear lady,' Dudley replied. 'It's a medicinal compound my specialist requires me to take. I have an ingrowing bowel condition.'

Miss Fosdyke took a sharp intake of breath. 'Oh, how awful. I do apologise. That must be extremely painful. You won't drop the paper on the floor, will you?'

'I expect he'll eat it,' Duggan muttered.

'Of course not. I have immense respect for the country code.'

'Splendid. Has your group got a pooter?'

Dudley looked blankly at her. 'Frankly, I'm not sure, dear lady. I've got a bit of a cold. I couldn't be certain if I have a pooter or not. Is it a medical condition?'

'No no no, one of these, dear.'

She took a small glass jar out of her bag with two transparent lengths of tubing attached to it. 'If you wish to keep one of your frame specimens, you suck on this end, and the specimen is drawn up into the tube, here, and then it pops into the jar.'

She handed one of the jars to him, turned to walk away, and then walked back again.

'I say,' she said, peering intently at Dudley, 'You're not the chappie who studies bees, are you?'

'I'm afraid not,' said Dudley, rolling up his trouser legs and exposing his blindingly white legs to the sun, 'but I'm very interested in bird migration and owls, if that's any help.'

'Really? How fascinating. You do look rather like him. He had a similar beard. Incidentally, it was mealy bugs, you know.'

'Really?' asked Dudley, wondering what on earth she could be talking about.

'Yes. I have to say I'm not at all surprised. I rather suspected phylloxera quercus, of course, but the snap was quite clear. Do you photograph, Mr... er...'

'Hornpipe.'

'Ah. Do you photograph, Mr Hornpipe?'

'Very rarely. I'm afraid I don't possess a camera.'

'Oh. That is unfortunate. And how are you getting on?'

'What with?' Duggan asked blankly.

'Your little job. What sort of results have you got?'

'I'm afraid we haven't started yet,' I explained. 'We were just about to begin when you joined us.'

'Oh, I see, I see. Well, don't let me spoil it for you. Just throw the frame, Mr Hornby, just throw it. It's very simple.' She wandered on to the next group, and Dudley watched her go, stroking his beard thoughtfully.

'Strange old bird,' he said. 'Might be worth studying her instead of the owls. Right, please stand well back, I intend to propel my frame.'

He took the metal frame from Duggan, looked at it cautiously for a second or two, and then raised it to his shoulder, lobbing it energetically in front of him. It flew in a jagged semi-circle like a faulty boomerang, and struck Major Beddington with great force in the back of the neck. The Major lurched forward, spun round, and gripped the back of his head with both hands.

'Who the devil threw that?' he roared, glaring round at the groups nearest to him and rubbing the back of his neck. Heads raised from poring over plants and metal frames, and Dudley stood quite still for a moment. Then he bounded over to the Major, hands outstretched.

'Oh, look, I really am most terribly sorry, old boy,' he apologised cheerfully, laying a meaty hand of reassurance on the Major's shoulder.

'I had no idea it would travel like that. I do apologise. I don't know how it managed to go like that at all.'

'You bloody fool!' the Major shouted, a portion of his neck turning the colour of a cooked beetroot. 'I said throw the frame, not try and hurl the bloody thing into the sea. What's the matter with you, man? First I find you trying to break into the place at midnight, then I'm told you need twice as many beds as anybody else. And now you try to kill me. Are you supposed to be a training college student or a bloody hired assassin?'

Dudley shuffled awkwardly in front of him, nodding in agreement. Then he put his hand out to soothe the Major's neck. 'Yes, I repeat, I am most dreadfully sorry. I do assure you I was only trying to...'

The Major slapped his hand away. 'I know what you were trying to do, you fool. Next time, either throw it underarm, or give me ten minutes to evacuate the valley.'

He rubbed his neck again and returned to an examination of the soil, muttering under his breath. Miss Fosdyke peered at him sympathetically, but decided it probably wasn't the best moment to say anything.

'I think it might be best if I moved some distance away to share in this dubious activity,' Dudley said to me. 'Devonshire perhaps. I had the same trouble with cricket balls at schools. I'm afraid I broke somebody's ankle, once.'

He picked up another frame and wandered off miserably. I walked in the opposite direction for fifty yards and then threw my frame a short distance away from my feet. It fell on the ground with a soft plop near a fallen tree, and I hurried forward to examine its contents. Apart from a slight movement of the grass I couldn't see anything at all, and for the moment I wondered if the sound of Major Beddington's voice had caused all the wildlife to beat a hasty retreat. I moved closer to the frame and examined it in greater detail, feeling a little ridiculous, as if I'd planted an orange pip and stayed around to watch it grow.

An ant carrying a tiny sliver of bark suddenly moved feverishly across the frame and disappeared among the blades of grass. I counted it, and put a note on my pad. Several minutes later, the ant appeared again, still carrying the same piece of bark. I assumed it had either taken the wrong route, or delivered it to the wrong colony and been told to take it away again. Though I scrutinised the area inside the frame carefully, nothing else seemed to be moving at all. I stretched my arms and lay back in the sunshine, wondering what Samantha was doing. I was surprised at how much I missed her, even though it was only three days since we'd been together. Perhaps I'd ask Major Beddington if I could dig up a few orchids for her…

Resting my head on my elbow so that I could scan the frame easily, I looked across the valley at the others. Daines was talking urgently to his group and prodding the ground with his foot. MacKenzie and two of his friends were chewing something furtively. Charlton and his group were on all fours around a counting frame, trying to hoover the area inside with a pooter, until Charlton suddenly realised he was blowing instead of sucking and was likely to end up with a mouthful of ants. Duggan was scratching the ground inside his frame with a piece of stick. Barton, nearest to him, was having a fierce argument about whether the two worms his group had spotted were really both ends of the same creature. Barton then suggested they should eat it rather than count it. In the distance, I could just see Dudley frantically waving a butterfly net. As I watched, the cane it was attached to suddenly became entangled with Dudley's legs, and in a spectacular somersault Dudley disappeared from view behind a clump of bushes. After several minutes, he reappeared holding his ankle with one hand and the two pieces of butterfly net in the other, and hobbled cautiously back towards the group.

Deciding that a single ant was a considerable disappointment, I scrabbled my hand in the grass. To my surprise, there was an immediate flurry of activity. Ants moved in all directions, a woodlouse lay on its back waving its legs at me, and two millipedes hurried off at the disturbance. I rushed to count everything, but by the time I'd counted the larger and slower creatures all the ants had promptly disappeared again.

I scrabbled again, and once more the area inside the frame sprang to life, except that I now had no way of knowing which of the creatures had been added to my list and which had simply turned up for a re-count. I decided this wasn't really my area of expertise, and after making what I considered to be a reasonable estimation of the contents of my frame, I wandered over to see what others had found. Duggan seemed mildly satisfied with his findings.

'Look at that,' he cried, thrusting his notepad towards me. 'I've got thirty nine ants to start with and a right collection of shelled stuff crawling about in there as well. It's a high density population area, this bit. What have you got?'

I showed him my list.

'Not bad, not bad. You can't beat mine, though. Have a look in my frame.'

The metal rectangle was indeed seething with life. Ants jostled and fought each other over a mound of tiny coloured particles in the centre, two millipedes inspected a matchstick with interest, a spider ran along the left hand side of the frame, and a dozen woodlice were sorting through the coloured particles. There seemed to be activity in all corners.

'That's interesting,' I said. 'I wonder what the stuff is that the ants are so attracted to.'

'It's fishfood,' said Duggan.

'Really? How do you know that?'

'Because I put it there. I don't know what's in it but they certainly don't waste any time in shifting it. I've got to admit I imported the woodlice, though. There's a rotten log over there with hundreds of them underneath.'

Major Beddington suddenly bellowed an instruction for the group to finish the count and gather round him again.

‘Some good results on the whole,’ he said approvingly as the group sat on the ground around him. ‘We’ll draw up a comparison grid when we get back to the Hall. Now, I’ll give you another forty minutes to collect some flora specimens and then we’ll move on up to Barrow Hill. Before you start, kindly remember that wild plants need to be protected. Flowers that were common once are often rare now. Pick only where there is an abundance of blooms. Don’t tread on them. And don’t dig ‘em up by up the roots. You might not realise it, but it’s against the law. Fortunately we don’t get many picnicking fools treading all over them at this time of year.’

Finding wild flowers was easier than recognising them, and after failing to identify four of the first six we collected, Duggan and I decided to combine efforts and fill a specimen bag between us.

‘Here’s an interesting one,’ Duggan called. He walked over with a small clump of yellow flowers.

‘They’re buttercups,’ I said. ‘My mother’s garden is full of them. And the other stuff is grass.’

‘Ah,’ Duggan cried, ‘That’s the layman’s point of view. This may look like grass to you, but it is in fact soft false brome grass. As opposed, say, to sheep’s fescu. Now what do you suppose the other plant is?’

‘Which plant?’ asked Miss Fosdyke, appearing behind him and examining his bag with interest. ‘That’s grass, young man. Brome. I shouldn’t bother collecting it. There’s a lot of it about.’

She smiled silently, savouring her joke to the full. ‘And what else have you collected?’ She peered in the polythene bag and thrust her hand inside.

‘There’s not much, I’m afraid,’ Duggan apologised. ‘Mostly buttercups.’

‘Ah, but creeping, meadow or bulbous, Mr Hornpiece? All of them nutlet producers, of course, and most of them having that typically acrid taste. Upright sepals, palmate leaves. Ah, now this is the bulbous, of course. Prefers dry grassland to marshy areas. What else have you got there? Pass me that one, will you, Mr Hornbeam?'

'I'm not Mr Hornbeam. Or Mr Hornpiece,' said Duggan.

'I do beg your pardon.' She pointed to a flower near the bottom of the bag and I pulled it out with a flourish like a conjuror producing a rabbit.

'Not that one, dear. The other one. Right at the bottom of the bag. The one you have there is a capsulla bursa-pastoris.'

'I'm afraid that's wasted on him,' said Duggan. 'He wouldn't know a capsulla bursa-pastoris from a daisy.'

Miss Fosdyke looked at me sympathetically. 'Really? Oh dear. We shall certainly have to do something about that, won't we?'

'Are we likely to eat, soon?' asked Duggan earnestly. 'It's half past one.'

'Good Lord, is it really?' said Miss Fosdyke. 'You must be very hungry. I'll tell Andrew. We normally have our lunch when we get to Barrow Hill.'

She hurried off and several minutes later Major Beddington bellowed at the group to come and sit round him again. When he was satisfied that every piece of equipment had been collected and returned, he announced his intention of stopping half a mile further on to eat. Putting the bag of sandwiches on his back, and entirely unsympathetic to the fact that Dudley was hobbling quite badly, he then set a strong pace at the front of the column and led the way through the valley and up to the brow of the next hill. Showing no sign of being even mildly fatigued by the walk, he stopped beneath a large oak tree and ordered everybody to sit down again. It was intensely hot, and my clothes stuck uncomfortably to my body. I felt as if I'd sweated half a stone during the climb.

Opening the canvas bags containing the packets of sandwiches, Major Beddington instructed everybody to come and collect one, and then he settled back with Miss Fosdyke under the shade of the tree. She opened her sandwiches, selected one carefully, and bit into it with contentment. Each packet contained two jam sandwiches, a dry sausage roll, a tomato and an apple. Barton leaned round the tree and signalled to Duggan.

'Do you two want to join the escape party?' he hissed. 'It's tonight. We're tunnelling out from Room Six.'

'Haven't got the energy, mate,' said Duggan. 'Do you want your tomato?'

"Fraid so. Do you want your sausage roll?'

'Well it's either that or I'll have to eat my plimsolls.'

After twenty minutes, Miss Fosdyke came round with a plastic bag for the sandwich wrappers, and then the Major stood up, lit his pipe, and called for everybody's attention again.

'Haven't got through as much as I'd hoped this morning,' he said. 'Can't think why they insist on these short courses. We'll have to push on fairly quickly or we won't get finished. I want to look at the floor of Fletcher's Wood this afternoon. Might even get time to do some beating. Pick up your kit and follow me, please.'

Setting the same pace as before, he led the group through a tortuous route of fields and footpaths. After a while nobody bothered to speak, concentrating instead on trying to reach the next destination and hoping that a cafeteria might rise, phoenix like, out of the ground in front of us. During the brief lunch period Dudley had strapped up his left foot and fashioned a crutch out of a fallen branch, and I noticed that he maintained a surprisingly good speed with it. Major Beddington stopped only occasionally, either to point out a changing feature of the countryside or to talk briefly about a particular plant or bird he felt everybody ought to be able to recognise. A sudden burst of song made him halt and listen expectantly, his hand cupped round his ear.

'Chaffinch!' he announced decisively, as if defying anybody to say that it wasn't. 'Listen. Whit-iu, whit-iu, whit-iu. There, hear it? Easiest bird to recognise, of course... black forehead, slate-blue nape... feathers often with a trace of white. Keep your eyes open. You might hear a whinchat. Or possibly a redstart or shrike.'

The noise he made sounded very little like anything I could hear but nevertheless, I admired the Major's ability to select a single sound from the various noises above us and make a positive identification of it.

'Clever, isn't it, Mike?' said Duggan, echoing my thoughts. 'I can only do a positive identification on the ones in Trafalgar Square. They're pigeons,' he added proudly.

By the time we entered the woods, the sky had changed to a muddy grey. Clouds began to mass above the trees and the stifling atmosphere was slowly replaced by a cooler breeze that gradually strengthened into a gusty wind. It stirred the patches of grass and flicked the dry leaves over restlessly, sending them scurrying along the footpath.

'Miss Fosdyke was right, then,' said Duggan, looking up at the sky. 'I thought it was too good to last.'

'It might be a benefit in disguise,' I said. 'I hate to admit it, but I wouldn't mind a quick storm. At least we'd have to stop for half an hour.'

Duggan laughed grimly. 'I shouldn't be too sure of that. He'll probably expect us to bivouac in the forest and build huts out of natural materials until the storm's over.'

Major Beddington suddenly stopped at the base of the largest tree he could find.

'Now, group yourselves around here, will you?' he said. 'I want to take a soil specimen from the floor here, and compare it with this morning's stuff from the valley. You'll find it quite different. Phyllis, where are the entrenching shovels? Phyllis?'

Miss Fosdyke was hovering around the back of the group, holding a handkerchief to her head and looking decidedly ill.

'I'm sorry Andrew,' she called. 'I'm feeling rather queasy. Must be the heat, I think. What was it you wanted?'

'Two entrenching tools, Phyllis, please.'

'I'm sorry, I thought they were with you. I'm sure you had them.'

The Major rummaged through the canvas sacks and gave a grunt of satisfaction.

'It's all right, Phyllis, I've found 'em. Now, you two men, take the shovels and dig out a large section, will you? Take the top turf off first. Want to leave things as we find them. I hope that's the first thing you'll teach children when you're showing 'em how to excavate. You'll need to go fairly deep. I want a sample from about two feet down.'

He handed the tools to Daines and MacKenzie, who cut away a square section of turf and then pushed the shovels firmly into the ground. The Major lifted the first complete section of earth from the shovel, like a proud father handling his first child.

'Good. Now while they're digging, the rest of you have a look at this section. What do you notice? More acidic, much darker humus, drier composition, fluffy texture in the upper layer. Good idea to watch for truncation too. Phyllis, pass me a soil tester, will you? Phyllis? Phyllis?'

He stood on tip-toe, and looked around the group. It was only when the back row of students turned round to look for her as well that he realised she was lying, immobile, on the ground behind them.

'Good God!' The Major exclaimed, more irritated than concerned, 'The bloody woman's fainted!'

Willing hands hurried forward to help Miss Fosdyke into an upright position. She groaned softly and held her forehead with her hands, while Charlton and Daines helped her to a fallen tree trunk by the Major's side. He immediately began fanning her face with the metal end of an entrenching tool. Her eyes fluttered open.

'I do apologise, Andrew,' she said faintly. 'Most unusual. I can't think what came over me. I'll be all right now, thank you.'

'Nonsense. You can never tell. Need to get the blood back to your head. Put your head between your knees.'

'I don't think that will be necessary,' she persisted firmly. 'I think I'll be quite alright now. I think it must have been the fish paste sandwiches.'

'Fish paste sandwiches? What fish paste sandwiches?'

'The ones we had for lunch, Andrew.'

'We didn't have fish paste sandwiches for lunch. We had corned beef. Or jam.'

'Look, I'm sorry Andrew,' Miss Fosdyke said weakly, 'but I think I know a fish paste sandwich when I see one. I can certainly tell the difference between fish paste and jam.'

Dudley suddenly looked vaguely guilty and hobbled to Miss Fosdyke's side.

'I think I can possibly explain, dear lady,' he said. 'Were these sandwiches wrapped in greaseproof paper, by any chance? If so, I rather fear you may have eaten some fish paste which wasn't as fresh as it might have been.'

'What the devil are you talking about, man?' the Major barked, looking at Dudley in disgust. 'Are you telling me Miss Fosdyke has been eating fish paste sandwiches belonging to you?'

Dudley leaned forward and stroked his beard. 'Well, I can't say that categorically, old boy, but I did leave a packet of sandwiches in the porchway last night. I think somebody may have put them in the lunch bag by mistake.'

The Major thought for a moment and then looked aghast. 'Good God, man,' he shouted. 'That was me! God in heaven, I've poisoned the bloody woman!'

Miss Fosdyke began to moan softly. The Major, embarrassed and annoyed, gripped her by the back of the neck and pushed her head violently into her lap. She gave a strangulated cry, and he stepped backwards into the hole that MacKenzie and Daines had dug a few minutes ago. A fat drop of rain splashed on his nose.

'Goddammit!' he shouted. 'Why didn't some fool warn me the hole was there?'

'Miss Fosdyke doesn't look at all good, Major,' Barton said kindly. 'I think we ought to get her back to the Hall. She probably needs a good meal inside her.'

The Major pulled his leg out of the hole, panting furiously.

'Damn and blast!' he shouted. 'We'll have to abandon some of this afternoon's work, that's all. I don't like the colour of her. Two of you make a stretcher, will you? You, the bearded fool. Get yourself on one end of it.'

Dudley swallowed hard. 'Look, old boy,' he objected, 'I'd be glad to oblige but I've hurt my ankle rather badly and I'm not sure if it would be a good idea.'

'Seems a very good idea to me,' snapped the Major. 'You've maimed me, poisoned my assistant and probably desecrated half the countryside catching butterflies, so it's the least you can damn well do. And don't call me 'old boy'.'

Daines and Charlton found two slim branches and constructed a makeshift stretcher using the string from the top of the canvas bags, two jackets and four animal counting frames. The Major hobbled over to it and prodded it with his fingers.

'Try it, will you Phyllis,' he ordered.

'Really, Andrew,' she said, 'I don't want to make a fuss. I shall be perfectly alright if I can just rest for a little while.'

'That's as maybe, Phyllis. Frankly, I don't intend taking any chances. It's a long way back. They can take turns in carrying you. Though on second thoughts it may be better to keep the bearded fool away from it, I suppose.'

There was a sudden rumble of thunder, and the woods darkened ominously. A few minutes later, rain began to spatter heavily through the leaves, and the group hurriedly after the Major, who walked with little thought for the stretcher bearers at the rear of the column. At the entrance to the wood, the stretcher suddenly collapsed, pitching Miss Fosdyke into the puddles that were rapidly forming under the trees. She refused to make the slightest attempt at remounting, and Daines and Charlton sighed with intense relief. Duggan and I pulled our open shirts over our heads in an effort to protect ourselves from the weather, but the rain sprayed our faces in bursts, running into our eyes and dripping down our cheeks. The countryside had been transformed, in a matter of minutes, into a wet and gloomy haze like a late February afternoon. Duggan swore as his feet sank up to the ankles in a puddle of mud.

'That's the end of Summer, then,' he shouted. 'I knew it wouldn't last. I've thoroughly enjoyed today, haven't you, Mike?'

'Thoroughly. I can't remember when I've had such a good time.'

'I wonder if the Major thoroughly enjoyed it too?'

'I'm sure everybody's thoroughly enjoyed it.'

'I'm sure, too. I love the countryside, don't you, Mike? Especially when it pisses down with rain and there's no shelter for miles. What do you think we've got for tea?'

'I couldn't care less. So long as it isn't fish paste sandwiches.'

'Scrambled eggs on toast with a slice of cheese on top,' said the waitress, putting four plates of food on the table. 'Pass it round, please. There's a tomato each as well.'

Duggan looked up at her.

'What, a whole tomato?

'That's right.'

'What, each?'

'Look, there's no need to take that attitude. If you've got any complaints, you tell Major Beddington. I don't buy the food. I don't cook it. I just serve it. I am not responsible. Okay?'

'Of course. What's the chef done to this cheese?'

'It's not a chef. It's a housekeeper. She's grilled it.'

'I should call her in then, love,' said Barton cheerfully. 'I think it's ready to own up.'

'I'll tell her that.' She looked at him in disgust and turned abruptly in the direction of the kitchen. After everybody had eaten in gloomy silence, Major Beddington rapped a spoon on the table and waited until he had everybody's attention.

'Miss Fosdyke was going to lecture to you this evening.

Unfortunately she is quite sick and I have called the doctor. I shall be lecturing to you myself tonight. We can't afford to waste any more time. We have wasted enough today already. Not through any fault of mine, I might add. Please go through into the laboratory as soon as you have finished your meal. And bring your specimens with you.'

'I haven't drunk enough to give him one,' Barton muttered.

I suddenly remembered I had left my polythene bag of wild flowers on the dressing table in our bedroom, and I hurried upstairs to fetch it. As I left the room, I noticed three pork pies, a french stick and a lettuce on Dudley's bed, and I wondered where Dudley had got them from. Like a man returning from a week's diet on a health farm, my hand tentatively moved towards one of the pies. Then I remembered Dudley's fish paste sandwiches and thought better of it. Perhaps the food had been left over from his grandmother's funeral. When I reached the laboratory, Major Beddington had already started his lecture. His eyes followed me to the back of the room, and he waited impatiently until I had found an empty stool.

'Now that we all seem to be here, kindly empty your specimen bags and spread your collection in front of you. You'll find a lot of the plants have been duplicated. This little specimen, for example. Hypericum perforatum if I'm not mistaken. Check it in your floras. Notice that the veins are pellucid, but the reticulations aren't. Look at this drawing of it. The leaves are thickly dotted with pellucid glands. Now, what else have you got?'

He walked around the centre table and stopped beside Samuel Charlton's stool.

'You'll notice we have collected a large variety of yellow flowers. Very common colour. Sometimes quite difficult to tell the difference between the varieties. Coltsfoot, fleabane, ragwort… all of them have similarities to the dandelion. This hawkweed, for example…'

Charlton coughed awkwardly. 'That's a hawkbit,' he said. Major Beddington looked at Charlton curiously, as if he had body odour.

'It's a hawkweed, young man. Look at the leaves. They're more linear. Look at the basal rosette.'

'No, I'm afraid it definitely is a hawkbit.' Charlton smiled nervously, not anxious to upset the Major again that day, but determined to prove his point. 'I've just dissected one and looked at it under the microscope. There's no latex.'

'He's probably right, Major,' said Barton. 'He's got a GCE in it.'

'What?' the Major frowned.

'He's very clever. He's got a GCE in it.'

'I've got an 'A' level in Botany,' said Charlton humbly.

'I don't care if you've got an 'A' level in woodlice,' said the Major testily. 'I have travelled every inch of Pinerose Valley and this is quite definitely a hawkbit.'

'Yes, that's what I said. It's a hawkbit.' Charlton nodded enthusiastically. The Major stared at him.

'What? You said it was a hawkweed. What the devil are you talking about?'

'No, I think I said it was a hawkbit. You said it was a hawkweed.'

'Whatever you said it was, it isn't, and never has been lad. And that's an end to it.'

Charlton looked extremely hurt, and the Major beat a hasty retreat to the back row of the laboratory, where Dudley was frowning into his microscope.

'Excuse me, old boy,' he said, 'but do you think we could have a rest from this? Frankly, it's getting a little tedious.'

The Major looked at him warily and raised his eyebrows. 'I beg your pardon?' he said.

'I'm afraid my particular interest doesn't happen to be flora. Do you think we could do something on butterflies or owls? I'm certain there's a family of Tawny owls...'

'If you were here for three weeks, I would be perfectly happy for you to sit in a tree and live with them,' the Major snapped. 'As it is, I can merely attempt to put as much nature into your mind as possible without fossilising your brain, and trust that at some time in the future you'll be able to teach children an appreciation of the countryside. Provided, of course, you haven't polished off much of the fauna by leaving your fish paste sandwiches everywhere.'

He stepped back from Dudley cautiously, like a child who has put a match to a firework and is uncertain what it might do.

'Now, where was I? Right, gentlemen, in this flower the yellow petals are grouped in cymose clusters. Large number of stamens... the calyx and corolla marked with dots and lines...'

He paused to pick up the next flower and I suddenly realised how tired I was. My eyelids drooped as Major Beddington's words travelled round the room in waves and seemed to merge into a blur of Latin names. I fought to keep my eyes open, but the day had taken its toll and I drifted on a tide of obscure botanical knowledge. A picture of Samantha floated into my mind. She was walking towards me carrying a plate of pork pies.

I was jogged into consciousness by Duggan's elbow, and I gazed round the laboratory like a blind man suddenly given sight. The room was quiet and students were peering intently down the barrels of their microscopes. Major Beddington paced up and down the benches, checking for focus and commenting on what he saw.

'I thought I'd better give you a nudge before he got here,' Duggan said to me, pushing a microscope across to me. I hastily loaded the small glass slide under the retaining clips and focused the eyepiece.

'You'd better give me some idea of what you're doing. I seem to have missed half of this.'

'About twenty minutes as a rough estimate. We're looking at the sex organs of a milkwort.'

'Really? Does Barton know?'

'Yes. It's given him an erection.'

Dudley lifted his eyes away from his microscope, blinked, and then scratched his chin vacantly. 'I can't seem to see very much at all,' he said to Duggan. 'I think I've got a faulty instrument here. Do you think I could have a look at yours for a moment?'

'What's the matter?' called the Major.

'It's my instrument, old boy. It doesn't work. I've cut a section with this, er... scalpel thing, but I can't see anything at all, unfortunately. Under the instrument, I mean. I can see it perfectly well with my spectacles.'

'Rubbish. Of course it works, man. They all work.'

'Well, that's as maybe, but I'm afraid mine doesn't.'

The Major strode over to him, removed his tiny spectacles and peered into the barrel.

'You've got the lens cap on, you clot,' he said. 'Good God man, is there nothing you can do right?' He paused and looked to the side of the microscope. 'What's this?'

'It's a flask, Major. It's full of hot cocoa. I...'

'Hot cocoa? Who the devil said you could bring hot cocoa in here?'

'I'm afraid I need it, old boy. I have a medical condition which requires me...'

'Stop waving your scalpel at me, man. A brain condition, more like. Get that flask out of the way of this equipment before you slop it all over my slides.'

They both reached across to move the box of slides, and accidentally pushed the thermos flask sideways. It spun round for a moment and then rolled to the edge of the bench, slopping its contents over Major Beddington's trousers. The Major jumped back forcibly, lost his balance against my stool, and put a hand on Dudley's shoulder to stop himself falling over. Dudley reacted automatically, and shot both hands out to steady the Major's legs, unfortunately forgetting he was still holding a scalpel. With a cry like a bull at the slaughter, Major Beddington backed away from Dudley like a haunted man, clutching his thigh and making strange roaring noises in his throat.

'Look, I'm most dreadfully sorry, old man,' said Dudley, horrified. 'I really can't imagine how I…'

His voice trailed away and he sighed deeply as he watched the Major hurry out of the door. For a full minute, Dudley stood staring after him, stroking his beard nervously and wondering whether he ought to go in search of bandages. Then he took a deep breath and turned to me.

'I think I'd better go and spend the night with the owls,' he said, and walked sadly out of the room.

JUNE

LAUNDERING, GUERNSEY... AND THE FINAL RECKONING

In general, students at teacher training colleges were cossetted from the harsher realities of everyday life, and St James's was no exception. Their rooms were dusted and tidied every day, the kitchen area, washrooms and bathrooms were cleaned twice a week, and their bed linen was changed by the domestic staff on Friday mornings. Text books, pens, paper and folders were the only really essential items for college work, and even then, most text books could usually be borrowed or shared. Though termly grants were not generous, it was certainly possible to make them last without too much hardship.

Washing clothes, however, was a grinding chore that couldn't really be avoided. Most students found they could get away with doing one main wash every fortnight. Leaving it much longer than that was really tempting fate.

At St James's, students had two basic options and each had its own disadvantages. The first involved sending washing out to a local laundry firm approved and recommended by the college. Every Friday, a large number of sturdy flat cardboard collection boxes would be left by the doorway in the main corridor, and if a student wanted washing done, he would simply put it in a box, fill in a card with his name and room number, and slip the card into the plastic pocket on the front. Then he prayed that the same laundry would be delivered back the following week.

The service was certainly inexpensive, but due to the volume of washing being handled by the firm it was quite possible to receive pieces of another student's clothing by mistake when the boxes were returned. On one occasion, Gerry had ended up with buttons missing from a shirt and three odd socks, none of which were his. Nevertheless, most students did take a chance and use the outside service until the last few weeks of a term. Funds were at a premium then, and if it was a choice between worrying whether the college machinery would ruin your shirts or going to the theatre, the arts usually won.

A session using the facilities provided in the college laundry room could be just as fraught as consigning clothes to the outside agency. After several frustrating mornings in here, David Barton had once likened the experience to buying a veteran car and trying to get to Land's End in it without knowing the slightest thing about mechanics. Even Gerry, a capable handyman, hesitated at coping with the idiosyncrasies of the laundry room equipment.

The room was situated in the basement, reached by a short flight of steep, stone stairs. Even negotiating these with a full bag of washing had deterred many students. Nevertheless, demand born of absolute necessity had made many persevere, and after a number of sessions it was almost possible to get a kind of bizarre enjoyment from battling with the laundry room machinery and winning.

The room was large, though badly lit and usually filled with condensation, which had caused the damp to attack the ancient plaster and peel the paint from the walls. It also caused some of the light bulbs to fail with monotonous regularity, so that even if a washing session had been completed successfully, it wasn't always possible to see if the clothes were any cleaner or not.

Four large Butler stone sinks were fixed to the shortest wall, relics of the original laundry provision, and eight industrial strength machines on the other side of the room represented the enlightened age of mechanised washing. Their doors often jammed, the thermostats frequently failed, the water sometimes wouldn't drain away, but on a good day about four of them usually worked for long enough to cope with at least one load. I'd been more fortunate than most, although on one occasion the machine I was using had pulled itself free from the wall and tried to walk across the floor. On another occasion the drum had mangled one of my shirt sleeves when it had caught on a button, but by and large I'd come to terms with the fortnightly battle in the basement and had chalked up a success rate of about seventy per cent.

A row of iron hooks lined the wall opposite the machines. Most of them had rusted so badly they wouldn't support anything much heavier than a string vest, but two were still strong enough to string a line between and hang a few sets of underwear on. A huge gas stove hulked in a corner, almost redundant now but too large to be removed from the room. It seemed to be defying anyone to approach it with a lighted match, though at a pinch it could be used for heating clothes in one of the galvanised tubs originally provided for that purpose. An enormous drying cabinet jutted out from the darkest corner at a disconcerting angle after two fitters had tried to coax it into the alcove and given up. It had not worked properly since Dudley had turned the heat control fully up to dry out the boots he had worn on the field course and then completely forgotten about them for two days.

Just after nine on the last Monday in May, I went as usual to the nearest sink and turned the tap on, intending to soak my shirt collars and scrub them before tracking down a working washing machine. Though the tap turned fully on and fully off, it refused to supply any water in between, and I moved to a second sink. The tap came off in my hand. I went to the third sink, checked the tap carefully and inspected the waste pipe to make sure the water would run away. Then I found the sink didn't have a plug. Since this was all part of a familiar pattern, I was by no means discouraged. I simply moved to the next sink and began the sequence again.

It was at this moment that I heard footsteps hurrying down the stone steps, and Duggan came into the room.

'I thought I'd find you in here,' he said. 'I've got some bad news.'

'Don't tell me. They've sent you the wrong shirts in the laundry again.'

'No. Worse than that.'

'I can't think of much worse than that. Milly's died in the bath?'

'No. It's the exams.'

I shrugged. 'Oh, we've talked about that. They're weeks away yet.'

'Three, actually.'

'Three? But we worked it out that...'

'I know. We were wrong.'

'But that's impossible...'

'The notice is up on the board. The written papers are five weeks away, but they've brought the orals forward.'

'You're joking.'

'Unfortunately, no. I don't joke about things like that.'

My mind raced. It seemed unbelievable. Three year's work to be revised in as many weeks. For one rash moment, I considered leaving my washing and rushing upstairs to start work immediately. Duggan watched the colour drain from my face.

'You'll get over the shock,' he said. 'Others before us have revised in half the time and passed, so there's no reason why we shouldn't.'

'But we aren't the others...'

My mind filled with images of Milly, uttering dire warnings about past students electrocuting themselves because they couldn't cope with the thought of their impending finals. For a moment, I couldn't understand where all the months had gone. A tap in the first basin I'd tried suddenly made a gurgle like a death rattle and cold rusty water began to pour into the end sink. I stared at it dismally. Duggan waited for a moment and then looked up sympathetically.

'Fancy a nice cup of tea?'

'What help is that going to be?'

'None. I'm just tendering sympathy, that's all. I think the best plan is to gather your smalls and prepare to do some work. I'm going to the library.'

I finished my washing as quickly as the ancient equipment would allow and went upstairs to check with the notice board. Duggan was right. There were just under three weeks to the science oral examinations, and the notice explained that this was the only way they could be fitted into the crowded examination schedule. The only person on corridor three with an optimistic outlook was Milly, who greeted me happily as I hurried into my room.

'Worried about yer exams, love?' she grinned, slopping a wet mop along the corridor. 'I told yer they'd come round quick. They all worry round this time o' year. You should be all right though. You've done enough, ain't yer?'

'Milly, I wish you were right, but I don't feel as if I've done anything at all,' I said quickly, anxious not to be drawn into a prolonged conversation.

'Oh go on love, you'll be okay. Anyway, there's no use in worryin' about it now. If you fail, you fail. 'Alf of 'em fail anyway, and some of 'em work really 'ard from the first moment they get 'ere and still fail. You won't be the first one, love. Not by a long chalk.'

She picked the mop up and sloshed it about in the suds bucket. Specks of foam flicked onto my shoes.

'Anyway,' she added, 'you can always take 'em again next year. I tell you what, though. My Violet 'ad a teacher what 'ad loads of degrees and stuff and 'e never taught 'er a bleedin' thing. Seems ter me, it ain't what yer got it's the way yer use it. Least, that's what my old man's always tellin' me, dirty bugger.'

'Well if I don't pass I'll have wasted a lot of time and money,' I said testily. 'I don't intend failing if I can help it.'

'I don't suppose you do, love. And I don't suppose you will. Anyway, if you're makin' a cup o' tea in a minute I wouldn't say no.' She pushed the mop slowly down the corridor, humming tunelessly to herself.

The following evening after dinner, Duggan presented me with a plan of action. He seemed enthusiastic and organised.

'Look, this is what we'll do. Since we both take science we might as well revise that together over the next week or so, while Gerry does his geography. The chemistry is probably our strongest line so we'll give part of the mornings to that. The rest of the day can be used for physics, biology and the field course stuff.'

'You think we're likely to be asked questions on that?'

'If we don't revise it we will. I mean, the life history of a mealy bug could be a relevant topic if somebody like Miss Fosdyke is testing us. Anyway, when we know that lot back to front we'll get Gerry in here and do the education stuff together.'

'What about the notes we haven't got?'

'Somebody'll have 'em. Gerry will have all the education lectures. I think he's recorded half of them on tape. And even if he hasn't got all the stuff we need, somebody else will be bound to have it.'

'Providing they're not using it at the same time.'

Duggan shrugged. 'We'll cross that bridge when we come to it. It's all in the text books, anyway. It just takes a bit longer to revise that way. Now, I suggest we start at eight o'clock in the morning and break for tea approximately every hour, with an hour and a half for lunch. The same with the afternoons with a quick game of table tennis sandwiched in between.'

'Just to keep us from getting stale?'

'Just to keep us from getting stale. Then there's the afternoon tea break of course, after which we could slip down to St James's Park for a breath of fresh air.'

'This is ridiculous. We'll never do it in time.'

'Of course we will. Provided we cram hard in the working sessions. You can do a lot in an hour. Believe me, I passed my GCEs like this. We might even get a couple of days over.'

The more we discussed the idea of revising, the more determined we became to actually make a start, especially as most lectures had now been cancelled to provide extra revision time. As Duggan still hadn't fully recovered from the thought that the final reckoning was imminent, it seemed a good idea to retire to the Barley Mow and forget about it for a few final hours.

The next morning dawned bleak and cheerless, doing nothing to raise any enthusiasm for changing our normal daily schedule and starting work earlier than usual. Duggan crawled out of bed with a hangover and missed breakfast altogether, and it wasn't until nine o'clock that he emerged from his room looking acceptably alert. We took all our notes into his room, and then spent half an hour drinking black coffee while we tried to decide which of the sciences needed the most urgent revision. The fact that half our notes seemed to be out of chronological order didn't help matters.

Nevertheless, once we had started, we made encouragingly steady progress, and I was surprised to find I could remember all the work on compounds, molecular structure and the properties of alkyl halides with relative ease. At half past ten, Duggan threw his folder on his bed and yawned loudly.

'Well, that's an hour gone,' he sighed. 'Drags, doesn't it. Put the kettle on and we'll celebrate our learning with a hot cup of tea. I think I'll pop out for a couple of doughnuts as well. Haven't got any cash on you, have you?'

I fished in my pocket and handed Duggan a small pile of change. Then I settled down to read the notes in my physics folder. This was much easier, because Dr Frost had insisted on seeing our folders at regular intervals throughout the course and my notes were immaculately filed. Dr Frost might not win a prize for his charm, I thought, but at least his aggressive attitude paid dividends when it came to revision. It didn't seem fair that his department had such a low pass rate, and I still couldn't understand why. When Duggan returned, we drank a cup of tea in thoughtful silence and then settled down again.

‘This is when I really envy people like Simon Daines,’ Duggan said unhappily. ‘I mean, the bloke probably doesn’t have to do any revision at all. He just soaks up knowledge like a bloody sponge. Why can’t I do that? There was a bloke at school who passed nine GCEs at Grade A. Nine! He worked hard, but I don’t remember him exactly flogging himself to death over it. Used to get really glowing reports. All I got was a report saying if I didn’t stop thinking life was a bowl of cherries I’d end up grinding my teeth on the stones.’

‘I know what you mean. Some people have a natural aptitude for passing exams. We don’t.’

Duggan settled himself into a comfortable position on his bed. ‘You know, the trouble is, Mike, they’ve spoiled us. This’ll probably be the toughest few days we’ve had since we’ve been at college. We’ve been fed, laundered, entertained, given money to spend and we’re up with everything that’s going on in the West End. We’ve leapt about on a trampoline, run a fantastically successful college society at a vast profit, torn up the Doc’s daffodils and counted millipedes marching up and down inside a metal square. And what’s more, we’ve even had considerable success with teaching London children. Now all we have to do is work extremely hard for a fortnight and we’ll be handed a license to teach children and a career for life. You’d think it would be easy, wouldn’t you?’

‘We’ll pass. I’m determined. And anyway, I want to teach.’

‘So do I, and I’m sure they wouldn’t dare waste our talents. Anyway, the country needs more teachers. It’s always needing more teachers.’

‘That’s because they’re not paid very well.’

Duggan pulled the paper bag towards him and pulled out another doughnut. ‘True, but teachers don’t need much money, you see. They’re dedicated, like nurses. And it’s such an easy job. Look at all those long holidays they get.’

‘Nine till three. And all Summer free.’

‘Exactly. Tell the kids to turn to page thirty five and get on with it. And to earn a place in this remarkable profession, all we've got to do is work hard for the next fortnight. Then off to Utopia.'

'I hope you're right.'

'Of course I'm right. How many blokes do you know that have done much studying at college? Not just keeping up with the work. I mean real study?'

'Quite a lot,' I said. 'Half our corridor, for a start.'

Duggan considered this for a moment.

'Okay then,' he said finally. 'I'll give you that. For argument's sake, let's say half our corridor. But they'll all get the same certificate in the end. Perhaps a couple of distinctions. But that doesn't mean they'll be any better in the classroom. Just remember what Milly said about her daughter. Anyway, enough of this mind-bending philosophy. How do you prepare butyl chloride? I've forgotten.'

He sighed, pummelled his pillow into shape, and settled back on the bed with his folder propped up on his knees in front of him. I picked up my chemistry file to check.

'Concentrated hydrochloric acid and alcohol. I think.'

'You think?'

'Yes, I'm not certain.'

'Sod it.'

He scratched his chin thoughtfully and then screwed up two sheets of notes, tossing them into the bucket. 'I seem to have notes on everything I don't need. I've forgotten half of it and the other half seems to be missing. What's the test for ether? Potassium something or other, but God knows what.'

I flipped through the pages of the chemistry text book, anxious to reassure him. I'd seldom seen Duggan so depressed. 'Potassium thiocyanate.'

'Never heard of it. Any more tea in the pot?'

'No. I'll make some more.'

I boiled the kettle again and refilled the teapot. When I went back into the room, Duggan was staring morbidly out of the window, watching a hearse move slowly along the road.

'Look at that, Mike,' he said, sipping the tea slowly. 'He's failed his as well.'

'Oh come on, we haven't exactly been overdoing it. One morning's work and you're admitting defeat already.'

'Well, it's not as easy as I thought. How long till lunch?'

'Another hour.'

'A whole hour? Oh well, let's try again.'

We settled down to the books once more, trying to concentrate on equations, formulae and experimentation that had been written up months before. Eventually, Duggan abandoned his file of notes and studied the text book instead, making notes on the areas he still had to revise on a sheet of exercise paper. The harder I concentrated, the more daunting I realised the task actually was. I had a sneaking suspicion that I simply hadn't done enough work to pass the chemistry strand. And I hadn't even started on the education subjects yet. After another hour, I still felt I hadn't accomplished very much.

'Hey look, that's interesting,' said Duggan, breaking the silence suddenly. 'There's a droopy little line on this page where I fell asleep in a lecture. Must have been an fascinating afternoon.'

There was a bang on the door and Gerry came in, rubbing his hands together in a manner that suggested he had learned all his notes off by heart.

'How goes it then?' he asked cheerfully. 'Coming down for an early lunch? It'll give us longer this afternoon.'

Duggan looked at him in disbelief. 'You sound as if you've almost finished. Know it all then, do you?'

'About half of it. I can't find the stuff on Argentina, though. I think I've stuck it in a film catalogue somewhere. I'm taking a punt here, but I suppose you don't have anything on fazendas in South America, do you?'

'No, but I've got something here on Fehlings solution if you want it.'

'That's the stuff made from copper sulphate, isn't it?'

'How d'you know that?' Duggan exploded. 'I've just spent the last hour trying to find out what it's used for.'

'Something to do with amino-acids, isn't it?'

Duggan's mouth dropped open. 'I thought your bloody subject was geography?'

'It is. I just remember doing something about it at school.'

'My God, you must have been bloody keen, then. I hadn't heard of it until ten minutes ago. You wouldn't like to do the exam for me, would you?'

'Not unless you want to try and cover the economic viability of the land north of the Nerbudda, livestock in the Ukraine or the various industries of Buenos Aires this afternoon?'

'I'll stick to Fehling's solution. You wouldn't know how to purify solid organic compounds by recrystalisation, I suppose?'

'No, you've got me there. I'll leave that to you. You're the scientist.'

'Yes, that's what I thought until I started revising. And we've got all Dr Frost's stuff yet. And Elderberry Hall...'

'That shouldn't take you long. You've only just been down there. You can't have forgotten the entire experience.'

'We remember the experience all right. We just don't remember much of the work we did. Perhaps we'll be asked about torture by hunger.'

'You could always fall ill on the day of the exams,' Gerry suggested brightly. 'I hear that one of last year's finals students swallowed a glassful of petrol and collapsed in the sickbay on the morning he was due to present himself in front of the oral examiners. You could always give that a try.'

'Only as a last resort,' said Duggan grimly. He stood up and put his jacket on. 'We'll wait and see how much we've remembered by the end of the week first. Anyway, let's go and get some lunch and worry about it afterwards.'

(iii)

'Come on then, tell me all about the history of education. In a nutshell.'

'What, everything? Are you staying the night, then?'

'All right, you don't have to tell me absolutely everything. Just the essentials. But I warn you. If you make more than one mistake, you fail, and you have to pay for the pictures on Saturday.' Samantha curled herself attractively into the rather uncomfortable chair beside my bed.

I looked at her and smiled. 'The entire history of education. It's going to be the easy ones first, then?'

'That's right. And you have to imagine I'm a very severe, spinsterly examiner who hates male students and intends to prove they don't have any knowledge of anything important in their minds at all.'

'Right, Miss. How far back do you want me to go? The sixteenth century? Independent grammar schools?' I flicked through my education file. 'Tell you what. I bet you didn't know a couple of grammar schools even claimed descendency from Alfred the Great?'

She raised her eyebrows and looked up, not sure whether to believe me.

'I didn't know, actually. Fancy that. He didn't just go around burning cakes, then?'

'Apparently not.'

'So come on, Mike. Where do you really want me to start from?' She placed the file delicately on her lap and opened it at the first page.

'Right there. The beginning of my file. Ask me about the 1944 Act.'

'All right then. Tell me about that.'

She scanned through my notes and then looked up at me expectantly. I put my knowledge of the act into careful mental order and counted off the main components on my fingers as I named them.

'It created a Minister of Education. It created local education authorities. It created the three stages of education. It made religious education compulsory. It gave local authorities welfare functions. It made local authorities educate handicapped children. Oh, and it made local authorities pay their teachers according to an agreed scale. There. How about that?'

Samantha looked up in admiration. 'Well, that's a very good start, you clever boy. Nine out of ten. You only missed out a couple of things. You've got a note here about arrangements for leisure time occupation. And something about fee paying schools, too.'

'Oh yes, I forgot those.'

'That's amazing. I thought the 1944 Education Act was just about free secondary education for all children. Or something like that, anyway.'

'So do most people. But it was pretty far sighted, really. And just think, you'd never have known all that if you hadn't been here on your afternoon off.'

Samantha smiled, pushing her shoes off and trying to find a more comfortable position on the chair. 'I consider myself to be very lucky, then. I bet there aren't many girls learning about the 1944 Education Act on a gorgeous afternoon like this.'

'No, I bet there aren't. I tell you what…'

'What?'

'I love that dress you're wearing.'

Samantha smiled and tucked her legs further into the chair.

'What's that got to do with the 1944 Education Act?'

'Not a great deal. I just think you look great in it.'

'Really? You don't think it makes me look too fat, do you?'

'Well yes, it does make you look too fat. It's nice though.'

She stared at me for a moment in disbelief, and then threw the chair cushion at me.

'You are a sod!'

'Well of course you're not fat. You've got a gorgeous figure and you wonder if you look fat? Anyway, I love the dress. Red really suits you. Ask me another question. Or do you want me to go into detail about the parts of the 1944 Act?'

'No, you sound too confident about that. I'll look for something else.' She shuffled through the pages of my file. 'Right, I'll ask you about the educationalists. Which one would you like? Rousseau, Montessori, Frobel, Dalton, Pestalozzi... sounds like a village in Switzerland. Who on earth was Pestalozzi?'

'Somebody who was very influenced by Rousseau. You'd better see how much I can remember about Rousseau first.'

I'd enjoyed the lectures on the educationalists, and I had little difficulty in recalling how their philosophies had changed and shaped educational attitudes. Almost without faltering, I managed to tell Samantha how modern teaching techniques had stemmed from Rousseau's ideas, his revolutionary thinking, and his profound effect on European education. She listened with interest, caught on the wave of my enthusiasm. Occasionally, she stopped me and asked for a deeper explanation of a detail in my notes, but she was obviously impressed with my knowledge of the subject. After an hour and a half of concentrated revision, she suddenly stretched in the chair and put the folder down.

'It's so hot in here,' she said. 'I think I've earned a cup of tea at least.'

'I think so too.'

I leaned across the chair and kissed her gently. 'Let's have a break for an hour and walk down to the park. I'll buy you an ice cream instead.'

'Okay. That would be nice.'

The late afternoon air was hot and still, and the grass in St James's Park was crowded with people making the most of the hot summer sunshine. I recognised many students from the college too, some asleep, some stripped to the waist and others propped up on their elbows with a small pile of books in front of them. I led Samantha to the small bridge over the lake, and we stood and watched two drakes diving repeatedly into the water beside the weeping willows.

'Beats revising, doesn't it?' I said, putting my arm around Samantha's shoulder and pulling her closer. 'What a lovely afternoon. Now if I was a duck, I wouldn't have to worry about educational theory at all. I could just dive headfirst into the water.'

'You'd get bored with it.'

'Ducks don't get bored.'

'How do you know?'

'Look at them. Do they look like bored ducks to you?'

'I'm not sure. I don't really know how to recognise a bored duck. I wonder if they know anything about the 1944 Education Act?'

'Probably not. They know a lot about bits of bread, though.'

'Do you think you'll ever get bored with teaching, Mike?' Samantha asked seriously.

'I don't know, love. At the moment, I don't think so. That's a strange question. I haven't even started teaching yet. Why do you ask?'

'Because you're so interested in it, that's all. I just wonder if you'll ever tire of it.'

'It's possible, I suppose. But I honestly can't think of anything else I'd rather do. I might have changed my mind if I hadn't liked my teaching practices. But I enjoyed them so much, Sam. Especially the first one. I really loved being with the children.'

'They were lucky, too. Having you to teach them, I mean.'

'That's a lovely thing to say, but I don't think I made that much difference. Anyway, I might not pass my exams. We've only just started to revise.'

'You'll pass. You're too interested in it not to pass. Why don't you stay on for a fourth year and do a degree?'

'I've thought about it. Really I have. I want to start teaching now, though. I don't want to study for another year. I've been studying all my life so far. With varying degrees of success. I can do a degree later on.'

'At least you'd still be near me if you stayed at college.'

I held her waist tightly and hugged her. 'I'll be near you anyway. I'm not going back home when I finish college. I want to stay and teach in London for a time. Duggan suggested we should rent a flat together. He's not going home either. We'll probably try to get jobs in one of the poorer parts of the city.'

'Don't tell me. You want to bring enlightenment to the underprivileged.'

'Oh God, I didn't mean to sound patronising.'

'I know. I'm only teasing.'

'Seems crazy, really. Out of three years at college we get fifteen weeks in actual schools. I mean, that's where you really learn to do the job. I learned more from Dorothy Bridgewood in a day than I did in an entire year of college lectures.'

'Well, you know what they say. People who can't teach go and lecture about it instead.'

'There's probably a lot of truth in that. My first teaching practice was so enjoyable. Those few weeks made me certain that teaching primary children was for me. And I saw both sides of the job. Genuine commitment from most of the staff.'

'And no commitment at all from the headteacher.'

'That was certainly true. Still, there may have been all sorts of reasons for that. The kids were marvellous, though. I got very attached to them. They're the sort of children I want to teach.'

'It's good that you feel like that. I envy you.'

We crossed the bridge and walked slowly round the lake towards the small wooden refreshment hut, where there was a queue for ice cream.

'Come on then, I'll treat you,' I said. 'Provided you come back and help me revise for at least another hour afterwards. What flavour would you like?'

'Pestalozzi.'

'I think they're right out of that. You can have Rousseau, Dewey, or tutti frutti.'

'Was tutti frutti a famous education philosopher?'

'It wouldn't surprise me.'

'I'll have one of those, then. A double cornet.'

'You'll get fat.'

'I'm fat already.'

'Oh yes, I forgot.'

I bought two cornets and we walked down a pathway shaded by cedar trees to a wooden bench beside a bed of yellow and purple tulips. For a moment, we both sat in silence, licking the melting ice cream.

'You're very lucky, Mike,' Samantha said. 'Knowing exactly what you want to do, I mean. I wish I did. I enjoy working in the library, but I don't suppose I'll stay there much longer. The trouble is, I'm not really sure what I want to do yet. I'll probably end up trying several things, but I do want to work with people. I couldn't stand being in an office. Maybe I could do something with Nursery children. I'd love that.'

'Sounds a good idea. Just don't go too far away, that's all.'

'You mean you'd miss me?'

'You know I would. I think about you all the time.'

'What, even more than Rousseau, Dewey and Pesta... whatever his name was?

'Pestalozzi. And yes, much more than them. You know exactly how I feel about you.'

She moved very close to me and looked at me steadily. Her hazel eyes were suddenly serious. 'Yes, I know. I do know. I just want you to be really sure, that's all.'

'I've never been more sure of anything.'

'Let's go back to your room,' she said quietly.

(iii)

As the examinations drew relentlessly closer, corridor three became enveloped in hushed and concentrated study.

Regardless of whether they had worked diligently throughout the course, the third year students moved about with drawn and vacant faces, their eyes glazed from the intensity of concentrated reading. As the days passed, the corridor gradually became silent at most hours of the day, but especially early in the morning and after the evening meal, when each student would retire quietly into his room to murmur facts, dates, names and theories to himself and then to his friends, who would check for inaccuracies before trying out their own knowledge in turn.

Kettles constantly boiled water for endless mugs of coffee. Figures with haggard faces hurried into the kitchen area at regular intervals, whispered greetings to whoever else might be in there, and then disappeared again. Students wandered the corridor, unable to sleep, muttering formulae and method, fact and hypothesis, before hurrying back to the solitude of their rooms, where pages of notes were pencilled on, amended, hastily consumed and mentally resurrected.

Faces of students I only vaguely knew suddenly appeared at breakfast tables, stocking up until lunchtime, their ashen cheeks and unshaven stubble hinting at the pages that had been ploughed through until the early hours of the morning. Society meetings were abandoned by the finals students and the television room was left virtually unattended.

At the start of the third week, we began work on the education subjects that formed an important section of the written examinations. We re-read Dewey's ideas of motivation, the theories of Robert Owen, the doctrines of Plato, the influence of Plowden. We discussed our periods of practical teaching and the techniques of classroom organisation we had tried. We tackled the psychology of the classroom, the merits of assessment and testing, the learning difficulties of children with special needs. Finally, at ten thirty on the final Friday of the three week period we had set ourselves, we emerged from our notebooks desperately tired but elated. At the very least, we considered ourselves capable of attempting a pass mark.

'That's it, then, Mike,' said Duggan triumphantly, tossing a text book back onto his bookshelf. 'If we don't know it all now we never will, so I'm going for a long beer and then I'm going to sleep it out until the first one on Tuesday morning. You are welcome to join me. In a beer, that is. I don't necessarily want you climbing in bed with me.'

For both of us, the next few days were the hardest of all. Rather than touch our books again, we were determined to let everything sift, settle and sort itself out into coherent order in our minds. Sleep was difficult; the small hours were punctuated by dreams in which ancient examiners leaned across huge mahogany desks to fire meaningless questions at me, until I woke in a sweat of anxiety convinced I knew absolutely nothing at all. Only Gerry seemed unaffected by the thought of airing his accumulated knowledge of the last three years in public. Or perhaps he was merely showing the unflappable exterior I had come to admire during our film society shows when a projector broke down.

I was woken in the early hours of Tuesday morning by an ominous roll of thunder and a storm that had been threatening to arrive for days. I screwed up my eyes to look at the clock beside my bed. Six thirty. The first day of reckoning had arrived.

I sighed, stared at the rain for a few moments and then turned over in bed, but it was impossible to get back to sleep and I tried to take my mind off the day by reading a chapter from a detective novel I'd picked up on a station bookstall. It was impossible to concentrate, and after fifteen minutes I decided that I might just as well get out of bed.

Breakfast was out of the question; the thought of sausages and bacon dished up on a greasy plate made me feel nauseous. I dressed slowly, as if it would help put off the final moment, and then sat on the edge of the bed trying to gather information into tidy mental compartments before venturing out for a wash. Nobody was about in the corridor. I wondered if everybody was still sleeping, or whether they simply hadn't bothered to go to bed. I made two mugs of tea, and carried one of them into Duggan's room, half wondering whether I should wake him or leave him lost in blissful oblivion. Duggan grunted, turned over as I touched his shoulder, and then sat up in panic.

'Christ, what's the time?'

'Ten past seven.'

'Ten past seven? Bloody hell Mike, what are you up already for?'

'I thought you might appreciate a cup of tea.'

'That's very sweet of you. I would. Any sugar in it?'

'Two spoonfuls.'

'Great. You're a treasure.'

'I know.'

He sat up in bed and shivered, rubbing the sleep out of his eyes.

'I could do with another ten hours sleep. Have a look in the desk drawer. I think there's a packet of custard creams in there somewhere.'

I found the packet and tossed it onto the bed.

'Look at that,' Duggan said in disgust, 'only three left. You don't get much for your money these days.'

'Are you going to revise any more?'

'No fear. My brain couldn't cope with it. Chuck the newspaper over. I think I'll finish the crossword puzzle and then go back to sleep for a while. My call isn't till eleven o'clock. Is Gerry about?'

'I haven't looked. I'll go and take him some tea.'

'He probably got out of bed at six for a quick run round the park,' Duggan said. 'Either that or he's thrown himself out of the window. Oh look, before you go. This is for you.'

He pulled out a large white envelope from between the books on his top shelf. Inside was a beautifully hand-drawn good luck card from Samantha, with a message telling me to come round to the library as soon as the first oral examination was over.

'Look at that,' said Duggan admiringly, 'she must have been working on that for days. What a lovely girl. You don't deserve her.'

'I know.'

'Don't fancy doing me a couple of slices of toast, do you?'

'I've just made you a mug of tea. What more do you want?'

'A couple of slices of toast?'

'There isn't any bread. I'll ask Gerry if he's got any biscuits.'

Gerry was already dressed and working at his desk, scribbling notes from his geography folder onto a pad.

'Hello,' he said brightly. 'All ready for this morning, then?'

'That's difficult to say. I mean, if I'm asked about magnets or Boyle's Law, I'm ready. If I'm going to be asked about the life cycle of an evening primrose, I'm not ready. Do you fancy a mug of tea?'

'Lovely. Put it on that beer mat. Oh well, you've got a couple of hours yet. Do you want me to go through anything with you?'

'What, like lists of alternative employment?'

'Everybody suffers from pre-exam nerves. Once you get in there, you'll be fine. Put a bit of litmus paper in your pocket as a lucky charm and smile sweetly.'

'I'll try. You haven't got any biscuits, have you? Duggan wants one.'

'Sorry. I don't dare buy them. I just end up eating them.'

At five minutes to ten, I gathered my science files together and walked slowly down to the tutorial room, where the oral examinations were being held. Four chairs had been placed outside the room. A folder rested on one of them, open at a page on halogens. A notice had been pinned on the door stating that examinations were in progress and under no circumstances were the occupants to be disturbed. A low murmur of conversation came from within the room. As I was about to sit on the end chair, the door opened and Simon Daines walked out. He smiled cheerfully at me and seemed very relaxed.

'Hello. Well, that went very quickly. Quicker than I expected, anyway. Are you next?'

'Yes, I think so. What's it like?'

'Very straightforward, but she went through the course pretty thoroughly. Asked questions on just about everything we've done. Especially the field study. Have you got your files with you? She looked through my folder very carefully. Glad I had everything in the right order. Anyway, best of luck.'

He held the door open and I tried to look positive as I walked into the room. A small, smartly dressed woman in a grey suit sat behind Miss Bottle's desk, scribbling notes on a piece of paper. She looked up as I entered, and pointed to the chair in front of the desk.

'What dreadful weather we're having this morning, aren't we?' she said pleasantly. 'Do sit down, please. Now, I am Mrs Smythe and you are Mr... um... Hornpipe, I believe?'

My eyebrows rose in surprise. 'No, I'm not, actually.'

'Really? Well, that's very odd. I suppose a Mr Hornpipe does actually exist?'

'Yes. He's in our group.'

'Well he's also supposed to have had his oral this morning. He was first on my list.'

'He's in the room next to mine. Do you want me to...'

Mrs Smythe waved her hand. 'No, not at all. Now, let's try again. You are Mr... um...'

'Kent. Michael Kent.'

She ran her pencil down the list of names in front of her. 'Ah yes, Mr Kent. Now then, I believe you have studied the combined science course? Chemistry, physics, plus some biology... and some field work. Is that correct?'

'That's correct,' I said softly.

Mrs Smythe leaned forward in her seat. 'You'll have to speak up, Mr Kent. Come now, it's not that much of an ordeal, is it?'

'I suppose not. It's just that this is my first oral exam and I seem to have been hibernating with education books for the past month.'

'Well, please don't worry. I have absolutely no intention of trying to catch you out. I just want to find out how valuable your course of study has been to you. I imagine the time here has gone very quickly for you?'

I cleared my throat and spoke in a louder voice. 'Very quickly indeed. I've really enjoyed it. Especially the teaching practices. I'm looking forward to actually starting.'

'You're not staying on for the degree year, then?'

'No. I'm going to do a degree later on. At the moment I just want to get into the classroom.'

'I admire your enthusiasm, but I hope you don't regret your decision. It's easier staying on to do your degree while you're in a receptive frame of mind. Would you hand me your files, please?'

I stood up, passed across the three folders of work and sat down again. Mrs Smythe took the physics folder from the top of the pile and looked through it for what seemed an eternity.

'And what about your science course, Mr Kent? Have you enjoyed that too?' she asked, without looking up.

'On the whole, yes.'

'On the whole?'

'Well, some of the work has been quite difficult. I tended to specialise in chemistry at school rather than the other sciences.'

'I see. Well, we'll start with chemistry, then, shall we?' She picked up the chemistry folder and opened it at random. 'I see you have some experiments here on steam distillation. We'll begin with those. Tell me about the experiments, with any observations of your own and what sort of limitations your methods might present.'

She removed her spectacles and looked at me with interest. I answered slowly and carefully, feeling that if I could prolong the chemistry answers there wouldn't be much time for her to ask about anything else. When I'd finished, she looked up and smiled for the first time.

'Yes, thank you. Very good. Of course, as steam distillation takes place below the boiling point of water we can purify many substances of high boiling point by low temperature distilling. But I see you have made a note about that anyway.'

She flicked through the pages of the file and ran her finger down some of the notes before looking up again.

'How would you standardise caric sulphate solution, Mr Kent?' I remembered this immediately, but held the answer in my mind for as long as I dared, not wanting Mrs Smythe to rumble my delaying tactics.

'Sodium oxalate, I think,' I answered carefully.

'Correct. Go on.'

'But I don't see...'

'Well, assuming you were going to do it by direct titration, you would use a catalyst, surely?'

'Oh, yes,' I agreed, 'you'd certainly need a catalyst.'

'Well?'

'Sorry?'

'Well, what would you use?'

'Oh, you mean you want me to tell you a suitable catalyst?'

'I should have thought that was obvious, Mr Kent.'

'Yes, of course,' I said slowly, trying to give the impression of weighing up and selecting from a hundred suitable possibilities. Mrs Smythe leaned forward in her chair.

'What would you use, then?'

'Iodine monochloride, probably. Yes, I think I'd probably go for iodine monochloride.'

Mrs Smythe sat back in her chair and drummed her fingers on the desktop.

'Yes, I think you'd be well advised to choose that, Mr Kent. Can I suggest that you try to answer the rest of the questions a little more promptly, or we'll run out of time.'

'I'm sorry,' I apologised. 'It's just that I seem to have been up all night for weeks on end going over my notes.'

'Yes, I'm sure you have. Still, so has everyone else, and so did I thirty years ago,' she said briskly. 'Now then, you have several pages here on diatoms. Would you like to tell me something about them?'

'Certainly.'

'Then... er... please do, Mr Kent.'

I concentrated on the page Mrs Smythe had obviously turned to, and I formed a mental picture of the information. Then I outlined the composition of diatoms, their characteristics, their reproduction techniques, and their place in the order of things. Mrs Smythe nodded vigorously as I spoke.

'Very good, Mr Kent. I think we'll talk about valency next, and then we'll have a look at your field study work. Oh, now what do you think of...um.. Guernsey, Mr Kent?'

For a moment I stared at her in disbelief. Had I imagined the question, or was she approaching a topic in my folder from an unexpected direction simply to throw me off guard.

'I think it's a very nice place,' I answered cautiously, wondering if I was dreaming. 'A very nice place indeed.'

Mrs Smythe smiled, took three colourful pamphlets out of my folder, and passed them across to me.

'I see you were revising Guernsey as well as your chemistry,' she said brightly. 'You left the brochures in your book. I assume they are there by mistake?'

I suddenly realised what she was talking about and laughed with embarrassment.

'Oh, yes. I... er... wrote off and booked a site there for a couple of weeks this summer. Some friends and I camped there last year and we were thinking of going again.'

'How very nice,' Mrs Smythe interrupted me. 'It's a delightful island and mercifully still unspoiled. I grew up there, you see. My brother and his family still live on the island. He's a teacher, too. His subject is history.'

'Really?' I asked, not quite believing my luck and anxious to exploit this opportunity as fully as I could. 'Which part does he live in?'

'In Torteval. Near Pleinmonth Point. Do you know it?'

'Not very well. It's at the tip of the island, isn't it?'

She settled back more comfortably in her chair, crossed her

legs and nodded enthusiastically. 'That's right. The 'Land's End' of Guernsey. It's a very pretty part of the island. Fascinating history, too. Lots of stories of haunted shipwrecks. The children in Alan's classes love hearing about them, specially as he usually embroiders his stories somewhat. Where are you going to be camping?'

'On a farm near Saint's Bay.'

'Oh lovely, I know it very well. Close to Icart Point. There's a footpath from Saint's that leads all the way up to it. Icart is the highest point on the island. An absolutely splendid view from the top of it. And the flora is delightful. Especially if you teach botany, of course.'

'Because of the mild climate, I suppose?' I was wary of getting too heavily into the area of science I was least sure about. Nevertheless, with a little luck and some judicious manoeuvring, I was certain Mrs Smythe's enthusiasm could be used to carry the conversation forward to my advantage.

'Oh yes, absolutely,' she said, biting her bottom lip and thinking for a moment. 'There are probably a thousand species of plants just growing wild. Some of them are very rare even in this country. I see you've made some notes about the varieties of buttercup in your field study, Mr Kent. Well, it may surprise you to learn there are even more unusual varieties of it in Guernsey. And there's a variety of sea-lavender you won't find anywhere in the world except the Channel Islands. Which month are you going in?'

'August.'

'Oh, ideal. And you'll be going to the Battle of Flowers, I imagine?'

She saw the puzzled expression on my face and laughed warmly.

'It's a flower pageant held in Saumarez Park. An annual competition between Guernsey and Jersey. Both islands make the most amazing floats from flowers and some of them are huge. A quite extraordinary experience. You really must try to go. There's a lovely horticultural exhibition, too. You seem to be very interested in botany, Mr Kent, judging from your file. Your drawings are very impressive.'

'We'll definitely make a point of going,' I said. 'We want to see as much of the island as we can.'

'Of course. There's so much of interest. Especially for history students. I don't know if you knew, but the island was once invaded by the Vikings. Mind you, they seem to have invaded everywhere, don't they?'

I glanced at my watch. If we continued in this manner, I thought, the oral would be finished in no time. Mrs Smythe leaned forward in her seat, warming to her theme.

'Oh yes, the island really has quite a history. The French invaded it, of course, and Victor Hugo was exiled there. And there's the German underground hospital, built near the end of the last war.'

'Yes, we visited that last year. Amazing that it was all built by slave labour.' I still had vivid memories of the visit, and the contrast between the boiling hot sunshine and the coldness of the concrete caverns excavated beneath the ground.

'That's right,' said Mrs Smythe. 'It took three and a half years to build and was actually used for about four weeks. Apparently half the workforce died and were just mixed in with the concrete. Dreadful thought, isn't it? Anyway, let's not be morbid. Have you visited the Little Chapel?'

There was a sudden, very loud knock on the door, the handle turned, and Dudley's face appeared.

'Ah, hello. I'm looking for the... um... would this be the oral examination for science?'

'It would,' Mrs Smythe nodded. 'And would you happen to be Mr Barton? Or are you the elusive Mr Hornpipe?'

'Hornpipe, actually.'

'I see. Then if I am not mistaken, you were supposed to be here some time ago, Mr Hornpipe.'

'I know,' said Dudley, scratching his beard miserably. 'Wretched alarm clock didn't work, I'm afraid. At least, it does work, but not when I want it to.'

'Perhaps you just slept through it, Mr Hornpipe.'

Dudley considered this explanation carefully. 'That's possible, of course. Yes, that's a distinct possibility. Still, I'm here now.'

'So you may be, Mr Hornpipe,' said Mrs Smythe bluntly. 'But as you may have noticed, I happen to be interviewing someone else at this particular moment.'

Dudley peered further round the door, recognised me, and smiled pleasantly.

'Hello, old boy,' he said. 'Didn't see you there. I hope it's going well?'

'Would you kindly sit and wait outside?' said Mrs Smythe curtly as Dudley showed no sign of moving away from the door. 'I will examine your work as soon as I have a spare half hour. That's the best I can offer.'

Dudley thought for a moment. 'Ah, unfortunately that does leave us with a slight dilemma,' he said. 'You see, I've got some trouble with my Claude Butler and I...'

Mrs Smythe clicked her tongue in exasperation. 'Mr Hornpipe, what exactly are you talking about?'

'My Claude Butler. My bicycle. I've got to go and collect the front wheel by eleven thirty. I rode the damn thing into a lamp post. I need it for this afternoon. The wheel, that is. Not the lamp post.' He laughed politely, noticed that Mrs Smythe hadn't found his joke even slightly amusing, and abruptly changed his laugh into an embarrassed cough.

'As far as I can see, you have two choices, Mr Hornpipe,' Mrs Smythe said, her voice rising impatiently. 'You can either sit outside and wait for me, in which case there is a chance that you could possibly pass the oral section of your science examination. Or, on the other hand, you can go away and mend your Claude whatever it is. In which case, I can assure you without the slightest fear of contradiction, you'll fail your oral. Hopefully, that clarifies the matter?'

Dudley squinted at her, pursed his lips, and then nodded. 'Perfectly, dear lady,' he said. 'I'll sit outside.'

The door closed softly and Mrs Smythe turned back to me. She smiled and raised her eyebrows.

'I just hope he can get himself into a classroom on time,' she said. 'He'll probably turn up at the wrong school. I'm so sorry that you've had to put up with this in the middle of your oral, Mr Kent.'

'That's all right,' I said graciously, aware that another five minutes of my examination time had been taken care of. 'He's actually quite a talented person. He just can't get it all together at times.'

'Really?' Mrs Smythe seemed distinctly unimpressed. 'Well, I'm not sure I'd want him teaching my own children. Anyway, your own files are most pleasing, Mr Kent, and well up to the required standard. I shall definitely be recommending you for a pass. I wish you every good fortune with your written papers. And indeed, your career.'

She stood up and held out her hand, indicating that the examination had come to an end. I stood too, and shook the outstretched hand warmly.

'Perhaps you'd send the next candidate in. I believe it should be a Mr Barton.'

Outside the room, Dudley was sitting on the last chair in the row with his left leg propped across two others. His trousers were partly rolled up and he was inspecting some bruises on his legs. His work, a haphazard pile of handwritten papers, was untidily stacked under the chair he was sitting on. Next to him, David Barton sat poring over his physics folder. He looked as though he hadn't slept all night.

'Hello,' he said unhappily. 'What's it like, then?'

'Not too bad, actually. Just a few questions on amino-acids and the sex life of the tsetse fly.'

'Yeah? I don't know much about the tsetse fly. Do you think he'd be willing to ask me questions about my own sex life instead?'

'I doubt it,' I said. 'He's a woman.'

'Really?' Barton smiled. 'Brilliant. I'll just have to put on my natural charm then, won't I?' He licked his forefinger, smoothed back his eyebrows, and strode into the room confidently. I hurried off in the direction of Duggan's room, to suggest he spent the remaining ten minutes learning something about the Channel Islands.

(iv)

Dr Bradley walked to the front of the hall, climbed the short flight of stairs, and strode to the centre of the stage. I was reminded of my first afternoon at St James's College, when he'd talked to the new students in this hall. It seemed such a short time ago.

The warm morning sunlight filtered through the high windows of the hall, and everybody sat quietly at their desks waiting for Dr Bradley to speak. He gripped the sides of the lectern, glanced at the large, loudly ticking clock on the wall and then slowly looked round at us all.

'Well, gentlemen,' he said. 'It is eight minutes to ten on the morning of reckoning. Your first written examination. Some of you may be wondering where the past three years have gone. By the end of the morning, some of you could well be wishing they hadn't gone at all.' Several students smiled lamely. Dr Bradley seemed amused by his joke and gave everybody time to appreciate it before he began speaking again.

'Frankly,' he said, 'I don't consider your first education paper to be a difficult one. It will give you a chance to evaluate and discuss your own experiences in the light of past developments and current thinking. It is a beautiful morning, the birds are singing, God's in his Heaven and you have three hours to answer this paper. More than enough, I'd say. Sharpen your quills, take a deep breath and turn your papers over, gentlemen. You may now begin. And, ahm, I wish you all the very best of luck.'

He put his hands behind his back and watched as there was a riffle of paper and every head looked downwards. I opened my paper and glanced through the questions. An icy panic gripped me for a moment, even though I was relieved that the time for the written examinations had actually arrived. The condensing of three year's lectures, the planning and the worry about whether the right things had been revised seemed less of an ordeal than the written paper itself. I'd never coped with examination conditions particularly well. At school I'd found difficulty in coming to terms with them even when I'd known I was well prepared.

I selected the questions I would answer, and scribbled some ideas on my roughwork pad as quickly as I could. Then, having made up my mind which question to tackle first, I picked up my pen and started to write. Answering a question always became easier after I'd written the first paragraph, and it was no different this morning. Dr Bradley had been right; the examination wasn't difficult, and with a feeling of relief I wrote quickly and enthusiastically.

Dr Bradley always invigilated during the first examination, and now he strode with measured steps along the lanes between the rows of desks, often pausing for a moment to read a paragraph or check a heading. At first many students found this a little distracting and looked up as he passed their desks, but as they gradually became absorbed in what they were writing, nobody really noticed his presence at all. When I next glanced up from my paper, more than an hour had passed. I glanced round the hall at my peers; Dudley Hornpipe sat awkwardly on his chair, writing with an elderly fountain pen that squeaked as he moved the nib across the paper. Gerry's lips moved gently as he silently mouthed the words he was writing, Simon Daines had a look of intense concentration on his face and had filled at least ten sheets of paper, and Duggan was writing frantically with his head propped on the palm of his left hand. Barton sat in the desk adjacent to me, scratching his head and looking at his paper doubtfully, as if he wasn't quite sure whether he had answered the right questions. He looked across at me and frowned.

'Tell you what,' he whispered miserably.

'What?'

‘It’s a right bastard, isn’t it?’

Though I hadn’t found it so, I nodded in sympathy.

‘How many marks do you get for writing your name?’

‘Two.’

‘Is that all? Christ! There isn’t a single question about exhaust gas analysers on this sodding paper. I think I’ll have to write about ‘The Glenn Miller Story’ instead.’

‘Are you talking, Mr Barton?’ Dr Bradley said softly but severely, moving swiftly behind his chair.

‘Sorry Sir,’ Barton muttered apologetically. ‘I was just wondering if I would be allowed out to the lavatory.’

‘Then kindly ask me, not Mr Kent. You’ve probably destroyed his concentration.’

‘Sorry. Would it be alright if I went to the lavatory?’

‘No, it wouldn’t.’

‘Oh, right.’

‘You have an hour and ten minutes left. I suggest you use them profitably, Mr Barton. Try to pass. It’s such a waste of public money when students fail.’

‘Thank you, I will,’ Barton said graciously and turned back to look at his paper again. Dr Bradley glided silently away.

I finished writing ten minutes before the three hours were up. I breathed a sigh of relief, put my pen down, and began to read through my answer paper from the beginning. It seemed quite satisfactory. I felt I knew a fair amount about the history of education, classroom practice, school organisation and curriculum issues, and I was pleased with my answers. I corrected the few mistakes I’d made, added a word or two here and there, and then carefully put my papers in order. The hands on the clock inched into the one o’clock position, and Dr Bradley checked the time on his watch.

‘That’s it, gentlemen,’ he called loudly. ‘Your first examination is over. Would you put your pens down now, please.’

There was a general shuffling of papers, and sighs from many of the students. Some were disappointed that the time had run out, a few were frantically putting the finishing touches to a last question, others were just thankful that the first ordeal was finally over. Doctor Bradley raised his voice above the murmuring in the hall.

'Please make sure your names are written clearly at the top of each page, gentlemen. Just as a precaution. The examiners who read your illuminating philosophies of education will no doubt wish to know who wrote them. Then put your answer papers tidily on your desks in front of you. When you have done that, you may stand up and leave the hall quietly.'

As we wandered out into the midday sunshine, groups of students clustered outside the hall entrance to discuss the ordeal of the previous three hours.

'Well, I suppose that wasn't too bad really, was it?' Gerry said emphatically, as Duggan and I joined him. He pulled his pipe out of his jacket pocket and began to stuff tobacco into the bowl with his finger.

'You must be bloody joking!' said David Barton, overhearing him. 'Not a single question on motor bikes in the whole paper.'

'That's because the school curriculum doesn't contain a great deal about motor bikes,' said Duggan. 'You'll have to wait till you get the physics paper.'

'I'll look forward to that. I couldn't do much worse than I've done today.'

'Probably just nerves, old boy,' said Dudley sympathetically. 'Come and see me before the next one. I've got one or two pills which might help.'

'Do you think you've passed that one, then?'

'Haven't a clue. I rather doubt it. My views don't always seem to tie in with what is recognised as current good practice. I rather think I've made a botch of the science oral. Wretched woman had an argument with me about the African Grey.'

'The what?' asked Barton with interest.

'The African Grey.'

'The African Grey what?'

'The African Grey parrot.

'Really? She didn't ask me about the African Grey parrot. She asked me about magnetic fields.'

'She shouldn't have asked me about the African Grey either, old boy. I know a great deal about the voice mechanisms of birds. On balance, I think I'll probably work in an aviary rather than a classroom.'

'Just goes to show,' Barton continued. 'I know a great deal about sex but she didn't have any questions on that, either. Shame, because I put in a lot of practical revision.'

'Anyway, I didn't think this exam was too difficult, did you?' Gerry said quickly, before Barton had a chance to describe his most recent conquests.

'We haven't had the hard stuff yet,' said Duggan. 'I mean, we've got Plato, Dewey, Rousseau and that lot to come yet.'

'That won't be difficult,' Gerry replied. 'We've got another four days before that one. Has anyone got a match?'

'We don't smoke, do we,' said Duggan severely. 'Nor should you. I could manage a pint, though. Let's wander down to the corner. We've got an hour before lunch. And we've got the afternoon to sleep it off.'

We walked slowly down to the main gate and into the street. As we passed the bus stop, a bus pulled into the kerb and a young man in a smart brown suit jumped off. He looked scrubbed and fresh, as if he had just climbed out of the bath.

'Excuse me,' he called, 'You're not from St James's Training College, are you?'

Duggan smiled at him. 'Indeed we are,' he said. 'You must have recognised the haggard look.'

'Can you tell me where I'm supposed to go?' he asked. 'I've got an interview for starting here in September.'

'You're a bit early, then. Its only July now.'

The young man smiled self-consciously. 'The interview's at two o'clock,' he said. 'Where can I find the college office?'

'Through the main gate about a hundred yards back,' said Gerry. 'Go through, across the lawn, up the steps and into the bottom corridor. It's just on the left.'

'Don't actually go across the lawn, though,' Duggan warned. 'My friend here did that, and look at him now. And when you come here in September, think twice before trying to borrow a projector. You haven't seen 'The Glenn Miller Story', I suppose?'

The young man looked baffled. 'No, I haven't,' he said. 'Why, should I have done?'

'It could be an advantage. Depends who's interviewing you,' said Duggan. 'If it's Miss Pratt…'

'Don't take any notice of him,' said Gerry. 'He doesn't know what he's talking about.'

'We're in the middle of our finals,' I explained. 'My friend is suffering from post-paper disorientation. Good luck with your interview. Tell him you were in the Scouts. That's what I did. We had a good conversation about that.'

The young man nodded earnestly. 'Thanks. I will. Good luck with your exams.'

He hurried off, and we turned the corner that led towards the Barley Mow. I felt elated. I'd been incredibly lucky with my science oral, the first written exam paper had proved far easier than I'd dared hope, I'd been very successful on my teaching practices and to top it all I was in love. A surge of confidence ran through me, and I breathed in deeply. I was going to pass my examinations, and I was going to do what I'd always wanted to do.

I was going to be a teacher.